PSYCHOPATHOLOGY OF COMMUNICATION

Officers of the
AMERICAN PSYCHOPATHOLOGICAL ASSOCIATION
for 1956

Oskar Diethelm, M.D., *President*

Howard S. Liddell, Ph.D., *President-Elect*

Leslie B. Hohman, M.D., *Vice-President*

Donald M. Hamilton, M.D., *Secretary*

Bernard Glueck, Jr., M.D., *Treasurer*

Merrill Moore, M.D., *Councillor*

Reginald Lourie, M.D., *Councillor*

Committee on Program

Paul H. Hoch, M.D., *Chairman*

Joseph Zubin, Ph.D.

Fred V. Rockwell, M.D.

PSYCHOPATHOLOGY OF COMMUNICATION

Edited by **PAUL H. HOCH, M.D.**
New York State Psychiatric Institute; College of Physicians and Surgeons, Columbia University, New York City.

and **JOSEPH ZUBIN, Ph.D.**
New York State Psychiatric Institute; Department of Psychology, Columbia University, versity, New York City.

THE PROCEEDINGS OF THE FORTY-SIXTH ANNUAL MEETING OF THE AMERICAN PSYCHOPATHOLOGICAL ASSOCIATION, HELD IN NEW YORK CITY, JUNE 1956.

GRUNE & STRATTON

NEW YORK • LONDON • 1958

Library of Congress catalog card number: 57-11344

Grune & Stratton, Inc.
381 Fourth Avenue
New York City

Printed and bound in the United States (A)

CONTENTS

FOREWORD

THE PROBLEM OF COMMUNICATION has received considerable attention from social scientists in the past decade because of the advances made in the field of information theory on the one hand and the discoveries in the field of linguistics on the other. While psychopathologists have regarded defective communication between the patient and his environment as one of the important earmarks of deviant behavior, the investigation of this type of deviation has remained largely descriptive or phenomenological. The form of communication in schizophrenia, for example, with its telescoping, condensations, autisms, etc., has been well described and documented. With the advent of Freud the content as well as the form of these communications has been subjected to psychodynamic interpretation.

Galton's word association technique, which originally was concerned with the mechanics of associative processes, was developed by Jung into a psychodynamic technique for the detection of complexes. These plunges into the unconscious aspects of speech fired the imaginations of psycho-linguists. Zipf, for example, soon discovered that certain regularities existed in the speech of the schizophrenic despite its apparent irrationality. Schizophrenics seemed to use fewer words with a higher frequency for each, which could be taken to indicate a lack of interest in communicating thoughts precisely and a tendency to be satisfied with mere expression regardless of whether the content was understood.

Narziss Ach studied the influence of the determining tendency on speech and Karl Lashley has sought the mechanism which controls the serial order of activities involved in the elaboration of speech.

Many attempts have been made to find "type-token" ratios in the speech of schizophrenics and normals. The number of adjectives, the number of verbs, the ratio of active to passive verbs, and a host of other indicators have been examined. In addition, the role of language in constricting or controlling thought has been investigated by Whorf and his followers.

The current volume, in trying to encompass this expanding area of psychopathologic research, ranges from the descriptive to the experimental and includes samples of normal as well as abnormal behavior. It is to be hoped that collaboration among a variety of disciplines will lead to a deeper understanding of the underlying factors producing deviation in communication and of the way in which such deviations affect the formal aspects of speech.

One primary result of this symposium has been to focus attention on the possibility of scientific evaluation of the interview regarded as a communicative act. Long neglected by social scientists, maligned as unreliable and invalid, the interview can now be brought into the storehouse of scientific tools and sharpened until it can cut effectively into the unsolved problems of mental disease.

Communication opens a window through which private experiences can be exposed to view. Since psychopathology has its roots in the private experiences of the patient, any method which will systematically uncover internal events to scientific scrutiny will be of great help in the search for the sources of mental disease and will thereby contribute significantly to its amelioration. There is an urgent need for a scientific model of the interview, and the current interest is a bright harbinger for the future.

THE EDITORS

SANDOR RADO

Samuel W. Hamilton Memorial Lecturer, 1956

To outline the scientific contributions and sketch the personality of any man in a few hundred words is never an easy task; its complexity is the greater if the man has both brilliance and a many-faceted personality. Such a man is Sandor Rado.

My first contact with him was as a member of the audience which had eagerly awaited the first course of lectures to be given by the newly appointed Educational Director of the New York Psychoanalytic Institute. Rumors of his brilliance had heralded his arrival. Word was passed around that he was the heir apparent to the throne of the psychoanalytic empire. Despite his early difficulty in mastering the English language, his organization of ideas and clarity of thought made this early handicap a matter of no moment. As the years went by, his incessant study of the language and his natural facility with words have made him a passable stylist and a competent editor of his own writings.

Rado, from his earliest days, has possessed the urge for inquiry and for assembling and codifying his conclusions which, taken together, mark a restless and critical intelligence. His eagerness for inquiry is equalled by his enthusiasm and skill in imparting his ideas.

Perhaps a better idea of the range of his interests and the scope of his intellectual attainments can be realized from a summary of the academic distinctions and scientific contributions which he has achieved. Born in Hungary on January 8, 1890, he was educated at the Universities of Berlin, Bonn, and Budapest. In 1911 he received the degree of Doctor of Political Science, and in 1915 the degree of Doctor of Medicine, both from the University of Budapest. In 1916 he was licensed to practice medicine in Hungary, and in 1923 was certified there as a specialist in psychiatry. He was a military psychiatrist during the closing years of World War I.

In 1923 he joined the faculty of the newly-formed Berlin Psychoanalytic Institute, having completed his own training in Vienna. In 1931, on the invitation of the late Dr. A. A. Brill, he came to New York to accept the post of Educational Director of the New York Psychoanalytic Institute. After serving for 10 years in this capacity his differences with some of the more rigidly traditional older members of the

SANDOR RADO

educational committee led to a parting of the ways, and the post of Educational Director was abolished.

Not long afterward, together with a few other colleagues who were not satisfied with the conduct of affairs in the New York Psychoanalytic Society, he began to work out plans for the establishment of a psychoanalytic training center connected with the Department of Psychiatry at Columbia University. These efforts resulted in the establishment in 1944 of the Columbia Psychoanalytic Clinic for Training and Research, of which he was appointed the first director.

Coincidentally with these developments he helped to found a new psychoanalytic society, which is now called the Association for Psychoanalytic Medicine. Just as the Columbia Clinic became the first fully recognized training center within the structure of a university medical school, and the first to break the previous tradition of limiting psychoanalytic training centers to one for each city, so the new society was the first to break the tradition by which only one recognized society was permitted to exist in any given city. He served as president of the association from 1950 to 1954, and as Director of the Clinic until reaching the age of retirement in 1955. In 1956 he was given the Samuel W. Hamilton Award of the American Psychopathological Association.

Sandor Rado was licensed to practice medicine in the State of New York in 1933. In 1938 he became a citizen of the United States and a diplomate (in psychiatry) of the American Board of Neurology and Psychiatry. He was an examining physician in the Selective Service System (1943-47) and was given the Selective Service Medal by Congress. His latest appointment (on August 1, 1956) was as Professor of Psychiatry and Director of the Graduate School of Psychiatry, State University of New York Medical College.

Second only to Rado's eminence as a teacher and organizer of psychoanalytic training programs have been his editorial accomplishments. From 1925 to 1934 he was managing editor of the *Internazionale Zeitschrift für Psychoanalyse* and of *Imago,* both under Dr. Sigmund Freud's direction. Since 1930 he has served on the editorial board of the *Psychoanalytic Quarterly,* the *Psychoanalytic Review,* the *International Journal of Psychoanalysis,* and the *Journal of Investigative Dermatology.*

Needless to say, Dr. Rado has made many contributions to the literature of psychoanalysis and allied fields, including articles in the foreign and domestic press; and his books, particularly *Psychoanalysis of Behavior—Collected Papers 1922-1956*, all embody his theoretical formulations. He is also a member or fellow of a number of scientific and professional societies, including the American Psychiatric Association and the American Psychoanalytic Association.

To review this wealth of experience and achievement leaves one wondering what kind of man it is that can have labored so strenuously for so long and still be engaged in launching yet another original experiment in the training of young psychiatrists. Those who have worked with him remember meetings at which the immediate business somehow got side-tracked when some student's problem started Rado going on a series of stories culled from his memories of the early years. Everyone felt so rewarded by these wandering reminiscences that they could easily accept the necessity of an extra meeting to conclude the business in hand. His "Hungarian temperament" often finds expression in mischievous defiance of his opposition; he loves to debunk the dogmas of traditionalism and unproved theory.

One curious contradiction has arisen from his enthusiastic presentation of his own theory which is often mistaken for authoritarianism—an attitude he strongly deplores. For him psychoanalysis must require of its exponents an untiring re-examination of theory and a discarding of all that cannot be proved. He has returned often to the biological teachings for a medical framework that has enabled him to formulate his "new look" at psychoanalytic theory, which is not a rival science but a watch tower looking out upon a human psychology in all its adaptational aspects.

As with most independent thinkers, his skepticism has brought much criticism down on his head and his combative nature has aroused many lesser men to take up arms against him. Whatever history may write concerning the validity of his theories, he will long be remembered as an enthusiastic, gifted teacher and a successful pioneer in psychiatric teaching and training.

John A. P. Millet, M.D.

1

SOCIAL STRUCTURE AND VERBAL PARTICIPATION IN THE PSYCHIATRIC CASE CONFERENCE

By WILLIAM F. KNOFF, M.D., JOHN H. MABRY, PH.D., AND EDWARD J. STAINBROOK, M.D.*

INTRODUCTION

Social Structure and the Therapeutic Community

THE INTERPERSONAL TRANSACTIONS associated with organizational status and role continue to be of considerable value to the behavioral sciences. Whether the primary interest be understanding the patient[1-4] or advancing theoretical knowledge,[5-7] interpretations of individual behavior require a knowledge of the behavior of persons in groups. Since a validated theory of the behavior of persons in groups leads to scientific prediction and control, any study of interpersonal relationships which tends toward the validation of theory should also contribute toward more effective patient-oriented therapy as well as toward the creation of more effective teaching programs.[8-11]

The focus of this study is the psychiatric case conference which may be viewed as an arena of interacting personalities, each with an interpersonal past history and each of whom has specific niches that are occupied within particular status systems. In this study we are concerned with the relationship between the department of psychiatry, the medical therapeutic community, the nonmedical therapeutic community, and those who have membership in two or more of these conference subgroups. The implications of this kind of study and approach extend beyond the psychiatric case conference. Ward culture and the dynamics of social interaction are important in other hospital settings (e.g., staff

* Departments of Psychiatry and Preventive Medicine, State University of New York, College of Medicine, Syracuse, N. Y. Prepared with the collaboration of Murray Wexler, Ph.D., and the technical assistance of Carl Snider, M.A., Paul Herman, M.A., Robert E. Burdick, M.A., and Mrs. Reign Hadsell.

meetings, research conferences) for staff members as well as for patients and their own perceptions of the various statuses and roles in the hospital (charwoman, aide, nurse, interne, resident, psychologist, social worker, occupational and recreational therapist, and psychiatrist). That status and role differences impinge upon and influence behavior in the therapeutic community, with particular emphasis upon the psychiatric case conference, is the basic *raison d'etre* of this study.

Methodology

Delineation of Conference Status Systems

The four consecutive psychiatric case conferences scrutinized in this report were held in September-October 1955, in the Department of Psychiatry, State University of New York, College of Medicine in Syracuse as part of the department's postgraduate teaching program. Because the Department of Psychiatry staffs and supervises the Psychiatry Service of the Syracuse Veterans Administration Hospital where the conferences were held, dual group membership in the Department of Psychiatry and therapeutic community sub-groups occurs for some of the conference participants. These weekly 90- to 120-minute conferences, four of which compose this study, are held in a large conference room comfortably accommodating the 25 to 30 medical and nonmedical personnel of the Department of Psychiatry and the therapeutic community who regularly attend. The conference room, located on the in-patient service, is furnished with a large conference table at which the moderator and the resident presenting the case are seated. If the patient is presented in person he is interviewed here. The moderator, the presenting resident, and any therapeutic team members such as the nurse, psychiatrist, occupational therapist, or social worker who may be called upon to present a report, constitute the formalized sub-group for administration of the conference and, therefore, take dual roles in group interaction. Such dual roles include (a) membership in both the Psychiatry Department and the medical therapeutic community and (b) formal conference presentors who have also other sub-group membership. For example, the moderator is chief of service in the therapeutic community as well as instructor in the Department of Psychiatry hierarchy. He interviews the patient before the group and may participate in the "free" discussion thereafter. The resident presents the case, answers questions, and may also participate in the "free" discussion period during which the teaching function of the conference is manifested. He is not only a formal presentor but also a member of the medical therapeutic community subgroup.

Those who attend the conference, although they do not all verbally participate, fall into four subgroups in addition to the formalized subgroup for administration of the conference defined above. These are:

1. Department of Psychiatry, medical, teaching.
2. Therapeutic community, medical, service.
3. Therapeutic community, nonmedical, service.
4. Visitors.

In terms of organizational position and assumed role relevant to occupational title, the hierarchical structure for the case conference group can be delineated as shown in table 1. These groups are further detailed in table 2.

Table 1.—*The Case Conference Group (of Subgroups)*

Participants
1. Department of Psychiatry, medical (teaching)
2. Therapeutic community, medical (service)
3. Therapeutic community, nonmedical (service)
4. Visitors
5. Formalized subgroup for administration of the conference

Table 2.—*The Subgroups*

Participants
1. Department of Psychiatry, medical (teaching)
(a) Professor
(b) Assistant Professors
*(c) Instructors
2. Therapeutic Community, medical (service)
*(a) Chief of Service
*(b) Assistant Chief
(c) 2nd Year Residents
(d) 1st Year Residents
(e) Interns (rotating)
(f) Nurses
(g) Medical Students
3. Therapeutic Community, nonmedical (service)
*(a) Chief, Clinical Psychology
*(b) Assistant Chief, Clinical Psychology
*(c) Clinical Psychologists
*(d) Psychiatric Social Worker

TABLE 2.—*Cont'd.*

(e) Occupational Therapists
(f) Recreational Therapists
(g) Volunteers

4. Visitors
5. Formalized Subgroup for Administration of the Conference
   (a) Moderator
   (b) Presenting Resident
   *(c) Reporting Nurse, Psychologist, Social Worker, Occupational Therapist, Recreational Therapist } If Called Upon

The formal operation of the conference begins with a remark by the moderator introducing the presenting resident who then proceeds verbally to reconstruct the chronological life history and treatment experience of one of his patients selected as a difficult clinical problem or for some other reason of high interest value. The resident is given the opportunity to express his own individuality, inasmuch as no prescribed form of presentation is rigidly followed, but he is guided by the principal information clusters of the usual psychiatric history, including presenting symptoms, initial interview, present illness, life situation, interpersonal developmental experience (including family history), medical history, and behavior status. The resident details his experience with the patient in therapy to date and proposes, especially if requested by the moderator, his own dynamic formulation. This presentation may be interrupted at any time by a member of the conference. Any and all such spontaneous utterances as well as those of the "free" discussion period are included in our analysis. Unless spontaneously offered, observations upon the patient's behavior are usually requested of therapeutic team members in other subgroups: the psychiatric nurse, psychiatric social worker, or occupational therapist. A formal report of testing is usually presented by the psychologist before or after the patient's appearance at the conference. The patient is fetched by the presenting resident who introduces him to the moderator. The moderator engages the patient in a 10- to 15-minute interview pertaining to the patient's problems insofar as he wishes to discuss and share them with the group. (This interview takes place only with the prior consent of the patient and with his full knowledge of the circumstances of the

* Dual Roles

case conference.) Members of the group may question the patient briefly, after which the patient departs and the conference is thrown open to "free" spontaneous discussion. This 30- to 60-minute discussion period is relatively informal and *constitutes the primary focus of our analysis*. Here the teaching function of the conference and the individual participant's role behavior become manifest. Group members of apparently greater knowledge and experience endeavor in characteristic ways to instruct participants of apparently less knowledge and experience, while participants representing different disciplines present interdisciplinary information. Conference leadership in this informal period may appear to shift from one speaker to another, or the participants may learn to expect the professor to "sum it all up," thus introducing a formal expectation into an otherwise relatively informal group action. However, the formality of the first two-thirds of the conference does not completely disappear inasmuch as the moderator can assert his role at any time, and it is the moderator or the professor who finally ends the conference with a closing remark.

Method of Postulates

Two of the writers have another paper in process which describes in more detail the logico-mathematical research procedure known as "the method of postulates."[12] Essentially, the method requires a rigorous logical ordering of postulates with a series of derived theorems which are so stated that a body of facts and empirical data may be enumerated with a view to verification, disproof, or modification.[13-15] Again, the treatment of empirical data is in conformity with the mathematical assumptions underlying statistical techniques.[16, 17] The advantages of this most precise and rigorous methodology are: first, the investigator is required fully and completely to think through his research problem and to examine carefully all of the ramifications of the questions that he initially thinks he wants to answer; second, it enables the investigator to know exactly how he must classify his data, as well as what data must be collected, in order to solve his research problem; third, it enables him to visualize exactly where he is going in the various phases of his research procedure and diminishes the possibility of fruitless ruminating; and fourth, it cannot help imposing on him a sense of humility as he realizes not only what he is doing in a specific research problem but also what it is that he is omitting.

The logical ordering of theorems and postulates for this particular study required four single-spaced typewritten pages, but since they are quite abstract and do not read easily with high interest, we are not presenting them here. Instead, we shall briefly describe them.

Our primary interest was in the relationship between two sets of variables: first, case conference sub-groups (as described above), and second, the frequency, amount, and kind of verbal participation. Furthermore, we were primarily interested in the more informal discussion periods so that we precluded the formal presentors (residents, nurse, psychologist, recreational and occupational therapists) from our analysis presented here today. The *amount* of verbal participation was measured by the number of lines consumed in the typewritten transcript of the tape-recorded case conference. The *frequency* was ascertained by the number of utterances other than those which were a part of the formal presentation of the case. In brief, we are concerned with *who says what to whom, when, and for how long.*

Since this was an initial effort to develop both methodology and substantive findings, a rather crude content analysis system was developed in order to arrive at the *kind of verbal participation* in terms of form and content of talk. The customary methods and procedure of content analysis as used in the behavioral sciences have been discussed elsewhere.[18] Suffice it to say that we analyzed each utterance in terms of the following content categories: *spontaneity*—an interruption in, or change in the flow of the discussion; *isolationality*—a comment or question ignored or not followed up by others in the group; *questioning*—not including rhetorical questions; *answering*—except when one answered his own rhetorical question; *interpersonal data*—how the patient descriptively and overtly gets along with others in the world around him; *socioeconomic data*—descriptive material about his job, church, social class, economic circumstances; *diagnosis*—nosological illness classifications as well as symptomatology; *dynamics*—covert psychological mechanisms and reactions to interpersonal and socioeconomic events; and *therapeutics*—plans and techniques of the treatment process.

It was not our intention to develop a set of mutually exclusive or exhaustive content categories in this first of a series of social structure studies. At this point we were basically interested in whether the conference subgroups could be described in terms of differential kinds of verbal interaction as well as differential frequency and amount. Consequently, an utterance could be classified as spontaneous, isolational, questioning, or answering, and either interpersonal, socioeconomic, diagnostic, dynamic, or therapeutic—or some other combination of the nine categories.

The two clinical members* of the research team assumed responsibility for the content analysis dealing with diagnostics, dynamics, and therapeutics. Considering the extreme difficulty one encounters in trying to get unanimous agreement upon the operational definitions of these terms in the behavior clinical sciences, a reliability check of 76.5 percent agreement between the two analysts was considered sufficient. Two nonclinical members† of the research team had responsibility for categorizing the other six kinds of verbal participation and achieved almost 85 percent agreement.

Content Analysis

Figure 1 indicates the general breakdown of the relative frequency of appearance of the different kinds of verbal participation for all of the

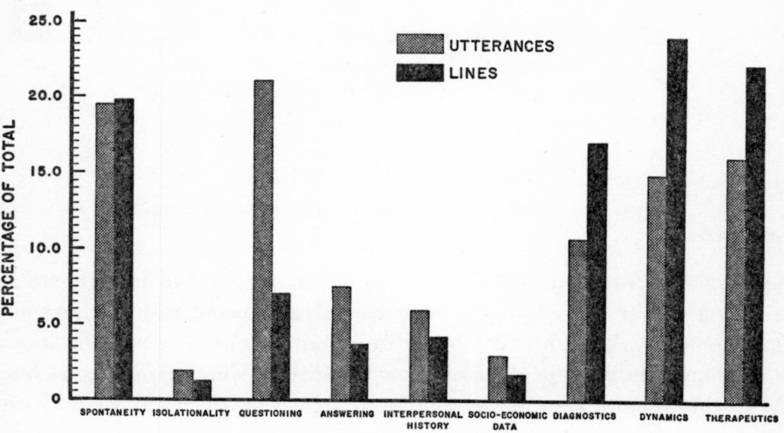

FIG. 1. Content analysis of five case conferences.

conference sub-groups. This content analysis does not include the formal presentors (which are given separately in fig. 2), so that the discrepancy between questioning (21.1 percent frequency, 6.8 percent amount) and answering (7.6 percent frequency, 3.7 percent amount) is partly accounted for by the fact that almost 85 percent of the total answers in

* W. F. Knoff, M.D., and M. Wexler, Ph.D.

† J. H. Mabry, Ph.D., and C. Snyder, M.A.

the conference were provided by the formal presentors. It may also be observed that the formal presentors asked almost 25 percent of the questions, but this is largely explained by the fact that the case confer-

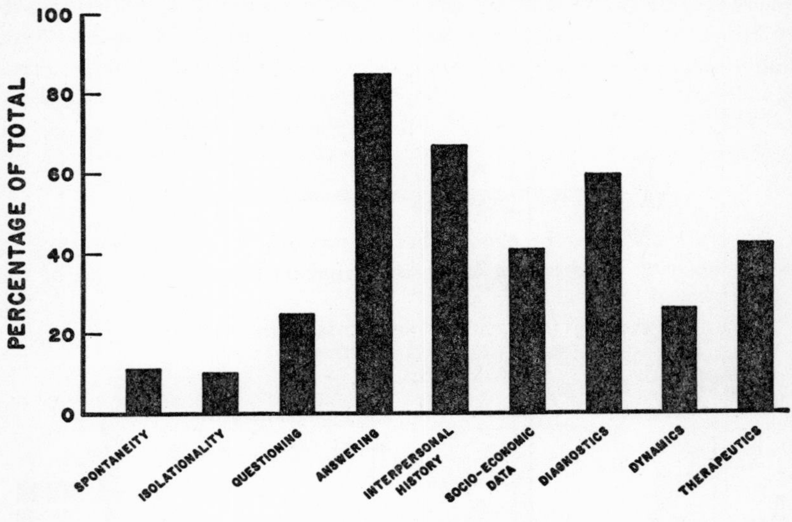

Fig. 2. Formal case conference presentors as per cent of the total conference utterances.

ence moderator (who had a triple role) was inclined to interrogate the resident, nurse, psychologist, recreational and occupational therapists, and social worker while the latter were more inclined simply to answer questions—only 11 percent of their comments were spontaneous ones. With this general view of the content of the case conference, we may now turn our attention to the relationship between these various categories of verbal participation and the social structure within each subgroup.

Findings

Frequency and Amount

Within the limitations of this study there was no doubt that the Department of Psychiatry made more comments and at greater length than did any other conference subgroup; those in a dual role participated more than would have been expected by chance alone but not as much as the Department of Psychiatry. Residents, for whose enlightenment the conference was primarily intended, participated much less than would have been expected, and the discussion participation of interns, medical students, social workers, and others was practically nonexistent. (The departmental social worker's low participation is partly due to occasional necessary absence from the conference.) Ten statistical calculations were accomplished which support the foregoing conclusions, and all were significant far beyond the 0.1 percent level of confidence.

Frequency and Amount for Nine Content Categories

Figure 3 shows the proportion of comments uttered by each of the

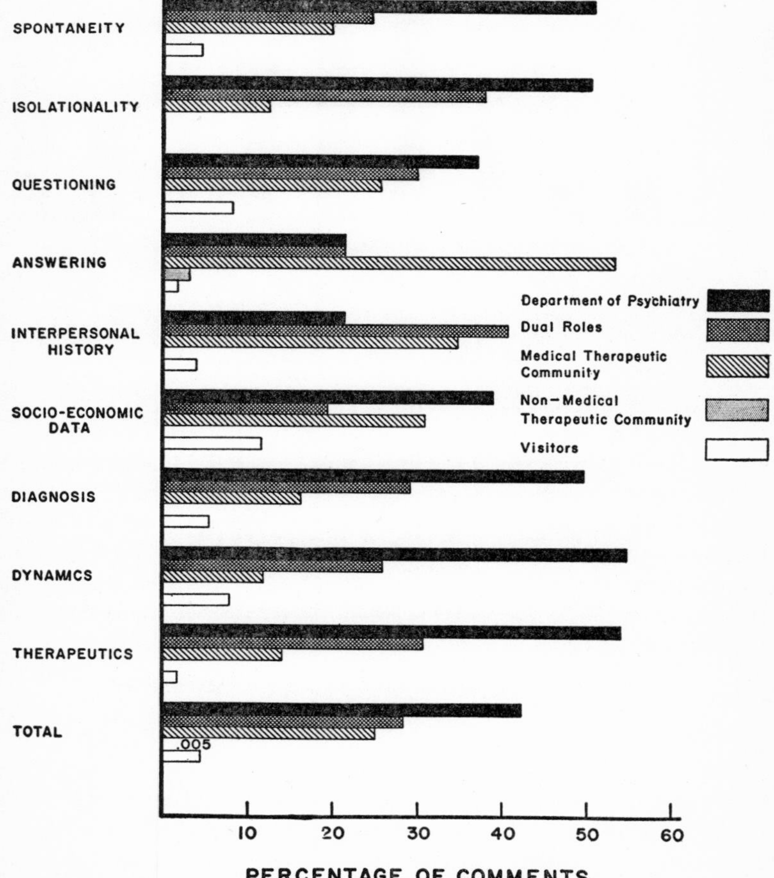

Fig. 3. Percentage of comments uttered in each category by the five conference subgroups.

conference subgroups in each of nine content analysis categories. With the exception of category #4, "Answering," there is a fairly consistent and significant trend for the Department of Psychiatry, those in a dual role, and the residents to participate verbally in that order for each of the categories. The following observations may be made:

First, those in the higher status groups (Department of Psychiatry, dual role personnel) were more inclined to participate spontaneously and to ask questions while those in the lower status subgroups (residents and interns, nurses, social workers, and others) were more inclined to

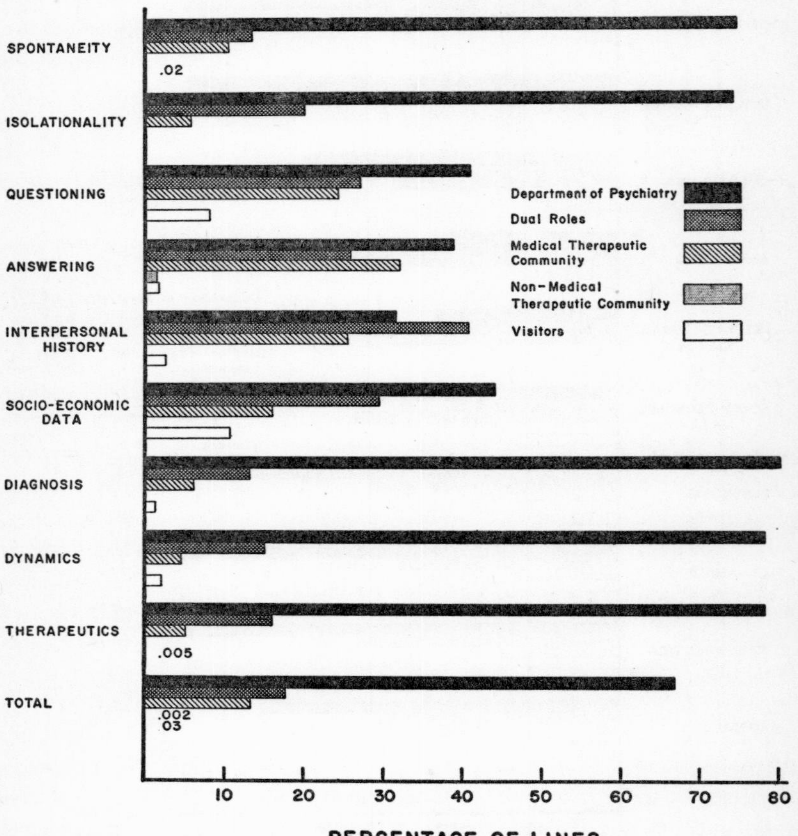

FIG. 4. Percentage of lines spoken in each category by the five conference subgroups.

answer questions non-spontaneously and to go along with the direction of the particular line of discussion.

Second, for diagnostic, dynamic, and therapeutic interpretations, the Department of Psychiatry clearly contributed the most comments while those with dual subgroup memberships were far below them and at the same time were appreciably above the other conference subgroups.

Third, interestingly enough, the dual role subgroup for administration of the conference verbally participated with more interpersonal data comments than did any other group, with the subgroup including residents ranking second. This may be partly explained by the fact that frequently a diagnostic, dynamic, or therapeutic question was answered *not* in these terms but rather with an uninterpreted interpersonal anecdote from the patient's history.

Fourth, it is intriguing to observe that the number of isolational comments were so few (16 in all conferences). By the same token, we dropped a relationality category because 99 percent of the comments were germane to some aspect of the patient and his illness.

Thirty-six statistical calculations were achieved and all of them supported the foregoing conclusions. Thirty-five were significant beyond the 0.1 percent level of confidence and one was significant beyond the 1 percent level of confidence.

Frequency and Amount by Category for the Department of Psychiatry and Medical Therapeutic Community Subgroups

In terms of the frequency and amount of verbal participation, the Professor of Psychiatry differed significantly from others in the department in that he participated more than any other department member. When we analyzed the *kind of verbal participation* within the Department of Psychiatry we found that, first, the Professor of Psychiatry participated more frequently and with longer utterances in terms of spontaneity, questioning, diagnostics, dynamics, and therapeutics; second, that he participated at no greater frequency but with longer utterances on comments classified as interpersonal history and socioeconomic data; third, on comments classified as isolationality and answering there were no statistically significant differences. These conclusions were supported by 45 statistical calculations whose significance levels were as follows: five were significant at greater than the 5 percent level of confidence and thus not interpreted as statistically significant; one was significant between the 5 and 2 percent levels; one between the 2 and

1 percent levels; and 35 at beyond the 0.1 percent level of confidence.

For the medical therapeutic community subgroup, including residents, it is equally strongly suggested that those in the upper hierarchy, i.e., second year residents, verbally participated with more frequency and at greater length, while first year residents were next, and others (interns, nurses, social workers, medical students, and occupational and recreational therapists) scarcely participated at all. This difference obtained also for the following kinds of verbal participation: spontaneity, questioning, answering, interpersonal history, dynamics, and therapeutics. It was not demonstrated to hold for comments classed as isolational, socioeconomic data, and diagnostics. A total of 12 calculations were computed in support of these conclusions and 11 were significant beyond the 1 percent level of confidence while one was significant between the 1 and 0.1 percent levels.

Summary with Implications

Assuming that each member of the conference group will tend to use the conference, particularly the discussion period which purports to encourage spontaneous "free" exchange of ideas, in his own particular way, depending upon his concept of his position and role in the group, we have recorded and analyzed this behavior as manifested in part by verbal utterance. In a teaching center involved in both undergraduate teaching and post graduate training, the psychiatric staff case conference supposedly functions as a teaching conference designed to impart knowledge relevant to diagnosis, prognosis, and psychodynamics and to assist the resident in the performance of his therapeutic task. This paper, which reveals the impingement of social structure on verbal utterance, presents a beginning attempt at seeing how and if this happens.

Although the case conferences were undertaken with an atmosphere of free and open equalitarian discussion, it is quite clear that there are status subgroup differentials in the frequency, amount, and kind of verbal participation as well as differences according to status within each of the subgroups here under study. Those participants with the most training, experience, and highest professional positions tended to participate more than would have been expected while those with the least experience, training and lower professional positions participated much less frequently than would have been expected on a purely statistical basis. *Our delineation of the conference status system in terms of organizational position was drawn independently of and prior to our analysis of verbal participation.* Interestingly enough, if we now derive the conference hierarchy from the evidence of utterance behavior we find exactly the same hierarchy. This suggests that it is possible to recognize status positioning in groups through talk behavior alone without knowledge of formal organization and shows an aspect of the relatedness of social structure to action. In this respect, this conference is not unlike other social groups which have previously been described in the literature.[19-21] Lest we suffer the "delusions of statistical accuracy,"[22] however, it is well to discuss the relevance of these descriptive findings.

First, it is quite inappropriate to contend that it would be "better" or "worse" to have verbal participation follow a pattern different from that described here. It would be necessary to ascertain definitively the specific learning outcomes of the case conference before any change in its structure and format as implementations of learning goals would be appropriate. There are a number of group structures and leadership roles,[23] ranging from authoritarian to relatively unstructured situations. Sociologically, there would not seem to be very much that could be done to change the conference status subgroup memberships, since clinical and research findings have shown that one needs to place himself with relationship to others, not only from the standpoint of administrative arrangements but also in terms of the individual's perception of himself and of others with whom he works. This paper statistically demonstrates the interdependent relationship between conference status subgroups and verbal participation. Each question about possible changes in the verbal participation pattern of the case conference would raise certain imponderables. Should the residents participate more frequently and at greater length? This would mean that the Department of Psychiatry, whose chief function is a teaching one, would have to participate less frequently and at lesser length. Should a larger proportion of comments by residents and others be diagnostic, dynamic and/or therapeutic? This would require less comment upon interpersonal material and socioeconomic data which serve as a basis for the derivation of diagnostic and dynamic interpretations and which aid in the realistic problems of outlining a therapeutic process. These and other questions require a great deal of thought about the teaching-learning process in its formal and informal, verbal and nonverbal aspects. This study has purported to describe the verbal participation patterns as they operate in a particular case conference at a given time. Although this study is limited to a particular on-going conference group, there is no reason why our method or modifications of it cannot be applied elsewhere by other observers. Presumably, increased understanding of conference behavior can sharpen group insight, thereby facilitating change in the direction of better teaching and improved problem-seeing and problem-solving in the psychiatric case conference.

Second, the psychiatric case conference is attended by non-physician representatives of the professional medical community although participation is much less for the non-physician groups. It is clear that the discussion period could not be completely equalitarian. There was an average attendance of 30 at each conference. If each individual were to have an equal amount of participation in time there would be an average of two minutes per person in a one-hour discussion period: the Department of Psychiatry would have 8 minutes, residents 16 minutes— it would be absurd to suggest that a moderator could effectively fulfill his role requirements with only two minutes. It goes without saying, of course, that a great deal of learning may occur through verbally passive participation and active listening. We should not be unduly distressed over the under-participation of some of the groups, for a certain amount of this would seem to be necessary. If increased participation is found to be desirable, we would suggest that an instrument for achieving this would require a different kind of case conference.

Third, the verbal participation patterns of residents may be considered as one of a series of acculturation processes[24] by which they become gradually incorporated into the medical therapeutic community. It would be expected that the participation patterns might change in time as they become better acquainted with the dynamics of personality, diagnosis and therapy, and as they gain more confidence in themselves as emergently fulfilling the role of psychiatrist. We have not yet studied the residents' perceptions of themselves and of those with whom they carry on interpersonal transactions, but we have certain impressions that the residents' participation pattern has changed somewhat in the nine months since our data were collected and that current data, unanalyzed so far, would reveal that residents early in the first year participate much less, and with different content, than they do toward the end of the first and the beginning of the second training year. It appears that spontaneity and amount of utterance increase while content moves from interpersonal history data about the patient to diagnostic, dynamic and therapeutic interpretations.

Finally, our establishment of clearly defined status structure and role behavior (as measured by verbal participation) has further implications for the hospital community. To what extent do psychiatrists, residents, interns, nurses, aides, and others behave differentially on the psychiatric ward? To what extent are status and role differentials among the medical and nonmedical ward personnel perceived and differentially responded to by patients on the ward? These questions do not permit a simple answer, but they must be reckoned with in any serious attempt to conceptualize and achieve an effective therapeutic ward community.

REFERENCES

1. Mead, Margaret: Some relationships between social anthropology and psychiatry. In F. Alexander and H. Ross, Eds., Dynamic Psychiatry. Chicago, University of Chicago Press, 1952, pp. 401-448.
2. Redlich, F. C., Hollingshead, A. B., and Bellis, E.: Social class differences in attitudes towards psychiatry. Unpublished discussion, Yale University.
3. Tavistock Institute: Social Psychiatry: A Study of Therapeutic Communities. London, 1952.
4. Caudill, W., Redlich, F. C., Gillmore, H. R., and Brody, E. H.: Social structure and interaction processes on a psychiatric ward. Unpublished discussion, Yale University.
5. Bales, R. F.: Interaction Process Analysis. Cambridge, Addison-Wesley, 1951.
6. Slotkin, J. S.: Personality Development. New York, Harper, 1952.
7. Marx, M. H., Ed.: Psychological Theory. New York, Macmillan, 1951, pp. 526-554.
8. Lynd, R. S.: Knowledge for What? Princeton, Princeton University Press, 1948.
9. Cohen, M. R., and Nagel, E.: Logic and Scientific Method. New York, Harcourt Brace, 1934, pp. 399-403.
10. Likert, R., and Lippitt, R.: The utilization of social science. In L. Festinger and D. Katz, Eds., Research Methods in the Behavorial Sciences. New York, Dryden Press, 1953, pp. 581-646.
11. Neurath, O.: Foundations of the social sciences. In International Encyclopedia of Unified Science, II. Chicago, University of Chicago Press, 1944.
12. Stainbrook, E., and Mabry, J. H.: The method of postulates: a research tool in the behavorial sciences. In preparation.
13. Huntington, E. V.: The method of postulates. Philosoph. Sci. *4*:482-495, 1937.
14. Murdock, G. P.: The cross cultural survey. Am. Sociol. Rev. *5*: 369-370, 1940.

15. ——: Social Structure. New York, Macmillan, 1949.
16. Yules, G. U., and Kendall, M. G.: An Introduction to the Theory of Statistics. London, Methuen, 1937.
17. Fisher, R. A.: The Design of Experiments. Edinburgh, Oliver & Boyd, 1949.
18. Berelson, B.: Content Analysis in Communications Research. Glencoe, Ill., Free Press, 1952. See also Bales, op. cit.
19. Linton, R.: The Study of Man. New York, Appleton-Century, 1936, pp. 113-131.
20. Lundberg, G. A.: Foundations of Sociology. New York, Macmillan, 1939, pp. 290-333.
21. Brown, J. F.: Psychology and the Social Order. New York, McGraw-Hill, 1936, parts 2-3.
22. Whitman, Roy M.: The rating and group dynamics of the psychiatric staff conference. Psychiatry (in press).
23. Stainbrook, E. J., and Caudill, W.: Background for Illness. New York, The Commonwealth Fund (in press).
24. Moroney, M. J.: Facts from Figures. London, Penguin Books, 1953.
25. Gouldner, A. W., Ed.: Studies in Leadership. New York, Harper, 1950.
26. Herskovits, M. J.: Man and His Works. New York, Knopf, 1947, pp. 523-541.

2

ULTRACONCEPTUAL COMMUNICATION

By D. EWEN CAMERON, M.D., F.R.C.P.*

INTRODUCTION

DURING THE LAST FEW YEARS we have been studying communication between individuals and it is surprisingly difficult to obtain a satisfactory definition of what is meant by communication. If one takes a broad statement, for example, that communication is any action on the part of the individual which evokes a response in others, he finds himself immediately confronted by actions which can by no manner or means be thought of as communication per se. For instance, an individual may by accident drive his car into a lamp-post, and this certainly will evoke a response in the passers-by and in the police force, but it cannot be thought of as communication. On the other hand, we can well imagine such an action being planned as a signal for a mob uprising or a conspiratorial outbreak. In this case one could just as certainly say it was a communication. If one then seeks to narrow the definition by saying that communication is any action which is designed to evoke a response in others we encounter two difficulties. First of all, quite a lot of communication is unconscious, for example, the patient in psychotherapy who unconsciously moves back from his therapist. This is perceived by the therapist and evokes a response in him in turn. A second difficulty which this definition encounters is that some communication consists in signals which we do our best to prevent. For instance, we may try to conceal our fear of our antagonist, yet we may betray it in our pallor and in our increased respiratory rate, and this certainly acts as a signal to him to take appropriate action.

We have found no satisfactory overall definition; hence we shall limit ourselves to stating that we are concerned in this paper with the signals that individuals make to each other or which they detect in each other

* Chairman, Department of Psychiatry, McGill University, Montreal; Director, Allan Memorial Institute of Psychiatry.

and which may be conscious or unconscious. And in particular we are reporting upon those signals which are not consciously perceived by the recipient but which may nonetheless evoke response in him.

The following are representative though not exclusive lists of the signals which we have studied:

Range of Signals

Verbal—form, content, intonation.

Gestures—including facial mimicry.

Bodily movements—tapping with impatience; childhood residues, e.g., curling an imaginary lock of hair; or moving of body to or away from therapist.

Autonomic changes—flushing, breathing.

Range of Verbal Signals

Content—repeated use of a word or of a phrase; unusual use of a word or phrase.

Form—hesitations; blocking; mispronunciation; transposition of words.

Intonation—general tone: hostility, anxiety, immaturity, and coldness; special intonations, which may occur at special points in the communication: loudness, softness, "tightening" of voice, "roughening" of voice; appearance of earlier foreign pronunciations.

More recently our capacity to study both the production and the effects of communication has been greatly increased by a number of mechanical devices. One of the earliest of these was the galvanic skin reflex. It has not taken us as far as its proponents at one time hoped it would, nor has a second method of study met our needs concerning communication and interpersonal action, namely the investigation of respiration during interpersonal actions. Others of considerably greater promise seem to be the electrogastrograph, with which the activities of the stomach can be examined during the interview, and, still more useful, the electromyograph, which in the hands of Malmo[1-3] and others has been exceedingly valuable. Movies, especially slow motion films, have still further expanded our knowledge of the signals and responses which individuals show in interpersonal relationships. But of all these forms of instrumentation the magnetic recorder has been by far the most important. The most recent models allow recording of vocal frequencies from 0 to 15,000 cycles. When this recording is coupled with a sensitive pick-up system and with a high fidelity speaking unit it constitutes a most penetrating and flexible tool for the study of communication.

Still other advances which do not lie in the field of instrumentation at all have been extremely useful. The first of these has been the development in our knowledge of psychodynamics and psychotherapy, and particularly the advances in training to listen with the third ear. Another tool which we ourselves have found useful is the working concept of the diploid. This concept visualizes two individuals in interaction with each other as constituting a single whole within which dynamic exchanges take place.[4]

Experimental

The material upon which these studies is based is derived primarily from tape recordings of the communications of patients undergoing long range psychotherapy and of the therapist. Productions of all patients under psychotherapy during the last three years by the present author have been continuously recorded. Pivotal statements have been transferred from the tapes to long-playing discs for playback and for special investigation.

Our studies fall into two major categories: (1) those based on driving (repeated playback) of recorded psychotherapeutic communications; and (2) those based upon the electronic analysis of such communication by an apparatus specially developed for this purpose.

In our studies of the *repeated playback* of the recording of psychotherapeutic communication we observed:

That repeated playback resulted in both the patient's and the therapist's being able to perceive and understand meanings in communication which they could not detect when the material was played back for the first time. Some of the reasons for this have already been reported.[5] Chief among them are that with respect to the patient it was found that a shielding exists which prevents the individual, whether patient or therapist, from grasping the full import of his own communication. This shielding is with respect to the synthesis of air and tissue conduction which normally occurs when one listens to oneself speaking. When, however, one listens to his own voice being played back this synthesis is broken down, since what one hears is produced purely by air conduction. Since the synthesis has been broken down the shielding is no longer effective and hence the individual begins to hear significances in his own communication from which he previously had shielded himself.

Another factor which has been studied is the amount of work involved in talking as contrasted with the amount of work concerned in listening. Briefly it may be said that talking involves a very great complexity of activities, among them being the development of a series of concepts whereby our communication may be transmitted, the choosing of words, the continual monitoring of our tone, the continuous calculating of the receptivity of the listener, the monitoring of a listener's response, and our continual seeking to maintain our goal idea, that is, to keep talking toward an objective. Listening, on the other hand, involves much less activity. However, listening in itself is not the purely mechanical recording which is apt to be our unthinking stereotype of what we do when we listen to somebody else. Actually, listening is a highly dynamic interpersonal relationship which results in the listener's periodically going off on side reactions of his own and then having to find his way back to the main theme of what is being said. Hence, listening to anything on the first occasion will not provide the listener with all the data being communicated. Listening has to be carried out on repeated occasions if full communication is to be achieved. Finally we have suggested that the increased communication noted upon repetition may also be due to three other factors, although these have not been conclusively demonstrated. First, the law of the summation of sub-liminal stimuli may come into operation, and, second, constant repetition, particularly as far as the patient is concerned, may result in an exhaustion of his defenses. This idea of an exhaustion occurring is one which is not well understood but would appear, at least theoretically, to be possible. The third factor is that of set. It has been found that the general set of the patient on a given day will determine in some measure his capacities to detect signals. The reasons for the increased communication which takes place upon repetition of a psychotherapeutic communication have been outlined above. The main import, however, is that since increased communication does occur only on repetition, one must say that in any given statement there is apart from the immediately grasped communication a range of other signals which are not immediately grasped and which can be understood only after certain special circumstances have come into operation. Among these circumstances are (a) repeated playback, and (b) the circumventing of the patient's shielding through the use of a recorder.

This was our introduction to the general idea that there may be a range of communication which cannot readily be perceived and conceptualized, and to this we gave the designation "ultraconceptual communication." The following is a key statement by a patient in which are contained a number of signals of very considerable importance. As will be seen, it deals essentially with her relationship to her mother. Many of the signals cannot be adequately represented in written form since they consist of shifts in intonation, blocks, pauses, hesitations, and emotional overtones.

> I don't know why . . . I'm supposed to listen to every little thing and I don't *want* to listen to every little thing. I can't give her what she wants. I'm *not* well . . . and she has pinned *everything* . . . she has blamed *all* her troubles and upsets on my *ill health* and on the fact that she feels that she has *failed* with me. She's pinning it all on *that* . . . (*pause*) And she . . . I guess she knows too much *about me* . . . and I *don't like that.* And I feel sort of *bound* to tell her everything . . . I don't know why.

At the time of first playing the patient was able to recognize with difficulty the extent of her resentment against her mother. On replaying two weeks later she was able to accept the fact that she actually hated her mother. She also perceived her own struggle for independence as implied in the words, "She knows too much about me." Played again a month later she perceived and understood the signal indicating her mother's interference.

2. There is in a verbal communication a range of signals, some of which could be picked up by one listener and others by another. It was found, for instance, that ordinarily the therapist could pick up more signals in a given communication than could the patient. It was also found that a group of therapists listening to a communication would all pick up many of the same signals, but that in addition there would be quite a number of signals which some therapists would pick up and others would not except when they were brought to their attention, and sometimes an individual could not pick up a signal even after

it was pointed out to him. Indeed, we have a few recordings which contain signals which most therapists agree that they can detect because of changes in emphasis and timing, but no agreement whatsoever can be reached as to their significance.

It was a matter of great interest to note the occasions on which the patient was able to pick up signals in his own communication which the therapist had not picked up, and perhaps of even greater interest to note that even when they were on occasion pointed out to the therapist he could not detect them nor could he conceptualize their significance. This second group of observations reinforced us in our conviction that signals might be made which could not be understood and even at times remain undetected by the signaler or by the recipient. Here is another key statement from a patient:

> I think I usually . . . I usually . . . thought about . . . her doing something *mean* to me and . . . it causing me great *harm* . . . and then she would realize . . . what a dreadful thing she had done . . . and would say she was *sorry*.

Many of the important signals are immediately available on reading this, but there is one which none of us has been able to understand, although it has been listened to by many groups of psychiatrists, that is the particular intonations with which the last phrase, ". . . and say she was *sorry*," was said.

3. An increase in the capacity to understand signals was achieved by both the patient and the therapist with practice. Detection is increased with practice, as is shown by the fact that the experienced patient learns to detect his hesitations, pauses, and blocks regardless of whether the loaded areas which underlie them are heavily defended or not. With regard to the increased capacity to understand the meaning of signals, we have developed a working theory that experience in this type of activity, namely the listening to communication, results in setting into the conceptual panels of the listener sets of additional abilities to respond to the appropriate cues in a given communication. We also confirmed the observations made by others that signals which could be detected and understood on a given day might not be understood on a subsequent occasion, and also that there were days both for the therapist and for the patient on which signals were harder to detect and much less easily understood than on other days.

These three sets of observations left us with the following provisional findings:

a. That signals are made which are not conceived as such by the signaler, at least at the time he makes them.
b. That signals are received which are not conceived as such by the listener, at least at the time that he first listens.
c. That a range of signals may be made which will only at times be conceived as such by the signaler and by the listener.
d. The ability of both the signaler and the listener to recognize signals may be increased and decreased.

We then conjectured that it was at least theoretically possible that a range of signals might be made which could not be understood by either the signaler or the recipient at any time but which might nonetheless evoke an appropriate response in the recipient.

We then proceeded to our second set of studies: those based upon the *electronic analysis* of such communication. In order to undertake this it was necessary to design a special apparatus.

A condenser-microphone is connected to a tape recorder. After a recording has been made of the patient's communication, representative samples are selected from the tape. Selected lengths are then made into endless loops and each loop in turn is analyzed by playing it back continuously through a number of band-pass filters which divide the speech spectrum into a number of frequency bands covering a range of audible frequencies, i.e. 30 to 15,000 cycles per second, approximately. The output of each band-pass filter (thirty are used in our apparatus) is measured directly by a meter in values which represent average acoustic energy produced by the voice as a function of the frequency.

In order to analyze conversational speech, an energy level integrator is connected to the output of the set of thirty band-pass filters and the spectrum level for each band is measured by means of an electronic counter. Repeated playback of words and sentences makes it possible to obtain an analysis over the desired frequency range. Our studies with this type of apparatus are still in the early stages and fall into three main groups, designed primarily to explore the versatility of the apparatus. These are as follow: (a) We have explored variations in the energy output of the voice from hour to hour during the day when the subject maintains a constant frequency hum. This can be achieved by having the subject hum into a microphone connected with a cathode ray oscillograph set in such a way that a regular pattern appears and is maintained only when the hum reaches a predetermined frequency. This is accurate within 1-2 c.p.s. When the output of a voice is examined under these circumstances, it is found that in some individuals the tonal quality of the voice indicated by relative energy values of the upper harmonics varies considerably. This suggests a variation in energy output, despite constancy of the fundamental frequency, and may serve as a signal under given circumstances. (b) Our second set of studies concerned repetition of a well-practiced statement made hour by hour throughout the day. This was achieved by ringing one of the secretaries on the telephone. She answered routinely, "Dr. —— office." This was recorded and the telephone replaced, leaving her with the impression that a wrong number had been called. In this way the voice was investigated primarily for loudness (amplitude) variations, and it may be noted that the unaided ear could by no means always pick up differences in the secretary's intonation. In actuality, considerable changes did take place throughout the day. Moreover, after a particularly tragic event had occurred at the Institute, there was a change in the secretary's voice as recorded by the machine. (c) Finally, we took a recording from a patient who was communicating in psychotherapy under very stressful situations. After approximately three months we had the patient read back precisely the same statement. Both recordings were then analyzed with regard to amplitude and there were very great differences.

This material is presented in order to demonstrate the extent to which signals may be superimposed upon content. The listener can certainly distinguish between the emotional content of the first statement and the rather placid reading of the second. However, this type of comparative approach suggests the possibility of our being able to detect whether or not there are actually concealed signals in a communication from the patient. We hope to be able to show this by comparing a more complete speech analysis of the statement as it was originally made with the analysis of the statement when it is read.

Discussion

From our studies on communication we have been impressed with the fact that signals may be made and received without either sender's or recipient's being aware of the fact.

Everyday experience and considerable literature indicate that such signals, even when not consciously perceived, may nonetheless evoke response in the individual. These facts tie in with another group of observations, namely those made by workers in the conditioned reflex field. Such signals, i.e., conditioned and unconditioned stimuli, do not usually constitute communication as we commonly conceive it, from person to person.

The most recent Russian work, as reported by K. M. Bykov to the 19th International Congress of Physiology in Montreal in 1953, illustrates the pervasiveness with which signals may operate. He points out, however, that workers who by reason of their occupation are constantly exposed to cold, such as train conductors and workers in refrigerator plants, show as a result of their work a considerable increase in heat production even during the complete absence of any muscular activity. If such individuals are placed in a situation in which the temperature is comparable to that which they experience while at work, but which is otherwise entirely different, then the temperature rise in metabolic rate does not occur to the same degree and, when it does take place, it comes into operation much more slowly than when they are in their work surroundings. In other words, their work surroundings constitute unconscious signals for a rise in temperature to meet the coldness with which their work surroundings have been habitually connected. Similar work has been done on the effects of a moving wind passing over the surface of the body. Our general experience is that a moving wind tends to reduce temperature. Hence the tactile stimulus of the wind becomes the conditioned stimulus which raises the heat production of the body. If, however, the temperature of the wind is raised to the point at which no heat loss takes place, the heat production nonetheless continues, for the simple reason that the awareness of the wind constitutes an adequate stimulus. Again, somewhat similar experiments have been carried out in sheep. It has been found that the oxygen consumption of sheep in pens is much less than that of sheep in the open field, even though the sheep under both circumstances undertake the identical amount of activity. The open-air situation carries with it to the sheep implications of the probability of increased activity and this tends to raise the oxygen consumption.

We should also like to draw attention to work carried out by Dr. R. B. Malmo in the Psychology Laboratories of the Allan Memorial Institute and reported at the Regional Research Conference on Psychiatry held by the A.P.A. under the auspices of McGill University in 1955. By running simultaneous electromyographic and other physiological records on the therapist and patient simultaneously during a psychotherapeutic period, Dr. Malmo was able to demonstrate that there was a remarkable degree of conformity between the physiological evidences of stress in the therapist and in the patient. This occurred in many instances without there being any conscious perception by the therapist of stress in the patient, or by the patient of stress in the therapist. In other words, these observations also would serve to suggest that signals may be made and communicated without either the signaler's or the recipient's being aware of their existence.

The importance of this concept of ultraconceptual communication is that it may well throw light upon responses which otherwise are hard to understand. Among these responses may be the triggering of anxiety attacks. It is well known that patient and therapist alike very often find it difficult to explain why a given psychosomatic response, particularly an anxiety attack, occurs apparently spontaneously. Ultraconceptual communication may also serve to explain some interpersonal responses which are likewise hard to understand, among them aversions as well as attractions. Possibly, looking at it in a wider sense, it may also be that regularly made signals by individuals having certain unconscious needs and certain unconscious deficits will serve to explain some of the otherwise hard-to-understand selections in friendship and in marriage.

Summary

1. Signals are made which are not conceived as such by the signaler, at least at the time he makes them.
2. Signals are received which are not conceived as such by the listener, at least at the time that he first listens.
3. A range of signals may be made which will only at times be conceived as such by the signaler and by the recipient.
4. The ability of both the signaler and the listener to recognize signals may be increased and decreased.
5. It is probable that there is a range of signals which cannot be understood by either, but which may nonetheless evoke an appropriate response in the recipient.

Acknowledgement

The author wishes to acknowledge the technical assistance of Mr. L.

Rubenstein in the development of the electronic analysis of verbal signals.

REFERENCES

1. Malmo, R. B.: Experimental studies in mental patients under stress. In M. L. Reymert, Ed., Feelings and Emotions. New York, McGraw-Hill, 1950, p. 169.
2. ——: Research: Experimental and theoretical aspects. In E. D. Wittkower and R. A. Cleghorn, Eds., Recent Development in Psychosomatic Medicine. London, Pitman, 1954, p. 84.
3. ——: Symptom mechanisms in psychiatric patients. Tr. New York Acad. Sci. *18*: 545-549, 1956.
4. Cameron, D. E.: Unorthodox working concepts for psychotherapy. Med. Ann. District of Columbia *22*: 226-234, 1953.
5. ——: Psychic driving. Am. J. Psychiat. *112*: 502-509, 1956.

3

SOME PSYCHOLOGICAL EFFECTS OF LANGUAGE STRUCTURE

By JOHN B. CARROLL, PH.D.*

ABNORMAL MENTAL PROCESSES are not merely the accompaniments of psychopathological disturbances but are their very substance. Because these disturbances manifest themselves in the patient's language behavior, the psychology of language in its normal as well as its abnormal aspects has engaged the attention of the psychopathologist. Slips of the tongue, the language of schizophrenia and of aphasia, taboo words, and the effects of verbal labelling, are some of the topics which have been studied. In most discussions of these topics, however, it is the *content* of the language which has been emphasized rather than the *form*. That is, language has been regarded as a mere carrier or vehicle of thought, with the cargo unchanged or unaffected by the nature of the vehicle. There are, to be sure, a few trivial instances in which the nature of the vehicle has had to be taken into account. For example, certain symbolic phenomena relying essentially on verbal puns or otherwise on phonetic similarities between words will obviously depend on the language being employed—English, French, German, or whatnot. There does not seem to have been an extensive consideration of the possibility that the nature of the language structure in general, or of the structure of particular languages, may have an influence on cognitive processes and hence upon pathologic mental states. In part this is due to the fact that to take account of language structure is a bootstrap operation: one must somehow "get outside" of one's own language in order to see how its mechanism really works. This is also due partly to the fact that the languages we are all accustomed to are in many fundamental respects highly similar; we do not often have occasion to become exposed to the characteristics of languages like Japanese, Bantu, or Hopi, with structures quite different from that of English and standard European languages.

* Harvard University, Cambridge, Mass.

It seems to be widely accepted that language is involved in the process of thinking in many ways. I am not concerned here with this general problem, however, but with the narrower and more specialized problem of whether the particular structure of one's language has some special influence on cognitive behavior. Let me define my terms.

By *language structure* we mean all those lexical or grammatical phenomena founded explicitly or implicitly on a language code and which imply categorization of referents or ways of ordering and patterning such referents. Every language has a certain structure, even in its vocabulary; that is to say, it has a finite number of lexical forms, ordinarily called *words,* which imply the possibility of classifying experiences to correspond with the vocabulary. Some languages have richer vocabularies than others and languages vary in the richness of their vocabularies in certain semantic domains. Eskimo has a rich vocabulary for varieties of snow; Arabic has a rich vocabulary for varieties of horses and their markings. A question which has not yet been satisfactorily resolved is that of how much languages differ in the way they classify common experiences, but I think every student of a foreign language soon finds that there are differences which he might not otherwise expect, like the difference in German between *essen* (to eat, said of human beings) and *fressen* (to eat, said of animals). Suffice it to say that differences are sufficient to make translation often difficult and sometimes impossible. Perhaps more interesting than lexical differences between languages, because of their pervasiveness and "unconscious" character, are the grammatical differences. Every language has grammatical processes by which words can be modified or put into syntactical arrangements; to illustrate, in English we can form plurals, the past tense, the comparative degree of adjectives, and designate subject and object of verb by word order. Such grammatical processes refer to certain patternings or potential patternings of our experiences. Languages differ markedly in the grammatical categorizations they impose on speakers: in Chinese and some other languages, it is not necessary to indicate plurality, as we customarily do in English; on the other hand, there are languages which impose much more than English does—such as certain American Indian languages which require one to report the truth-value or "source of evidence" for any declarative statement. (That is, grammatical markers are required which indicate whether one saw something at first hand, heard it from someone, or is purely imagining something.)

Linguistic scientists rarely pay much attention to the meanings of words or of grammatical processes, treating them as formal givens. To state the meanings of words and of grammatical processes is essentially a psychological problem, and to me it is essentially a matter of stating the generalized discriminations which the members of a speech community have developed and associated with linguistic entities. To take a simple example: what is the difference between a *stick* (of wood) and a *block* (of wood)? If we present a subject with a graduated series of pieces of wood varying from a perfect cube to one which is quite long and slender, he will designate a range of objects to which *stick* can apply and a range to which *block* can apply; we should expect a certain degree of overlapping in these ranges, varying somewhat from subject to subject. The point is that our English speech community has developed and reinforced a discrimination between certain experiences, the words *stick* and *block* being associated with this particular discrimination. One can conceive a community where this discrimination has not been reinforced, or where the ranges of the discriminated responses are different. This sort of thing is certainly known to have happened with colors. Even when we take more or less "standard color names" like *red, orange, yellow, green, blue, violet,* it is often impossible to find color names in another language which will match these in terms of the ranges of physical color stimuli to which they apply. If this is so, one would expect to find discrepancies between languages with respect to many other domains of experience, perhaps even more in such "subjective" domains as terms for judgments, feelings, and emotions.

It will be noticed that the statement of meanings inevitably involves an appeal to certain types of cognitive processes, for by *cognitive behavior* we refer generally to behavior involving the making of discriminations, generalizing these discriminations, structuring experiences, and making inferences and predictions.

Having defined our terms, we see that the problem we are confronted with is one of whether the categorizations of experience implied in a particular language structure influence the way in which we interact with our environment behaviorally. The problem is not new. It would make an interesting essay in the history of ideas to trace it back to its origins. But I shall skip this history. In recent years the problem was brought to attention largely through the writings of Edward Sapir, the linguist and specialist in American Indian languages, and his student, Benjamin Lee Whorf. In 1929 Sapir wrote: "The fact of the matter is that the 'real world' is to a large extent unconsciously built up on the language habits of the group. . . We see and hear and otherwise experience very largely as we do because the language habits of our community predispose certain choices of interpretation." Whorf wrote in an even more positive manner in the following excerpt: "The background linguistic system (in other words, the grammar) of each language is not merely a reproducing instrument for voicing ideas but rather is itself the shaper of ideas, the program and guide for the individual's mental activity, for his analysis of impressions, for his synthesis of his mental stock in trade. Formulation of ideas is not an independent process, strictly rational in the old sense, but is part of a particular grammar and differs, from slightly to greatly, as between different grammars."[1]

The prime difficulty in accepting the conclusions of Sapir and Whorf is that their evidence always consists solely of observations concerning linguistic structures: the ways in which they are alike and the ways in which they differ. Almost never do we find observations concerning the mental operations of the speakers of the various languages brought into discussion, much less the results of experimentation with cognitive behavior. The mere fact that language structures differ is not satisfactory as evidence for corresponding differences in cognitive behavior. Satisfactory evidence, one would think, would be the demonstration that differences in cognitive behavior on the part of speakers of different languages could be traced to differences in the structures of the respective languages.

The *linguistic relativity* hypothesis, as it may be called, has intrigued linguists, anthropologists, and psychologists, but a common complaint is that the hypothesis has not been sharply defined and stated in testable terms. There are several possible varieties of linguistic relativity hypotheses; in what follows it is my purpose to state several hypotheses quite explicitly and consider the possibility of testing them and accepting or rejecting them.

There is first, of course, the null hypothesis—the hypothesis which states that there is no relation (other than a trivial one) between language structure and cognitive process. In support of this hypothesis is the conclusion which many have reached that there is some sort of semantic invariance which remains despite translation, and that anything which can be said in one language can be translated into any other with only minor losses. But we would be inclined to accept this null hypothesis only after certain alternative, positive hypotheses are no longer tenable.

I shall consider two such positive hypotheses. The first is what I shall call the "mold theory" and the second is the "lattice theory." The "mold theory" is the classic form of the hypothesis which Sapir, Whorf, and others seem to have espoused. It states that the language structure we have learned maintains a tight control over our cognitive behavior, such that our perceptions are possible only within the "molds" provided by language structure. That is to say, if our language recognizes a certain series of categories or patternings, these are the categories or patternings within which our cognitive behavior is inevitably constrained. Whorf describes at length what he calls, for English, "the contrast of two artificial classes, substantives and verbs, and the bipartitioned ideology of nature," all of which forces us to think of "holding" as an action even though it is no action but a positional relation. At another place Whorf proposes that English, with its system of past, present, and future tenses, is committed to a certain conception of time which finds no exact parallel in a language like Hopi, with its system of validity-forms (reportive, expective, and nomic). In Hopi, one speaks of an action either as reportable as a fact (in past or present time), as expected (in some future time), or as a customary, repetitive one. Other examples cited from Hopi by Whorf suggest that Hopi speakers do not think of phases of time (days, months, seasons, and years) as objectified, pluralizable entities as we do, and that they tend to identify certain common objects as animate, for example, *clouds*, because the Hopi word for cloud falls into a class of words which according to Whorf are "always pluralized in the animate way."[2]

Unfortunately, the evidence presented for this "mold theory" is extremely unconvincing. In the first place, the evidence is purely linguistic. Secondly, it is difficult to make psychological sense out of the hypothesis. If it were true that we can perceive or conceive only what can be codified in our language, a child could hardly learn this language, for how could he learn the conceptions basic to a language which would itself be prerequisite to the learning of those conceptions? Linguistic codification could hardly be expected to operate prior to perception. We may illustrate this discussion by seeing how this theory would apply to the problem of color terminology. The "mold theory" seems to say that we will perceive or discriminate colors only in the broad categories provided by our color terminology. This does not seem to be the case, for experiments on the sheer discriminability of colors do not reveal any such dependence on color terminology. Perception, here, is antecedent to linguistic symbolization. And if the "mold theory" were true, it is hard to see how an individual could acquire the color terminology presumably necessary for him to perceive or discriminate the various colors. Nor does our color terminology provide us with a theory of color; it does not even say that there are just so many colors, and it does not tell us in what order the colors come in the spectrum. Finally, it is well known that we can be highly inventive about color terminology. I suggest that it might be safe to rule out the "mold theory."

Let me now turn to the "lattice theory," which I believe is more reasonable, and to which Whorf's work is not inapplicable. The virtue of the "lattice theory" is that it is a genetic hypothesis, recognizing the way in which a language is learned. It says that language structure is like a lattice or screen through which we see the world of our experience. This lattice, as it were, may obscure little bits of our experience, perhaps, but it lets through the rest in larger or smaller hunks, perhaps clarifying some parts, clouding other parts, and suggesting a larger pattern for still another. All the while, however, we see the pattern of the whole and are as little bothered by the lattice as if it were a screen installed on our front porch. In more behavioral terms, this hypothesis simply says that in the life-long process of learning language, we automatically learn the categories provided by the language; hence, insofar as a language may be selective with respect to the total range of possible discriminations, we are predisposed to notice or pay attention to certain discriminations and neglect others, even though those other discriminations are possible for us to make and are capable of being elevated into full potency under suitable conditions of reinforcement. We could therefore expect that the predispositions to discriminate (or to classify or conceptualize) would reveal themselves in various overt behaviors such as sorting, recognition, recall, and reasoning. Similarly, it is natural to find that we generalize the process of learning linguistic structures in such a way that we come to expect (1) some referential contrast to correspond with any linguistic contrast, and (2) a referential similarity in all instances covered by a single linguistic entity. If we show a person a series of strange forms or objects and tell him that some of them are BLIXes and others are JULKs, he will take us at our word and look assiduously for criteria by which to distinguish BLIXes from JULKs. If we tell him that some of the objects have been GRECKed and others have not been GRECKed, he will probably assume that "grecking" is some sort of process which has resulted in a "grecked" condition common to some of the objects and not to others, even though in actuality perhaps "grecking" refers to an event like giving, selling, or holding, which does not result in a visible condition. This last example also illustrates the way in which grammatical categories become invested with certain generalized properties even though they may not apply in every instance; it would seem that the linguistic category *verb* in English has become invested with the generalized property of referring to *action* or *process*. But of course not all verbs in English involve such a concept.

Linguistic categories often thus provide us, according to the lattice theory, with a set of possible hypotheses about the similarities and differences in our environment. In general, they are the stable similarities and differences which have provided satisfactory guides to behavior for previous generations, but we always have the possibility of testing them out. Things coded similarly may turn out to be more desirable to differentiate, as where we discover subspecies of birds and label them accordingly; or things coded differently may eventually appear to be one and the same thing, as where it was found that a number of psychotic syndromes could be grouped under the concept *schizophrenia*.

As I have stated it, the lattice theory appears to be plausible in terms of the theory of learning and in terms of relevant experimental results. The hypothesis is essentially a restatement or application of a well-known finding in discrimination learning—that we learn those discriminations which are reinforced; in the present case, linguistic symbols are themselves the cues for the discriminatory responses. Certain experimental results seem particularly germane, for example the experiment of Carmichael et al.[3] which showed that subjects' reproductive recall of visual shapes after a lapse of time was dependent upon the linguistic labels which were attached to them by the experimenter; more recently, the experiment by Brown and Lenneberg[4] which showed that an individual's recognition memory for colors is dependent on the extent to which he has available appropriate names for these colors.

We can raise a question, of course, as to the actual extent to which languages are selective either with respect to the total possible range of discriminations or in comparison with each other. Stated otherwise, this question asks, are languages really so different from each other, especially with respect to those discriminations which the human race has found it useful to make most often? This question needs further investigation; my guess is, however, that there are a number of important differences between languages, both in the lexical codification of even the common objects of the environment and in the grammatical codification of various modes of experience. At the same time, the universals of language are probably wider in extent than has been imagined. For example, I see evidence to suggest that all languages have something like a nominal category and something like a verbal category—the former comprising ways of referring to things that are subject to, or are responsible for, states of change or lack of change, and the latter comprising ways of reporting these changes. But even the universals of language demand our attention, for they represent universally useful ways which man has found to categorize and manipulate experience as perceived.

One particularly important implication of the lattice theory of the language and thought relationship is that language is an *organon* or instrument of thought, because according to it one's language provides—or fails to provide—"built-in" discriminations or contrasts which play either a facilitating or an inhibitory role in thinking. We would predict that ratiocinative behavior will vary in kind and in quality depending upon language structure. This proposition could presumably be put to test by seeing what transformations might have to take place in various objects of logical investigation on being translated into different languages. For example, logicians[5] have recently had a field day pointing out certain difficulties in ascertaining by rule the truth-value of a condition contrary to fact like, "If that match had been scratched, it would have lighted." Time does not permit me to discuss this topic, but I will simply say that it is my belief that some of the difficulties can be resolved by introducing certain logical distinctions which are not made in English grammar but which surprisingly enough *are* made in the grammar of certain American Indian languages.

I should like to turn attention now to the possibilities of studying the influence of language structure on the psychopathology of thought. A peculiar difficulty presents itself at once. If language is the common property of all members of a speech community, how can we explain any differential effects on those members? If language structure contains within itself the discriminations of experience which the experience of the race has found necessary for survival, how is it that people who have learned this language do not equally well guide their behavior in terms of these discriminations? Or conversely, if language structure should happen to be in some sense a hindrance to thought, how is it that some speakers of a language are able to overcome such a hindrance, while others remain victimized by it? Such questions are in the main meaningless because they are founded on the false assumption that language structure is the only determinant of thought processes. Perhaps language structure has about as much effect on thought as a stone dropped into churning waters has upon wave formation. Frequently one finds, I suppose, that the mental activities of a patient are dominated by some delusional system which appears to have little or nothing to do with language structure, and which can be analyzed in terms of personality dynamics. Nevertheless, it is conceivable that there will remain certain tendencies or schemas of thought which may be traceable to phenomena of language structure.

For instance, consider a whole class of statements that can be made by patients with paranoid, anxiety, or other obsessional states, statements like—"They are going to kill me"; "My son hates me"; "You're taking advantage of me"; etc. Such statements conceivably represent the response of the patient to his perception of some vague threat or hostility directed at himself. He then searches for the source of this threat, much as if he were searching for the subject of a verb. So strong is the pattern of English sentences containing subjects, verbs, and objects that in a sentence like "It rains," it seems entirely natural to ask the question "What rains?" and answer it with "IT." What I am suggesting is that the tendency of a paranoid to identify the source of some perceived threat or hostility is a consequence of the way he has learned to build sentences in his language.

Perhaps this example is not convincing. It would take a great deal more experience with clinical materials than I have at my disposal to develop better and more convincing examples. My purpose here is solely to call attention to a possible factor in psychopathological behavior which may have been hitherto neglected. I should be eager to learn whether members of this audience could offer any observations which might tend to support or refute the notions which I have presented.

REFERENCES

1. Whorf, Benjamin Lee: Language, Thought and Reality. Selected Writings, *ed. by* John B. Carroll. New York, Wiley, 1956, pp. 212ff.
2. ——: Ibid., p. 79.
3. Carmichael, L., Hogan, H. P., and Walter, A. A.: An experimental study of the effect of language on the reproduction of visually perceived form. J. Exper. Psychol. *15*: 73-86, 1932.
4. Brown, Roger W., and Lenneberg, Eric H.: A study in language and cognition. J. Abnorm. Soc. Psychol. *49*: 454-462, 1954.
5. Goodman, N.: The problem of counterfactual conditionals. J. Philosophy *44*: 113, 1947.

4

THE TANGENTIAL RESPONSE

By JURGEN RUESCH, M.D.*

MID-TWENTIETH CENTURY ADVANCES in science and technology have brought about profound changes in our views of man and nature. No longer are we concerned with the transmission, storage and transformation of energy; instead we have moved on to problems of control of forces through information and self-regulation.[4] Today, workers in factories no longer adjust machines manually, nor do home owners go to the cellar to shovel coal into the heating plant. They all rely on automatic control. These technological advances have left psychology and psychiatry not unscathed and in recent years attempts have been made to consider disturbances of behavior in a new light. Outstanding among these modern trends is the view that behavior is a function of social relations which in turn are dependent upon human communication. The study of communication is thus based upon the acceptance of two theoretical notions: first, that behavior is controlled by what is conveniently referred to as information and, second, that information about the physical and social effects of action is fed back to the organism or to the group and that this relay of effects steers subsequent behavior.

The notions of control of behavior through information and feedback, which have been so brilliantly summarized by Wiener,[12] shifted the emphasis from behavior per se to the forces which control behavior. But in contrast to the older schools of psychology and psychoanalysis which assumed that behavior is controlled by forces within the organism—by instincts, habits, the id, or the superego—modern communication theory does not limit these controlling forces to the organism. Instead, messages are thought to flow in large networks of communication which involve many people and even material structures. Whether these messages are coded in terms of electronic signals, speech or nervous impulses is not particularly relevant. What does matter is that the informa-

* Professor of Psychiatry, University of California School of Medicine, San Francisco; Research Psychiatrist, The Langley Porter Clinic, San Francisco.

tion contained in the messages steers human behavior. The switch in emphasis from behavior to the message as the unit of observation was a boon to the social scientist, for it enabled him to throw overboard the shackles that bound his thinking to the individual.[7]

The consideration of biological, psychological and sociological aspects of existence within one system is based upon observations of verbal expressions, gestures and actions as well as of signals that reflect contraction of the smooth muscles and secretions of glands. Within the framework of communication, the scientist is able to follow the behavior of an individual through a variety of situations—when he is alone, in two-person situations, or in groups. With communicative behavior as the center of his studies, the psychiatrist no longer has to search for parallelisms between action behavior and personality structure, nor does he need to assume—as he did in the past—that the causes of behavioral pathology are found inside the boundaries of the organism. Today, the psychiatrist may assume that in all cases of disturbed behavior the network involved extends beyond the confines of one organism.[6]

The search for single causes of behavioral pathology inside the organism thus is not on sound theoretical ground. What in the past was called a "cause" of abnormal behavior frequently does not fulfill the rigorous scientific criteria demanded of chains of causation. Often such a cause, although preceding the pathology in time, was not specific for the phenomenology in question. The attribution of causes and the localization of a disturbance thus have merely pragmatic significance in ascertaining the most convenient spot for therapeutic intervention. For example, abnormal behavior associated with central nervous system disease traditionally is tackled by influencing through surgical or medical means the structures located inside the organism, in spite of the fact that the cause of the disorder may be a poison which the patient ingested in interaction with his physical and social environment. And abnormal behavior in the functional disorders has been approached first as if it were due to an abnormal personality structure and confined to the patient; later as if it were the result of interaction with another healthy or sick person; and most recently as if it constituted maladjustment vis-a-vis a group or society at large.

At first sight, then, it would appear as if the empirical assessment of abnormal behavior depended entirely upon the psychiatrist's intuitive appraisal or the school of thought to which he belongs. Detailed study of communicative behavior, however, reveals that diagnostic decisions as to the locus of therapeutic intervention are not entirely arbitrary. It is possible to pinpoint those networks of communication in which an individual encounters failure and to describe the specific nature of communication pathology. From the evidence we have today we must assume that successful participation in networks of communication which involve other human beings is necessary if the individual is to survive.[11] Subjectively, the individual experiences failure in communication as frustrating. If the frustration is very intense, of long duration, or repeated, the individual's thinking, feeling and reacting become progressively more disorganized and inappropriate. In turn, such behavior is regarded by others as abnormal. Prolonged frustration diminishes the individual's ability to establish and maintain social relations, regardless of whether the frustration is the result of central nervous system disease or of social interaction. The basic hypothesis—that information and feedback direct human behavior—has therefore to be amplified to state that defective feedback involving intraorganismic, interpersonal and group networks is responsible for abnormal behavior. So much for theory.

Since time precludes the elaboration of the many possible ways in which communication can break down[9] within the individual, in two-person situations, or in groups, I shall confine my discussion to one phenomenon: the tangential response. This is a disturbance which arises out of certain selectivities which a recipient of a message can exercise in replying to the statement of the sender. If in terms of language, content and emotional concomitants the reply fits the initial statement, as a key does a keyhole, then the sender experiences pleasure and feels that he has been understood; however, if the reply does not fit, various degrees of tension are experienced. Perfect fit of reply rarely is achieved with the first comeback. But if the replier expresses his willingness to listen and to understand he may after a series of exchanges arrive at a reply which satisfies the sender. But matters become more complicated if one considers that, in the course of communication, the one who made the original statement frequently changes his position so that the second person then answers a statement which already has lost its actuality value. Intentions, emotions and roles of the participants are subject in two-person situations to such rapid change that the study of initial statement and reply usually has to be confined to a time segment of the order of seconds or minutes.

A selective reply, one which does not quite fit but is nonetheless acceptable to the sender, constitutes a negative feedback pattern which is commonly used by people to influence one another. In the course of conversation, for example, it can be observed that the receiver picks up the topic presented but continues to spin the yarn in a direction which differs from the one that the sender had anticipated. Taking up another aspect of the same topic or a related topic may be disappointing to the sender but it might still be acceptable. Such an unexpected turn of events may produce tension and often has an effect similar to that of a joke. Expectations are set in one direction but the conclusion comes as a surprise. In the case of the joke, people, after having been deceived in their expectations, discharge their tension by laughter. The same may occur in ordinary conversation if the change of direction in the conversation is consciously recognized.[2] But often the participants are completely unaware that they talk past each other. In these circumstances tension mounts and the unawareness of the participants as to what is going on prevents appropriate correction of behavior.[1]

Selective acknowledgment does not occur only in adult conversation. In responding to one aspect of communicative behavior rather than to another the parent exercises his prerogative of steering the child in a desired direction. Selectivity in reply, therefore, is not to be confused with pathology. Almost all families profess some specialized interest in one area or another. Through repeated exposure to particular topics or approaches, a child gradually acquires information and techniques which prepare him for particular fields of endeavor: scholastic achievement, art, music, crafts, technical pursuits, sports, trade, or homemaking. But selectivity is not confined to topics; it involves all of the subtleties of human communication. Through verbal or nonverbal reply, the parent teaches the child to emphasize one function more than another. To illustrate this process, some of the possible verbal and nonverbal replies to some initial statements of children and adolescents have been reproduced in table 1. If in the course of time the parents' replies are heavily concentrated on one issue in neglect of another, this selective exposure will determine the preferred ways of communication of the child. However, as long as the selectivities of reply insure continuous communication and growth of all participants they have to be considered as constructive devices of normal interchange.

TABLE 1.—*Varieties of Part Functions Selected for Reply*

Function Emphasized in Reply	Examples of Reply	
	Nonverbal Comments	Verbal Comments
System of communication		
Being alone	Pointing and directing child to his room after some misbehavior	"This you will have to think over by yourself"
Two-person situations	Crossed fingers indicating "just like that"	"Just the two of you"
Group situations	Cooperative preparations for family picnic	"Let's all join forces"
Perception		
Proximity receivers and proprioception	Taking an object out of a child's hand and mouth	"Do not put that in your mouth"
Distance receivers and exteroception	Pointing to a flock of geese in flight	"Take a look with the binoculars"
Evaluation		
Memory	Puts palm to forehead (gesture of having forgotten)	"I forgot our appointment"
Thinking	Points index finger to temple to indicate poor thinking	"He sounds cracked"
Feeling	Puts hand on chest	"You must have felt awful"
Decision-making	Looking determined after having looked doubtful	"I have made up my mind"
Action and expression		
Motivation	Looking questioningly	"Whatever made you do that?"
Implementation	Applause by clapping hands	"Superbly played"
Effect	Bull's-eye sign	"You really hit the jackpot"
Language		
Organ language	Blushes, pales, trembles	"I am scared"
Action language	Signals to come over	"Come on over"
Verbal and gestural language	Waiting for report	"Tell me what happened"

TABLE 1.—*Cont'd.*

Function Emphasized in Reply	Examples of Reply	
	Nonverbal Comments	Verbal Comments
Semiotics		
Pragmatics	Looks at trophies on the mantelpiece	"You really must have been good to win all those competitions"
Semantics	Points to a mysterious sign	"Let us consult the dictionary"
Syntactics	Recovers furniture in daughter's room	"I want your chair to match the curtains"
Universes of endeavor		
Knowledge	Nodding head	"You really know your stuff"
Skill	Catching ball	"You are a good pitcher"
Topic of Discourse	Shuffling deck of cards	"We'd better stick to card playing"
Instruction		
Roles	Pointing to badge	"I am the captain"
Rules	Pointing to a notice: "It is forbidden to . . ."	"You should not trespass"
Explanations	Getting somebody a set of instruction sheets	"I had better tell you how to do it"
Correction and learning		
Problem-solving	Exploring an unassembled kit	"Have you found the solution?"
Learning by imitation	Demonstrating the technique of pointing the shotgun	"You have to swing the shotgun with the birds"
Gratification and Frustration		
Pleasure	Grunts and looks pleased	"I get a kick out of . . ."
Frustration	Groans, mutters, looks exhausted, ready to collapse	"It does not pay to go up there"

Under certain conditions selectivity may lead to the development of pathology[9]:

If the adult's complexity of response is not matched to the child's state of development, the response being either too discriminating or not discriminating enough

If the adult's selectivity fails to stimulate certain functions which have to be learned or continues to emphasize functions that have already been mastered

If the selectivity of response steers the child in a direction that does not coincide with his innate abilities

If the replies are such that the child cannot link his statements in a satisfactory manner to the statements of the adult.

All of these selectivities produce frustration in the child which may exceed his immediate or long-term tolerance limits. The responses are tangential inasmuch as they are not adapted to the core of the child's conscious or unconscious intentions.

As an illustration, Johnny, age five, comes running toward his mother, joyously shouting, "Look, I found a snail." Mother looks at Johnny and in a dry, pleasure-killing voice remarks, "Go and wash your dirty hands." The child, entirely deflated, disappointed, and confused, enters the house. By directly initiating a new message—the order to wash hands—when she saw the mud-covered fingers of the youngster, the mother disregarded Johnny's intentional statement and refused to share his joy. Had she said, "Yes, this is a lovely snail," and paused, she then could have conveniently initiated a new message—"Now you go and wash your dirty hands."

In responding, the mother took cognizance of her child's intention to communicate and obliged him with a reply. But by countering with a response to an unintentional expression—the mud on his hands—that the child could not readily link to his initial statement, she interfered with his expression of pleasure and responded in a tangential way. Instead of being enabled to fuse the mother's answer with his own statement, the child was exposed to a new statement. Instead of dealing with one subject—snails—he now deals with two subjects—snails and washing hands. And his concern with snails remains unanswered. When a mother repeatedly refuses to pick up an intended statement, to carry it, and to develop it further, she kills one of the greatest social pleasures of the child. If this recurs often, the information in the mind of the child is split into many unconnected fragments and the process of integration lags behind. The repeated inappropriate fit of statement and reply not only is frustrating but also represents a serious interference with the communicative growth of the child. After all, the function of communication is one of the ways to insure self-extension and relatedness to others, which processes in turn have a deep influence upon the child's self-respect and sense of security.

There exists another kind of reply, closely allied to the tangential response, which might suitably be called a "jumping response." In this form of reply, the person who answers the initial statement jumps two or three intermediary steps in anticipation of statements to come. For example:

First statement—Person A: "How do you feel?"

Second statement—Person B: "Fine; and you?"

Third statement—Person A: "All right, except that I feel worn out from moving furniture."

Fourth statement—Person B: "Why don't you get the movers to do it?"

Fifth statement—Person A: "It costs less."

Sixth statement—Person B: "No sense saving money."

By omitting steps 2 to 5, the exchange looks as follows:

First statement—Person A: "How do you feel?"

Sixth statement—Person B: "No sense saving money."

In this latter version, Person B's reply is at first incomprehensible and only after searching inquiry does one understand that he reacted to A's overworked appearance. This kind of jumping response is frequently met in conversation with schizophrenics. It interferes with communication not only because it confuses the sender but also because the one who jumps imperceptibly changes the direction of the exchange and frequently loses the sense of what he wanted to say. The initial advantage that a person gains by giving a jumping response is soon forfeited because feedback ceases to steer the interaction. The jumper thus pays a heavy penalty; in getting ahead, he loses the other person who, not understanding what is going on, gradually withdraws from participation. As in the case of the tangential response, the disturbance is characterized by failure to match statement with statement and therefore to insure acknowledgment and gratification.

Both the tangential and the jumping response are observed not only in verbal discourse but in nonverbal communication through gesture, action, or object as well.[6] In the first few years of life, before the child has mastered symbolic expression, the mother has to respond through facial expression,[10] voice modulation, and action to the bodily and autonomic manifestations of the child. Her response to vomiting, diarrhea, constipation, sneezing, wheezing, coughing, flushing, or crying, if selective and out of proportion, can become the nucleus around which the interaction with the child becomes organized. In such a case, the parent initially may have responded to the expressions of the child quite appropriately; but this healthy response may later assume tangential characteristics if it is not modified in accordance with the biological and social maturation of the child. Particularly among bearers of psychosomatic conditions one encounters patients whose mothers could not express their feelings vis-a-vis their children in verbal or gestural terms. Instead, such mothers continued to treat their children as if they were babies; they attended to the body hygiene of their growing children by giving enemas, brushing hair, or powdering the skin—a care which did not match the concern of a sixth- or eighth-grader.

Closely related to this kind of organ language is action language.[8] When the child's speech is still in its infancy the youngster also has to use nonverbal action as a means of communication. An object proffered by the child has to be received; noises made have to be acknowledged. But already to a child of this tender age a mother may respond tangentially. I remember, for example, a two-year-old who, alone in his room, was crying after having been fed. The mother, instead of picking him up and investigating the matter, merely gave him an additional bottle. Or a three-year-old who reached for his mother and was given a teddy bear to hug instead. There are parents who continue to respond in terms of action at a time when the youngsters have outgrown this language development. If parents selectively respond to their children's transactions of material goods or to their expressions in terms of action, doing ceases to be an implementation and becomes a form of language. Psychopathic personalities usually have had parents who selectively responded to action. Fathers whose principal contacts with the child consisted of bouncing the baby, rough-housing with the six-year old, or engaging in athletic competition with the teen-ager in exclusion of other pursuits may serve as examples.

Verbal replies can become tangential when the nonverbal manifestations of the child are neglected. If parents ignore the somatic manifestations of their children, if they fail to stimulate the proximity receivers mediating the sensations of touch, temperature, pain, smell, or taste, if they do not provide opportunities for exercise but selectively react to the children's verbal expressions, then the child becomes nonverbally retarded. Under these circumstances the child is not encouraged to drape his body over his mother's shoulder or to fit himself within her arms, nor does he learn to wear his clothing gracefully as if it were an extension of his skin. As a result, his appreciation of space, beauty and movement lags behind the skill displayed with verbal or digital symbols. Such a child may become a verbal genius while he remains nonverbally feebleminded.

Tangential replies sometimes are brought about by circumstances. In wealthy families the nurse attends to body care, the athletic instructor to action, and the parent to some aspects of the verbal exchange. The same is true if children are reared by a widowed mother who is an invalid. As in institutionalized children, we find a complete splitting of functions; strangers attend to the body care, mother attends to verbal communication, but nobody takes care of interpersonal action. At no time does the child obtain a complete response to all of his expressions by one and the same person.

But tangential responses are not confined to various types of language or action. Some parents may be enchanted with the fantasy of their three- or four-year olds; if such practices occur at an age when the children have to learn action, skill and conformity, selective acknowledgment of fantasy becomes a tangential response. To perceive certain events and to ignore others likewise can be steered by directive acknowledgment.[5] Some people selectively acknowledge feelings and sensations that refer to their own organism—the subjectivists; others acknowledge only those feelings and sensations that refer to others and the environment—the objectivists. Some people specialize in reacting to the decisions made by others, either opposing, criticizing, or supporting. In tangential responses to decisions made by others, the person, situation, or decision itself is ignored. Instead, the fact that a decision is made is reacted to, or some of the inevitable flaws in the decision are picked upon.

The tangential response becomes particularly deadly when it slices the togetherness of action, thought, feeling, and word.[3] The motive-oriented parent selectively responds to the child's intentions, needs, and desires. The effort-oriented parent specializes in rewarding expenditure of energy and time regardless of the outcome of the action. Parents who encourage such an approach rear children who specialize in pretending that they work hard, who learn all the gestures and symbols of an action without producing results. At the opposite extreme we find those who merely care for end results—the salesman who seeks dollar volume and sales regardless of the means by which they were achieved has become proverbial. Some people isolate the popularity of an action or its social prestige and much advertising and sales success is based on this kind of response. Again, others emphasize the nature of the procedure. For example, some of our academic institutions have been known to reward beautifully designed research work, although the questions asked were irrelevant and the results added nothing new to our body of information. A particular split of the individual's experience can be observed when the reply singles out emotions. If parents react only when the child cries, or if adults react on the condition that the other person is in a good mood, or if only the feelings of a person are considered in neglect of the goal of the action, such selective attitudes can exert their destructive effects.

The criteria which characterize the tangential response can be summarized as follows:

The reply inadequately fits the initial statement.

The reply has a frustrating effect.

The reply is not geared to the intention behind the original statement as it is perceivable through word, action, and context of the situation.

The reply emphasizes an aspect of the statement which is incidental.

The effects of tangential responses can be summarized as follows:

The tangential reply influences through feedback the initial intention of the sender, who may begin to doubt what he really wanted.

The tangential reply structures action sequences in such a way that relatively unrelated actions or pieces of information become connected while related actions or topics become unconnected.

Repeated tangential replies interfere with corrective feedback of both participants because the statements of one person cannot be linked to the statements of the other person.

People who have been unduly exposed to tangential replies learn not to derive pleasure from enlightening communication. They conceive of communication as a means to achieve power over others, and by not giving appropriate replies themselves they in turn deny others the pleasure of feeling acknowledged.

Tangential replies given in action or word to infants or children constitute significant interferences with their mastery of communication and their integration as persons.

REFERENCES

1. LEE, I. J.: How to Talk with People. New York, Harper, 1952.
2. MEERLOO, J. A. M.: Conversation and Communication. New York, International Universities Press, 1952.
3. PIAGET, JEAN: The Language and Thought of the Child, ed. 2. London, Kegan Paul, Trench, Trubner, 1932.
4. RAPOPORT, A., WEAVER, W., GERARD, R. W., SAMSON, E. W., AND KIRK, J. R.: Information theory. *ETC. 10*: 241 320, 1953.
5. REDL, F., AND WINEMAN, D.: Controls from Within. Glencoe, Ill., Free Press, 1952.
6. RUESCH, J., AND BATESON, G.: Communication. The Social Matrix of Psychiatry. New York, Norton, 1951.
7. ——: Synopsis of the theory of human communication. Psychiatry *16*: 215-243, 1953.
8. ——, AND KEES, W.: Nonverbal Communication. Berkeley and Los Angeles, University of California Press, 1956.
9. ——: Disturbed Communication. New York, Norton, 1957.
10. SPITZ, R.: The smiling response: a contribution to the ontogenesis of social relations. Gen. Psychol. Monogr. *34*: 57-125, 1946.
11. SULLIVAN, H. S.: The Interpersonal Theory of Psychiatry. New York, Norton, 1953.
12. WIENER, NORBERT: Cybernetics, or Control and Communication in Man and the Machine. New York, Wiley, 1948.

5

REACTIONS TO DELAYED AUDITORY FEEDBACK IN SCHIZOPHRENIC CHILDREN

By WILLIAM GOLDFARB, PH.D., M.D., AND PATRICIA BRAUNSTEIN, M.A.*

THE SPEECH OF A GROUP of schizophrenic children has been demonstrated to diverge significantly from normal.[4] The deviations from normal occurred in every aspect of speech, for example, phonation (quality, volume, pitch, duration), rhythm, intonation, articulation, and facial and body reinforcements. Although there was no specific pattern of divergence in speech for all schizophrenic children, the general effect for each child was one of flatness in speech. For each child, however, the flatness was associated with specific alterations in the many other aspects of speech. The universal generalization was that none of the schizophrenic children had a normal speech pattern and that the normal associations between speech and meaning and between speech and mood were lacking. Such aberration was attributable to a number of possible factors. The speech models available in the family and which the children may have imitated could have been divergent, or the children themselves may have been intrinsically aberrant in receptor and self-monitoring processes, in central and coordinative functions, or in motor and executive responses.

There has been cumulative evidence of perceptual alterations involving all sensory modalities in childhood schizophrenia.[1] Schizophrenic children, too, demonstrate a divergent pattern of sensory preferences.[5] They tend to avoid the distance receptors of vision and audition though the neuroanatomic substrate for these receptor activities is intact; they do not look or listen. Rather, they depend more upon the contact receptors of touch, smell and taste. Specifically in hearing, some show so much auditory hypersensitivity that they actively exclude sound by covering their ears with their hands; others show a marked pseudo-deafness difficult to differentiate from true deafness. In auditory avoid-

* Henry Ittleson Center for Child Research, Riverdale, New York.

ance or inattention there is striking auditory insensitivity demonstrated by an absence of reaction even to extremes of noise. One wonders to what extent the exclusion of auditory and visual stimuli blocks the schizophrenic child's learning of normal speech patterns. Certainly, in the clinical treatment of schizophrenic children, improvement in their educability coincides with the emergence of visual and auditory awareness. Beyond this, it may be postulated that the altered receptor tendencies produce aberrations in self-monitoring and feedback processes which in turn influence the act of speech.

Because of the schizophrenic child's departure from normal patterns of perception and receptor preference, we have become increasingly interested in the study of self-monitoring processes in relation to speech and general behavior. During the past five years, there has been developing attention to the phenomena which accompany delayed auditory feedback.* As a consequence of a personal experience with delayed auditory feedback, the present investigators felt it was a phenomenon worth exploring with schizophrenic children. Among normal adults with normal speech, the disturbance in auditory self-monitoring by the delayed feedback produces speech impairment.[3, 6] In our own introspections during the experiment, we felt a strange vigilance and heightened attention to the speech performance and related behavior. We were conscious of a mildly uneasy bewilderment. These emotional reactions seemed linked to the psychic experience of personal identity or self, its fumbling expression and action due to an abrupt shift in one system of external referents. The hypothesis is offered that the phenomena which accompany delayed feedback represent the dual effects of interference with speech and with the individual's self-awareness system. It is further hypothesized that schizophrenic children should differ from normal children in their reactions to delayed auditory feedback. Thus, if schizophrenic children pay less attention to the auditory stimulus than do normal children, the speech of schizophrenic children should be less affected by the delayed feedback. In addition, the ego disturbances of the schizophrenic children are such that it might be anticipated that they would tend not to recognize their own voices and that they would show problems in self-identity.

* Oral speech involves the transmission of sound in two directions: one leads to an external listener and the other feeds back to the speaker. The hearing of his own spoken word by the speaker by air and bone conduction has been designated auditory feedback or side-tone.

The present study was undertaken to test out the above-stated hypotheses. Schizophrenic children would be compared with normal children. Speech would be elicited and recorded in a standard fashion, first under normal speaking conditions and then under delayed feedback conditions. Emotional reactions and behavior relating to self-awareness under delayed feedback conditions would be evaluated by behavioral rating and interview. The speech data would test previous conclusions about the speech of schizophrenic children[4] through standard observational and recording procedures against corresponding observations of a control group of normal public school children.

The Delayed Speech Feedback Experiment

Delayed speech feedback and delayed side-tone are synonymous. Delayed speech feedback is produced by transmitting an individual's speech to his own ears a fraction of a second after he has spoken. The technique for producing delayed auditory side-tone is essentially that used by Black[3] and Lee.[6] The subject wears a pair of earphones to block out the normal air-conducted sound. A magnetic tape recording machine is employed. The heads of the recorder are fixed so that the tape automatically passes from the erase to the record to the reproduce heads. For normal recording conditions, the record head functions when recording and the reproduce head during the playback. For delayed speech feedback both these heads are used simultaneously. The amount of delay is determined by the tape speed and by the time required for the tape to pass from the record head to the reproduce head. Thus, as the subject records, his speech is returned through the earphones after a designated delay. In this study the delay time was .16 seconds. The instruments used for recording were an Ampex Corporation high fidelity, magnetic tape recorder, model 600, at 7½ feet per second; an *Electro-Voice* microphone, model 654; and a set of *Permoflux* PDR-19 earphones.

The Subjects

The experimental group consisted of 16 children diagnosed as schizophrenics. In each case, there was diagnostic concurrence between the treating psychiatrist and the clinical director. However, of these, three were nontestable, so that the reactions of only 13 children will be described. All schizophrenic children were being treated in a residential setting at the Henry Ittleson Center for Child Research. The schizophrenic children in this group included nine boys and four girls with an average age of nine years and a range of ages from eight years, four months to ten years, two months.

The normal control group consisted of 25 children attending a New York City public school and living at home. The normals were comprised of 17 boys and 8 girls, with an average age of 8 years, 10 months and a range of ages from 7 years, 11 months to 10 years, 5 months.

The normal group included 23 white and two Negro children, while all the schizophrenic children were white. Aside from this, the two groups were equivalent in sex, age, background, and father's occupation.

Utilizing the whisper test, both schizophrenic and normal children were observed to have hearing grossly within normal ranges.

The Experimental Procedure

Tape recordings were made of each child's complete verbalizations under the following conditions in sequence:

Normal recording. The child was instructed that he was going to make a record for which he was to speak as he usually does. It was stressed that the procedure was not a test. The microphone was placed approximately six inches from the subject's mouth. The volume control was monitored during recording and left at the same level for the subsequent playback and feedback recordings. An effort was made to maintain similar conditions for all recordings. In order to obtain speech in a variety of communication activities, each child was instructed to

1. Say, "My name is——."
2. Read a passage. (The reading material used was the first paragraph from the Grey Standard Oral Reading Paragraphs.)
3. Recite the Pledge of Allegiance.
4. Sing, "My Country 'Tis of Thee."
5. Tell a story.

Playback conditions. When the above recording was completed the earphones were placed on the child and he was merely told to listen. No other instructions or information pertaining to what would be heard were given. Following this the earphones were removed and each child was asked the following questions:

1. Whose voice did you hear?
2. Did you like the voice?
3. Why?

Delayed feedback conditions. Each subject was given the same instructions for verbalizing as given previously under normal conditions.

He was also told that he would be wearing earphones throughout the recording. The same speech material was used. The feedback was introduced immediately.

The child's behavior was noted during delayed feedback. At the completion of this recording the earphones were removed and a guided interview to elicit information regarding voice recognition and self-awareness was held. The following questions were utilized:

1. Whose voice did you hear?
2. What did it sound like?
3. Where was the voice coming from?
4. How did it feel?

Each child's behavior during feedback was rated on the following scales:

1. Restlessness
   1. Can sit still with excellent control.
   3. Average self-possession when sitting.
   5. Cannot sit still with self-possession; exceptionally restless; hyperactive. (Underline appropriate one.)
2. Sustained Effort
   1. Capable of exceptionally sustained effort.
   3. Average maintenance of effort.
   5. Not capable of sustained effort. Effort quickly lags and deteriorates. Leaves work unfinished.
3. Confusion in Self-identity
   1. No evidence of confusion.
   2. Mild confusion. Slight uncertainty.
   3. Moderate confusion. Evident uncertainty, but fluctuant.
   4. Severe confusion. Evident uncertainty, consistent.
   5. Very severe confusion.
4. Gross Speech Impairment by Delayed Feedback
   1. No impairment.
   2. Very slight impairment.
   3. Slight impairment.
   4. Considerable impairment—articulation errors, repetitions, hesitations, etc.
   5. Severe impairment—halting, stumbling, blocking, etc.
5. Discomfort
   1. No evidence of discomfort.
   3. Mild discomfort. "It bothers me a little."

5. Severe discomfort. "It hurts me."

6. Awareness

1. That the voice under delayed feedback is the subject's voice though changed.

Items 1-5 were rated on five levels, while "awareness" was recorded as either present (+) or absent (—).

The speech of each child was evaluated by a speech expert under normal conditions and then under delayed feedback conditions. All the ratings were on a five-point scale ranging from "very good" (rating 1) to "very poor" (rating 5). Estimates were made of specific voice and speech characteristics, general characteristics of speech and language, and gross or over-all speech level. In addition, specific voice and speech faults were noted (table 1).

TABLE 1.—*Speech Evaluation**

A. *Specific Voice and Speech Characteristics*	1	2	3	4	5
1. Volume—adequate	......	......	......	......	......
2. Pitch—appropriate in level	......	......	......	......	......
3. Quality—pleasant, clear	......	......	......	......	......
4. Rate—appropriate	......	......	......	......	......
5. Phrasing—accurate	......	......	......	......	......
6. Stress—accurate	......	......	......	......	......
7. Intonation—appropriate	......	......	......	......	......
8. Pronunciation—acceptable	......	......	......	......	......
9. Diction—satisfactory	......	......	......	......	......
B. *General Speech and Language*					
1. Fluent	......	......	......	......	......
2. Grammatical	......	......	......	......	......
3. Expression of meaning	......	......	......	......	......
4. Communication of mood	......	......	......	......	......
5. Physical behavior	......	......	......	......	......
C. *General Estimate*					
1. Very good					
2. Good					
3. Fair					
4. Poor					
5. Very poor					

* Derived from the Teachers College Speech Examination, Speech Department, Teachers College, Columbia University.

TABLE 2.—*Comparison of Speech of Schizophrenic and Normal Children Under Normal Recording Conditions**

	Schizophrenic (n = 13)					Normal (n = 25)				
	no. at each level					no. at each level				
Variable	1	2	3	4	5	1	2	3	4	5
1. Volume	1	3	3	5	1	21	2	2	0	0
2. Pitch	0	5	4	3	1	20	1	3	1	0
3. Quality	0	0	0	11	2	0	10	11	4	0
4. Rate	1	0	1	6	5	19	3	3	0	0
5. Phrasing	2	1	1	9	0	21	3	1	0	0
6. Stress	1	2	4	5	1	25	0	0	0	0
7. Intonation	1	2	4	5	1	23	0	2	0	0
8. Pronunciation	1	1	8	3	0	23	0	2	0	0
9. Diction	0	1	8	0	4	0	11	10	4	0
10. Fluency	1	0	5	6	1	24	1	0	0	0
11. Grammar	2	1	7	2	1	23	1	1	0	0
12. Meaning	2	2	2	4	3	24	0	1	0	0
13. Mood	0	2	1	6	4	23	1	1	0	0
14. Physical Behavior	0	2	1	6	4	23	1	1	0	0
15. General Estimate	0	0	4	4	5	6	13	4	2	0

* Using Chi^2, P of all data except Diction is below .001; P of Diction is below .01.

TABLE 3.—*Effect of Delayed Feedback on Behavior and Speech of Schizophrenic and Normal Children*

	Schizophrenic (n = 13)					Normal (n = 25)						
	no. at each level					no. at each level					Chi^2	p
Variable	1	2	3	4	5	1	2	3	4	5		
1. Restlessness	2	0	2	1	8	13	1	9	1	1	16.83	< .01
2. Effort	2	0	5	0	6	16	0	5	2	2	12.30	< .02
3. Confusion	5	0	1	2	5	25	0	0	0	0	23.89	< .001
4. Discomfort	8	0	1	0	4	6	0	19	0	0	18.51	< .001
5. Speech Impairment	3	2	2	4	2	0	0	9	12	4	11.45	< .05
6. Awareness*	5	....	....	....	8	23	....	....	....	2	10.03	< .01

* 1 = awareness +; 5 = awareness —

The Speech Findings

One limitation of the study is the fact that the individual responsible for speech appraisal knew the sources of the subjects. Nevertheless, objectivity was maintained through careful listening and rigorous recording.*

There were differences between the speech of the normal and schizophrenic groups. Under normal recording conditions, the schizophrenic children were poorer than the normal children in all the specific aspects of voice and speech, e.g., volume, pitch, quality, rate, phrasing, stress, intonation, pronunciation, and diction (table 2). The schizophrenic children were also less fluent, less grammatical, less able to communicate meaning and mood, and less prone to use appropriate gestural reinforcements. The general estimate of each child's over-all speech level confirmed the strikingly aberrant speech patterns of the schizophrenic children. While 70 percent of the schizophrenic children showed poor or very poor speech (ratings 4 and 5), 76 percent of the normal children showed good or very good speech (ratings 1 and 2). Viewing the data somewhat differently, none of the schizophrenic children showed good speech or better, in contrast to 76 percent of the normal children. Similarly none of the normal children showed very poor speech, in contrast to 38 percent of the schizophrenics.

Under conditions of delayed auditory feedback, gross speech impairment was noted in all the normal children (table 3). Again, the schizophrenics were clearly differentiated. A dramatic finding was in how many schizophrenic children either no additional impairment or very slight additional impairment in speech by delayed feedback was noted. Five of the 13 schizophrenic children showed very slight or no impairment in speech. Two of these children were stutterers whose stuttering actually diminished under delayed feedback conditions.† However, an additional factor must be assumed inasmuch as three of the five children who were slightly impaired by feedback delay were not stutterers.

Behavior During Delayed Feedback (*Table 3*)

During the delayed feedback the schizophrenic children were more restless and less capable of sustained effort than the normal children. This finding, of course, is not unexpected.

Behavioral ratings were made to appraise reactions of discomfort to the delayed feedback experience. Four of the 13 schizophrenic children (31 percent) expressed severe discomfort, frequently elaborated in terms of physical symptoms. Illustrations of severe discomfort follow:

* It is clear, too, that judgments by others must be made.

† This finding seems related to the clinical improvement in stutterers under conditions of auditory interference.

1. When the delayed feedback was initiated, Ruth put her hands to her ears and asked what was going on. She shook her head violently as though to shake the sound away. She held her head with both hands and screamed in a frenzied fashion, "*What's happening? This is terrible. I don't like it. I don't like her. Please stop that noise.*"

2. Billy became extremely upset and screamed wildly. He frequently covered his earphones with his hands in a seeming effort to shut out the voice. He hit his head and ears with his hands. He flung his arms and legs about wildly, twisted and contorted his entire body, grimaced at a reflection of himself in the mirror, clenched his fists, and pounded his head.

3. Roger yelled, "*This thing is driving me crazy.*" He gritted his teeth, hit the recorder with his fist, shook his fist at the microphone. Frequently he grabbed the microphone with both hands in an attempt to cut off the sound. He shouted, "*I can't do it. It's terrible. It makes me dizzy. I got a headache.*"

Eight schizophrenic children (62 percent) gave the opposite reaction of no sign of discomfort at all. It is, therefore, noteworthy that virtually all the schizophrenic children showed either severe discomfort or no evidence of discomfort.

In sharp contrast to the schizophrenic children, 19 of the normal children (76 percent) showed just mild discomfort, largely in terms of hindrance in speaking. None showed severe discomfort and six of the normal group (24 percent) offered no signs of apparent discomfort. The severe discomfort reactions of the schizophrenic children were all spontaneously expressed, while the characteristic mild discomfort reactions of the normals were elicited only after interview probing.

An appraisal was made of each child's awareness that the voice under delayed feedback conditions was his own. All but two of the normal children (92 percent) were clearly aware that the voices they heard on delayed feedback were their own, though modified on reproduction. The schizophrenic children were distinctly different in this regard. Eight of the schizophrenic children (62 percent) were unaware that the recorded voices they heard were their own.

The appraisal of confusion was based on vocal, verbal and gestural behavior. Verbal behavior alone was found to be insufficient evidence of confusion. Thus, when the delayed feedback was initiated, a typical reaction of the schizophrenic children was to peer about the room as if to locate the mysterious voice, a behavior never observed among the normals. The more typical reaction of the normals was to smile understandingly at the experimenter and then to indicate unmistakably, by manner and word, the realistic recognition that the machine had altered the normal sound cycle. None of the 25 normal children gave evidence of confusion in self-identity under playback or delayed feedback conditions. In contrast, eight of the schizophrenic children (62 percent) showed moderate to very severe confusion in personal identity.

To what extent was the confusion a result of the auditory interference and the voice distortion produced by the delayed feedback? To what extent was the confusion a consequence of the arbitrary location of the voice source outside the child? The playback procedure offered a partial answer to these questions. Under playback conditions the auditory interference and the voice distortions of delayed feedback do not occur. However, as in delayed feedback, the voice source is outside the child. It is, therefore, worthy of note that under playback conditions four of the schizophrenic children (31 percent), but none of the normal subjects, showed serious confusion in self-identity. The dislocation of the voice source was a crucial disturbing factor.

Some illustrations of the emergence of defects in self-identity under playback or delayed feedback conditions follow:

4. After listening to the playback of her recording and preparing to leave the room, Marjorie said: "*You know something . . . that voice sounds like a boy. The voice was a boy's voice. Does he have to go now? Will he make another record again? Can the boy come soon again?*"

Examiner: "*That was your voice on the record.*"

Marjorie: "*It wasn't me. That was a boy on the record. Didn't he sound funny? He was a silly boy.*"

Examiner: "*That was your voice.*"

Marjorie: "*Yes, I think that was his real voice.*"

5. As soon as he heard his voice under delayed feedback conditions, Billy spontaneously said: "*Two Pats* . . . two Pats are saying that? Two Pats are singing it?*"

Examiner: "*No, there's only one Pat.*"

Billy: "*Is a boy talking? That boy is talking? That boy? A boy?*"

Suddenly, Billy began screaming, and then said: "*Who's yelling . . . another boy? That boy better shut up!*"

Examiner: "*You were yelling.*"

Billy: "*And who else? Stop it! Stop it!*"

Examiner: "*Who are you talking to?*"

* The examiner whose voice was also heard on the tape.

Billy: "*That boy. That boy better shut up!*"

He began to touch and feel the recording equipment cautiously and then asked in a pleading fashion: "*Where is he?*"

Examiner: "*That's your voice that you hear.*"

Billy: "*No. I talk funny. Who brought him?*"

6. After listening to the playback of his first recording, Roger commented: "*That's the weirdest, mystical voice I ever heard. You know what that sounds like? An adult . . . a man . . . a man who isn't in his right mind . . . you know what I mean . . . an insane man.*"

Later, Roger was asked to identify his voice.

Examiner: "*Whose voice did you hear?*"

Roger: "*Martin's*"

Examiner: "*Are you sure it was Martin's?*"

Roger: "*Sure. That wasn't my voice. I'd know it anywhere. It was Martin's voice. Who else?*"

Examiner: "*Could it be you?*"

Roger: "*No, if that's me, then I got corn the size of a house. That wasn't my voice. I've been cheated! I've been robbed! The owner of the cafe should be arrested.*"

Examiner: "*But that was your story, wasn't it?*"

Roger: "*That was my story, but that was somebody else telling it.*"

As soon as the delayed feedback was initiated, Roger spontaneously remarked in an angry, frustrated manner: "*This darn thing is talking back to me.*"

Examiner: "*What's talking back to you?*"

Roger: "*Something in there.* (Pointing to the equipment.) *It says it the wrong way. It's talking back at me. It makes me confused.*"

Then talking into the microphone, he said: "*Will you shut up?*"

Examiner: "*Who are you talking to?*"

Roger: "*A brat in there . . . talking back at me.*"

Examiner: "*Who is it?*"

Roger: "*I don't know. Somebody else. They're on the other side of this wall. They have a microphone in back of the wall, on the other side. The workmen could have been crooks. They built a false floor and they're hiding under it and they got a microphone hidden in the wall.*"

After the recording, when asked whose voice he heard, Roger said: "*A bum. I don't know. He must have been a crook. Only crooks listen in on other people's conversations.*"

7. After listening to the playback of his recording, Barry said: "*It sounds funny. I talk like a baby. I say the wrong words. It sounds like 6 years old.*"

8. After the delayed feedback recording Millie was asked to identify her voice.

Examiner: "*Whose voice did you hear?*"

Millie: "*Eleanor's. I'm positively sure.*"

Examiner: "*How could that be Eleanor's voice?*"

Millie: "*Well, okay Eleanor. What's your name? My name is Eleanor.*"

Examiner: "*Are you Eleanor?*"

Millie: "*Yes, Eleanor. Is that another girl talking? It's another girl. A little girl. Her name is Eleanor Millie. That's what her name is.*"

9. While talking under delayed feedback conditions, Ruth suddenly began to scream: "*Who is that? Who is talking in my ear? I don't like her!*"

She then turned to the examiner and asked: "*Who are you? Are you my sister? Are you Pat? No, you're my sister . . . aren't you? What's happening? I don't like it! I don't like her! I hate her!*"

10. During the recording under delayed feedback conditions, Eleanor stared off into space and spontaneously said: "*My mommy don't love me. I don't love my mommy till she loves me. My mommy don't take me home. My mommy won't write me a letter. My mommy says, 'I hate Eleanor.'* "

Then, directly into the microphone, Eleanor said: "*Shut up, Mother.*"

It is apparent from these illustrations that the manifestations of the defect in self-awareness were multiple and varied. These include all of the following:

1. Defects in self-reference.
   a. Confusion in sexual recognition. The voice is referred to a child of the opposite sex (Case 4).
   b. Third person reference. "*That boy is talking.*" (Case 5).
   c. "Other person" confusion. The voice is attributed to another specific individual (Case 6).
   d. Age confusion. Mistakenly the voice is attributed to an infant or to an adult (Cases 6 and 7).
2. References to multiple or duplicated figures. The child perceives two selves or more (Cases 5 and 8).

3. Total disorientation and bewilderment (Case 9).
4. Animism or the projection of human characteristics onto inanimate objects. Commonly, the schizophrenic children talked to the microphone as though it were alive and talking to them. As noted, among these children there was no recognition that the voices were initially their own (Case 6).

From a dynamic point of view, the schizophrenic children had difficulty in maintaining unified images of themselves. This was represented in the implicit fragmentation of the self and absence of boundaries of self, expressed in the following:

1. Perception of two selves (Case 8).
2. Interweaving of self and another (Cases 8 and 10).
3. Projection of the voice onto another human being. The sexual and age errors fit into this group (Cases 4, 6 and 7).
4. Projection of the voice onto inanimate objects (Case 6).

Discussion

The present investigation confirms the absence of normal speech patterns in a group of schizophrenic children. The study also supports the hypothesis that schizophrenic children react differently from normal children to the sound stimulus. Under conditions of delayed auditory feedback, all the normal children show significant impairment of their natural speech, involving changes in the specific aspects of speech and voice. Individual imperviousness of speech to the effects of delayed feedback does not occur at all in this group. In contrast, under similar conditions, the schizophrenic children show less impairment of their natural voice and speech. This finding confirms the trend to auditory exclusion in schizophrenic children. It is in accord with previous observations of auditory inattention in schizophrenic children, often to the point of pseudodeafness.[5] In all likelihood, auditory denial accounts in part for the high ratio of schizophrenic children with a total absence of discomfort reaction during delayed feedback. On the other hand, when the barrier of denial is penetrated and sound reception is enforced by the closely applied earphones very much like an intrusively loud voice, most of the remainder of the schizophrenic children spontaneously display a severe discomfort reaction shown by none of the normal children.

A smooth, fluent, delicately expressive vocal utterance requires an effective machinery for continuous self-monitoring. This self-guidance comes through immediate auditory feedback. Interference with the latter in normals produces the above-noted dissolution of many of the learned speech forms, an alteration which is detectable in the appraisal of over-all quality and the specifics of voice and speech. The aberrant speech of the schizophrenic children may be functionally related to their tendency, on one hand, to exclude verbal stimuli or, on the other, to react to verbal stimuli with marked discomfort. Yet, for the same reason, the experimental attempt to interfere with the normal auditory feedback by the delayed side-tone has less effect on the speech of schizophrenic children than on that of normals.

Of equal interest is the relationship between the experience of sensory feedback and the achievement of a sense of personal identity. We are referring here to the inner awareness of one's identity as discrete from the rest of the world. Beyond the direct relationship between self-monitoring systems and efficient, self-controlled action, a steady and predictable stream of feedback experiences constant in the matter of reception time seems to contribute to the maintenance of a stable awareness of self. The self in action produces a complicated but constant sequence of inner experiences that repeatedly affirm the responsibility of the self for the action. The importance of proprioceptive experiences in the achievement of self has been described.[9] It is likely, however, that the feedback of all the sensory modalities, including the auditory, is involved in the differentiation of self.

Aside from feedback experiences, the differentiation of the self from the outer "not-self" is facilitated and sustained by sensory perceptual experiences of external origin. Such experiences occur in a setting of the self in interaction with the outer world of people and objects. It may be postulated that the diminished use of the distance receptors, vision and hearing by the schizophrenic child interferes with the development of a concept of firmness and permanence of the outer world and therefore of the self.*

The absence of such referents is presumed to impede the development of the "self" as differentiated from the "not self." Further, the present study demonstrates that the shifting of such referents, as by delayed auditory feedback, acts to a varying degree to unsettle self-identification, with the emergence of bewildering symptoms of disorientation to the self.† A variety of adaptive and protective operations are observed.

* The general disorientation of schizophrenic children is well known clinically and has been systematically demonstrated.[8]

† Findings in the same direction with normal adults have been supplied by Lilly.[7]

These include

1. Pleas for environmental sameness (Case 1).
2. Outbursts of unfocussed rage with outwardly directed assaults, even against inanimate objects (Case 3), or against the self (Case 2).
3. Compulsive questioning (Cases 4, 5 and 9).
4. Confabulation (Case 6) to explain the gaps in awareness and perception.
5. Total denial of the uncomfortably confusing perceptual experience. Such denial would be implied in observations of pseudodeafness or in the relative imperviousness of the schizophrenic child's speech to the interfering effects of delayed feedback.

Present findings are in accord with the postulate that the psychic experience of self-awareness is dependent on inner and outer referents. Vulnerability of self-awareness to referential shifts is determined by individual differences in integrity of ego. In the stress of the delayed feedback, normal 8- to 10-year-old children retain clear self-awareness. In contrast, schizophrenic children are more dependent on constancy of external referents. In this light, the delayed auditory feedback experiment may be viewed as a useful device for appraising unity and strength of personal identity.

REFERENCES

1. BENDER, LAURETTA: A quantitative test of theory and diagnostic indicators of childhood schizophrenia. Arch. Neurol. & Psychiat. *70*: 413-427, 1953.
2. BEXTON, W. H., HERON, W., AND SCOTT, T. H.: Effects of decreased variation in the sensory environment. Canad. J. Psychol. *8*: 70-76, 1954.
3. BLACK, JOHN W.: The effect of delayed side-tone upon vocal rate and intensity. J. Speech & Hear. Disord. *16*: 56-60, 1951.
4. GOLDFARB, WILLIAM, BRAUNSTEIN, PATRICIA, AND LORGE, IRVING: A study of speech patterns of schizophrenic children. A. J. Orthopsychiat. *26*: 544-555, 1956.
5. ——: Receptor preferences in schizophrenic children. Arch. Neurol. & Psychiat. *76*: 643-652, 1956.
6. LEE, BERNARD S.: Effects of delayed speech feedback. J. Acoust. Soc. A. *22*: 824-826, 1950.
7. LILLY, JOHN: Effects of physical restraint and of reduction of ordinary levels of physical stimuli on intact, healthy persons. Paper presented at the Meeting of the Group for the Advancement of Psychiatry, November 1955.
8. POLLACK, MAX, AND GOLDFARB, W.: Patterns of orientation in children in residential treatment for severe behavior disorders. A. J. Orthopsychiat. *27*: 538-552, 1957.
9. RADO, SANDOR: Hedonic control, action-self, and the depressive spell. In Paul Hoch and Joseph Zubin, Eds., Depression. New York, Grune & Stratton 1954, chap. 11.

6

AUTISTIC PATTERNS AND DEFECTIVE COMMUNICATION IN BLIND CHILDREN WITH RETROLENTAL FIBROPLASIA

By W. R. KEELER, M.D.*

SINCE NOVEMBER 1953, there has been a research program under way at the Hospital for Sick Children in Toronto on the subject of childhood schizophrenia. Emphasis of study to date has been on that subgroup designated by Lauretta Bender as psuedodefective or autistic schizophrenia[1] and by Leo Kanner as early infantile autism.[2]

From the beginning the project made it known that children suffering from this disorder would be welcomed. As a result, children were referred who suffered from a variety of basic conditions other than infantile autism, but who manifested symptomatology sufficiently similar to it to cause this diagnostic confusion. This group of children suffered from mental deficiency, various "organic" states, aphasia (organic and congenital), deafness, and blindness. Among them, the blind children presented the most strikingly similar picture to infantile autism.

This group of blind children consisted of five preschool children referred during the past two and one-half years to the Hospital for Sick Children by the Canadian National Institute for the Blind for psychological and psychiatric evaluation because of their strikingly abnormal behavior and mental development. All of these children had been born prematurely with a gestation period ranging from six to seven months and with a birth weight ranging from two pounds up to five pounds, thirteen ounces. There were three girls and two boys. Two were identical twins. All had been placed in an incubator, had received oxygen, and had during the ensuing 3 to 14 weeks developed blindness resulting from the develop-

* Formerly Research Associate, The Research Institute of the Hospital for Sick Children, Toronto, Ontario, Canada; at present, Associate Professor of Psychiatry, University of Michigan, Ann Arbor, Michigan.

This study was supported by funds allocated by the Province of Ontario under the Mental Health Grants Program of the Department of National Health and Welfare, Ottawa, Canada.

ment of retrolental fibroplasia. Two were totally blind and the remaining three had only extremely slight light perception in one eye.

Upon first contact with this group of children one was immediately struck by the marked similarities of the histories and clinical picture to those of children suffering from early infantile autism. The main features of similarity appeared to be their self-isolation and their lack of the use of language for the purpose of interpersonal communication. They would sit by themselves for hours at a time showing no effort to initiate any activity whatsoever. When spoken to they would not respond. However, they showed evidence of full understanding of spoken language. They also revealed remarkably good memory. When physical contact was made with them they did not appear to distinguish between one person and another, i.e., they appeared to make the same type of contact with complete strangers as they would with their own mothers. Two of them became very disturbed if any physical contact was made with them whatsoever.

These children manifested autistic patterns of activity such as rhythmically rocking back and forth, usually to music. They also showed an exceptional liking for and preoccupation with music. They did not play normally with toys; they showed no interest in the animated type such as teddy bears, dolls, etc., but preferred playing with things which would make a noise or were of a mechanical nature, e.g., some household article. Repeated unscrewing and screwing back on again of a jar lid and spinning a pot lid around are typical examples.

As indicated, language had not developed normally, i.e, it appeared delayed and when it did develop consisted of echolalia, repetitive use of apparently meaningless words or phrases, and referring to oneself in the third person. Sometimes words were not repeated but a very similar sound was made using the exact tone and fluctuation of the voice. Bizarre guttural vocalizations were frequently present.

In contrast to their inability to use language properly all of them had, at a very early age (about two), learned to hum and to sing songs of a fairly complicated nature, sometimes putting the correct words to them.

Primitive patterns of perception of their physical environment, e.g., smell, touch, sound, and taste, were present. Exploring their environment by going about smelling or tapping everything was outstanding.

Abnormal patterns of motility strikingly similar to those observed in the autistic schizophrenic child were seen. There was toe-walking, body rocking, turning the head or the entire trunk in a rhythmical fashion, bizarre choreoathetotic posturings in the upper extremities, and peculiar arm and hand waving with rhythmical apposition of the finger tips of both hands. These children would also frequently run around in a circle. In addition there were other bizarre mannerisms usually classified as "blindisms", e.g., putting the backs of the hands to the eyes, putting the fingers in the eyes, putting the fingers in the ears, or putting the palms of the hands over the ears.

All five cases showed a peculiar but characteristic retardation in their developmental histories. I say peculiar because the retardation was not identical with that seen in the usual type of mentally retarded child. Learning to hold their heads up and to sit up were reported as being normal. Learning to walk, however, was delayed. Toilet training was also slow and difficult. The establishment of a normal sleep pattern was difficult, there frequently being a reversal of day and night. These children would not feed themselves and would respond to attempts in training by throwing the spoon away. They preferred soft foods and stayed on the strained baby foods up to the ages of four and five years.

Physical examination, except for the eye condition, was essentially negative in all five cases. Electroencephalograms done in three cases (all of which had some slight light perception) were normal.

Formal psychological testing of the blind preschool child is in itself a very difficult task and was found to be impossible in this particular group of children.

The psychological environment in all five cases had not been good. In all cases the first month or so had been spent in a hospital and most of this time in an incubator. In all cases, the mothers were greatly disturbed by finding their children blind and tended literally to put them out of their minds by leaving them in cribs and playpens off in a back room of the house or in the back yard for long periods of time, attending only in a minimal way to the most imperative of their physical needs. In three cases the mothers have worked off and on to the present time, hiring someone to come in and look after their children. A few of these mothers repeatedly made the statement that they would rather see their children dead than the way they are.

The family histories in all five cases, although not as complete in one case as one would wish, did not reveal any evidence of mental illness.

For the purpose of illustration, I should now like to present the histories and findings of two of these cases.

Case 1

Cheryl T., a six-year-old white girl, was referred to the Hospital for Sick Children for evaluation of her mental status when she was four years of age. Her mother complained that she would not pay attention to her, remained aloof and off by herself, never used language to communicate but did appear to understand what was said to her, and showed an excellent musical ability, being able to hum and to sing.

The history indicated that Cheryl's parents had been living in a common-law relationship. The mother had two grown sons by a previous marriage. Lenore is the only child by the present relationship, although her mother has had two miscarriages since Cheryl was born.

Cheryl was born prematurely on September 2, 1950, coming at six months and weighing two pounds. She was placed in an incubator and received oxygen for an unknown length of time but we do know that she was not discharged from hospital until the age of two months.

According to her mother, Cheryl did not pose any particular problem and she appeared to be developing normally until her parents noticed when she was six months old that there was something wrong with her eyes. At that time she was admitted to hospital for one month during which time she was investigated and diagnosed as suffering from retrolental fibroplasia and received ACTH therapy. At the time of discharge she was proclaimed to be totally blind.

During the ensuing months, Mrs. T. observed various abnormalities in Cheryl's behavior and development. Cheryl sat up at seven months and ever since then had rocked back and forth excessively in a rhythmical fashion. She stood up at nine months but could not walk on her own until the age of two years.

Cheryl remained on the bottle for a long time and up until recently has been able to take only strained baby foods. Toilet training has also been difficult. She has never let her wants be known and will not use a regular toilet but only her own little one. About this her mother stated, "If I talk to her and tell her to go to the po-po, she just mimics me, you know, says 'po-po' and just sits there, and she carries on like that, but she still won't go until I take her off and put her on her own little po-po and she goes on that where she won't go on the regular toilet." Cheryl still wets the bed occasionally at night.

During the latter part of her first year and the first part of the second, Cheryl would wake up during the night for several hours, would laugh, giggle, and appear to wish to play. This has by now largely subsided.

As an infant, Cheryl was never a cuddly baby. She did not want to be picked up, always preferring to be by herself. The latter behavior has persisted, her mother describing her as being socially isolated. She will remain in one spot for hours, usually rocking, perhaps humming, and at the same time moving her arms and hands in a bizarre fashion. Her mother's chief concern at the present time is her lack of wanting to communicate by spoken word. For example, her mother said, "If only she would talk with me, we could get along so well together and she would be happy."

Cheryl's language development was markedly delayed. She first spoke single words at around the age of three. She now repeats words, phrases, and sentences but does not make spontaneous conversation or let her wants be known through verbal communication. She has always liked music and has shown an extraordinary talent for carrying a tune. She does not put words to the music, however. Although exposed to children of her own age, Cheryl has never shown a tendency to want to play with them. When someone approaches her physically, she will go with him, but this can be with anyone, and according to her mother, she and her husband believe that Cheryl would never miss them. She has never played normally with toys, usually just tearing books apart or throwing her toys about. She is reported, however, to have a remarkable memory, knowing a place where she has been before even though this may have been on only one occasion a year or so before. She also shows very good ability at finding her way about the house.

The family history was negative for any type of mental illness although our data in this regard are not too satisfactory.

Mrs. T. is a rather pleasant but dull woman who has not openly rejected Cheryl but who has never been very close to her. As an infant Cheryl was left in a crib or playpen by herself a great deal of the time. Cheryl was about one year of age Mrs. T. went out to work and has worked off and on since then. When at work. Mrs. T. has some hired woman look after Cheryl. More recently she has wondered if this has been bad for Cheryl and has stopped working in hope that giving the child more attention might improve her condition. This was tried for most of a year, and because dramatic results were not produced, Mrs. T. felt discouraged and is now out again working in a restaurant for part of the day.

Examination of Cheryl revealed her to be a rather good-looking child. General physical examination except for her eye condition was essentially negative. Psychiatric examination revealed the predominant features of self-isolation and lack of verbal communication. She did not respond to the spoken voice of the examiner but did go with him when taken by the hand. When she walked she did so on tiptoe.

Cheryl preferred to stand by herself, rocking rhythmically backward and forward, from one leg to the other, with the right one forward. While doing this she would chant away, wave her arms and hands in a bizarre fashion, bringing the finger tips of one hand into apposition to those of the other. This activity would come in spells alternating with the blindism of placing the backs of her hands up to her eyes.

When spoken to, Cheryl would occasionally respond verbally in an echolalic fashion, e.g., when I asked, "Do you want to go home, Cheryl?" she responded by saying, "Do you want to go home, Cheryl?" She did not respond at all when other, less meaningful things were said to her. She also indicated that she had full grasp of what was being said in her presence.

Case 2

Betty A. This little white girl, born on March 26, 1951, was referred to the Hospital for Sick Children when she was four years of age. The chief complaints were that she had not developed the proper use of language and that she did not relate to adults or to children in an adequate fashion.

The history indicated that Betty was an illegitimate baby. She was born prematurely with a gestation period of six and one-half months, weighing three pounds. The length of time she was in an incubator and the amount and concentration of oxygen she received are not known. She remained in the hospital, however, for almost two months, being discharged on May 22, 1951.

Betty went immediately from the hospital into a foster home where she has remained ever since. Very shortly after her placement it was noted that she had trouble with her eyes and in June, 1951, she was diagnosed as having retrolental fibroplasia with a minimal amount of light perception.

In regard to her early development, Betty's foster mother said in response to my questions: ("Now you got her when she was how old?") "Well, she was a premature by three months and I got her when she was about five or six weeks old." ("And how was she at the beginning?") "Just as perfect as any other baby, just as normal, that is, as any other baby." ("She took her feedings all right?") "Definitely, yes." ("When did you first notice a change in her?") "Well I mean, she changed as she got older, all the time like, you know in her ways and her habits and all that." ("Was there a change in the first five or six months?") "Well, she was slow in coming along, if you mean that, I mean slower than the other baby. She never walked until she was nearly two. She never said words until she was well over a year, but other than that she was as normal as can be." ("Did she hold her head up all right?") "Yes, definitely yes." ("Did she sit up all right?") "Yes." ("But the walking was slow?") "Yes, the walking was slow, and when she first started to walk, she walked on her toes. That was close to two when she started." ("Does she walk on her toes now?") "Yes, until I remind her to put her feet straight and she does it. You know, she understands perfectly what I say." ("She does?") "She knows exactly what I say and she knows right from wrong."

From the beginning Betty was content to be by herself and was described as being a very quiet, good baby. She liked to play with anything which made a noise (e.g., a rattle) and would remain quietly by herself doing so by the hour. There was a pet chihuahua dog in the house regarding whom she showed no fear or affection. She acted as if he did not exist. As an infant she never wished to be fondled and since then has never sought out anyone for help, comfort, or company. She usually remains in one spot for long periods not initiating activity on her own.

During her second year, Betty started to kick her feet rhythmically a great deal —"twenty-four hours a day," according to her mother. During her third year, this was replaced by a rhythmic rocking of her body. At about this time she would wake up during the night and would talk to herself. About this her foster mother said, "Not crying or temper—just making a noise to hear her own voice and kicking her feet and rocking her head."

Betty was difficult to get onto solid food, and even now, at the age of five, prefers strained baby foods. She was also very slow in learning to feed herself.

Up to the present time Betty has not made any effort to use language for the purpose of interpersonal communication, although she can enunciate single words, short phrases, and sentences. She reportedly vocalized early and said "mama" and "dada" at the usual age. At the age of three she made sounds resembling phrases in songs. As stated, however, no useful language has developed to date. She does not ask for what she wants. She utters repeatedly irrelevant words and phrases such as "want a drink of water?—want a drink of water?" or "cookie—cookie," etc. When greeted or when spoken to by an adult she will immediately start up an incessant repetition of words or commands used by adults. For example: "Get down, Betty." "Come here, dear." "Water." "Po-po." Her foster mother reports that she will keep this up for hours. At other times she will just utter peculiar, guttural sounds. Echolalia is also described by her mother. In this regard Mrs. A. said, "She is just like a parrot. She'll say any word in this world, just to say it, but it means nothing to her. If I say, 'Betty, go and sit down like a good girl,' she will say, 'Betty, go and sit down like a good girl,' and she'll go and do it, but she'll say it also."

When asked how Betty communicated her wants to her foster parents, Mrs. A. said, "If she wants to eat—I've always taught whoever feeds her to feed her in a high chair, therefore, if she wants to eat she'll go in the high chair and go 'ugh, ugh, ugh, ugh,' you see—well, I've just got to use my own imagination as to what she wants and I'll say, 'Do you want water?' and she'll shake her head and make a face and I'll say, 'Do you want a glass of milk?' Well then she won't say anything, she just sits there, so I give her milk. If I say, 'Do you want cookies?' she'll just put her hand up for it." ("I see.") "If I say, 'Do you want to go the bathroom', if she doesn't want to go she'll shrug her shoulders and make a face. If she wants to go, she'll get down off the high chair and go, but you have to ask her for each thing. She won't ask you for them. She'll stand there and wet herself rather than ask you to go."

When asked if Betty liked music, Mrs. A. replied, "Oh, yes, and she can carry a tune as well as anybody else can." ("What sort of music does she like?") "Well, just whatever comes on the radio, I mean these commercials, she can say them as good as the man that's saying them, and she can say them word for word the right way. And yet she won't carry on a conversation or ask anything."

When asked what sort of toys the child liked to play with, her foster mother said, "Anything that makes a noise, if it don't make a noise she just tosses it away." Her foster mother was then asked if Betty went about smelling things, and she said, "She smells everything before she eats it. She won't put a thing in her mouth. How she knows it, I don't know, but if you give her a cookie or a piece of bread or an apple, anything at all, she'll smell it, then she'll eat it. And to prove to my husband that she knew the difference, I unwrapped a bar of soap and gave it to her. She smelt it, she put it down, she picked it up and smelt it again, she still put it down; she never put it in her mouth."

When further questioned about Betty's relationship with children, Mrs. A. said, "She hasn't any desire to bother with other ones." Mrs. A. was then asked about Betty's relationship with adults and she said, "She'll play with them by the hour. She'll really tire you out more than she'll be tired. If you just take her hand you've had it then, because she wants to climb all over you, jump off your lap; throw her in the air, do anything, just use her like a football, and she's quite happy to go through all that. But when you're ready to stop, then she don't want to stop, then she'll sit down and rock and get mad, and sulk and sit there till you pick her up again and do it." Further, in regard to physical contact, it was stated that Betty does not appear to discriminate between one person and another.

When asked if she thought Betty was smart in any way, Mrs. A. replied, "Well, I don't think she's stupid by any means. I really don't think so. I think if she had somebody that could spend a lot of time with her and she was with other children, I think she would come on wonderful. That's my opinion of her, and I think I know her pretty well."

In regard to Betty's psychological environment, this has been far from ideal. As indicated, she spent the first two months of her life in the hospital. Her foster mother has worked off and on and she has never received very much individual attention. This was particularly true during her first year or so of life, when her foster mother left her by herself in her crib or playpen a great deal of the time.

Examination of Betty, as with the other children, did not reveal any gross physical abnormalities except for her eye condition. As indicated, she has slight light perception in one eye. An electroencephalogram did not reveal any abnormality.

The predominant clinical feature was Betty's apparent lack of social awareness. She did not respond to the spoken voice except by manifesting echolalia. When physical contact was made with her, she immediately sought anti-gravity play. This she enjoyed immensely, showing great pleasure by squealing and laughing. When this was discontinued, she tried very hard to reestablish physical contact, and when she could not do this she showed marked evidence of displeasure, jumped down to the floor, sat there and began to rock rhythmically backward and forward. Bizarre motility in the form of waving her arms and hands in a peculiar fashion was also noted. A blindism in the form of putting her fingers to her eyes was quite prevalent. As she rocked she hummed to herself. This autistic behavior pattern could be interrupted by making physical contact with her, at which time she would attempt to involve the examiner in anti-gravity play. It could also be interrupted by giving her a musical toy, like a small music box. She would listen to this intently, give it to the examiner to re-wind, and then hold it very close to her ear again. This pleased and amused her immensely, as evidenced by her laughing aloud when she did this. When walking about the room she manifested marked toe-walking and peculiar choreoathetotic posturings in her upper extremities. Her movements were very similar to those of the young schizophrenic child.

In order to give us some insight into the nature of this disorder, it was decided to investigate a group of children with the same eye condition (i.e., retrolental fibroplasia) but who had not been brought for psychiatric evaluation and who therefore were presumably doing well in the community. This was done on 35 preschool and school age children who live in Ontario and who had been registered with the Canadian National Institute for the Blind.* All suffered from approximately the same degree of blindness as did the five cases referred with a psychiatric disorder. This group of 35 cases was considered to be a fairly representative sample, there being, as of March 1, 1956, 102 children of all ages with retrolental fibroplasia from Ontario who were registered with the Institute, 78 of whom were under six years of age.

Twenty-five of these 35 children were in the preschool age group and 10 were of school age, i.e., six to twelve years. Five in the preschool group were attending the Institute's special nursery school in Welland, Ontario, and all of the school age group were attending the Ontario School for the Blind in Brantford, Ontario. In the latter two groups of children, i.e., those attending regular and nursery schools, perusal of their histories was supplemented by personal observation.

The histories and behavior patterns of all of these 35 children were in many ways similar to those found in the 5 children under intensive study who were referred because of abnormal behavior. The chief difference between the two groups was that the symptoms and deviations in development were much more marked in the latter. Predominant were the features of delayed motor maturation, feeding difficulties, difficulties in toilet training, delayed language development, the presence of autistic patterns, the liking for music, the exploration of their environment through the sense of smell, the presence of blindisms and other bizarre motility patterns, etc.

Although all of the school age group were up to grade, their teachers reported that they were somewhat slower than the other children in their classes who suffered from blindness of a different origin.

In summary, therefore, we may say that all of these 35 children with retrolental fibroplasia who had not been referred for psychiatric appraisal showed, qualitatively speaking, similar histories and behavior patterns to those of the five children with psychiatric disorders. These features were much milder in degree, however, in the former.

In order perhaps to advance our knowledge even further regarding the nature of this disorder, it was decided to study two other categories of blind children: one group blinded at birth and another group blinded later on in infancy or in early childhood.

*Acknowledgement is made to the Canadian National Institute for the Blind for permission to use data from their records and for their cooperation in this research.

The first group consisted of 18 children who were congenitally blinded by such conditions as cataracts, familial macular degeneration, buphthalmos (congenital glaucoma), and endophthalmitis, etc. In all of these cases the amount of vision present was much greater than that present in the children with retrolental fibroplasia. In all of them, however, there was less than 20/200 vision in the better eye. This is the maximal amount of vision which an individual can have and be registered with the Canadian National Institute for the Blind. This was considered a representative group since it included all cases of congenitally blind preschool and school children who were registered with the Institute as of March 1, 1956.

The developmental histories of these congenitally blind children were quite different from those found in the children with retrolental fibroplasia. There were not the developmental delays in motor maturation, feeding, toilet training, etc. One did not see the same degree of autistic patterns of behavior, although some of these children were somewhat withdrawn. Abnormalities in motility were noted but were not so prevalent and not so severe, although in two cases they were quite marked. For example, the blindism of putting her hands in her eyes was so marked in one child that her mother tied down her hands. Another child would jump up and down almost continuously, suck her tongue, and twist her head from side to side.

The group of children blinded from other causes than retrolental fibroplasia which were studied consisted of 17 children, the majority of whom lost their vision later on in infancy or in early childhood as a result of the operative removal of both eyes because of the presence of retinoblastoma. Other causes of postnatal blindness were trauma, infection, and neuromyelitis optica.

Abnormalities in development and in behavior were least conspicuous in these children blinded postnatally from causes other than retrolental fibroplasia. Their motor maturation, acquisition of language, development of toilet and feeding habits, etc., had in many cases been established before the blindness had occurred. In those cases in which it had not, the developmental pattern approximated the normal. As indicated, the majority of these children became blinded during the first or second year of life. Problems of physical and emotional rehabilitation, especially for the older preschool and school age children, were the predominant features. One child who became blind at the age of four because of neuromyelitis optica showed the syndrome of anosognosia, i.e., a denial of her blindness. On the whole, children of this group showed more anxiety and were disturbed by changes in their environment. For example, one child was badly frightened by the sound of falling leaves in the autumn. Another child was frightened by the strange feeling of the bare ground in the spring after walking on the snow-covered ground all winter. This group of children, more markedly than the less severely handicapped congenitally blind children, showed blindisms in the form of putting their fingers in their eyes, head and body twisting, turning in a circle, etc.

As indicated earlier, the school age congenitally blind and the children blinded postnatally from causes other than retrolental fibroplasia did much better at school than the children with retrolental fibroplasia. This was particularly true in the earlier grades. By the time the latter had reached grade three, however, they appeared to be catching up.

The psychological environment of the 35 children with retrolental fibroplasia who were not referred for psychiatric reasons, of the 18 congenitally blind children, and of the 17 children postnatally blinded from causes other than retrolental fibroplasia, was evaluated as average to excellent.

Discussion

The number of cases in this study is too small and the range of data too narrow to allow us to draw any definite generalizations and statistically valid conclusions regarding the nature of this disorder. This was not, however, the main purpose in presenting this material. Rather, this presentation was meant to bring to our attention the fact that such a bizarre pattern of development and behavior does exist in some children blinded with retrolental fibroplasia, and that this disturbance simulates early infantile autism in a striking fashion. It is hoped that future research will further elucidate some of the points regarding the nature of this disorder, its etiology, etc. At present, however, the presented data do give us material upon which to speculate and leads by which future research may be guided. It is also hoped that perhaps the psychopathological features and possible mechanism shown in these blind children may give us some further insight into the nature of early infantile autism.

We may now go on to ask several questions regarding the possible mechanisms of the psychopathological syndrome observed in these blind children.

First, are we perhaps dealing with a condition resulting from brain damage and mental retardation due to an insult to the brain brought about by the prematurity factor or perhaps through vascular involvement of the brain, similar to that which occurs in the retina? There is no conclusive proof that there is such cerebral vascular involvement in this condition, although this has not as yet been disproven. Such a factor could account for the differences in severity of the condition within the group of children with retrolental fibroplasia, i.e., those with a marked psychiatric syndrome may have marked cerebral involvement and those without much symptomatology may have cerebral involvement either to a very mild degree or perhaps not at all. This would also explain the fact that this syndrome was not observed, at least to the same degree, in children blinded by other causes (where the disease was confined to the eyes exclusively). Against organic involvement, at least as being the only etiological agent, is the observation that the clinical picture is not like that of other brain-damaged or mentally retarded children. Perhaps, however, it is a combination of the brain damage with mental retardation and blindness. Although inconclusive, the presence of a normal electroencephalogram in three cases does suggest that possibly a brain damage factor is not operative.

Next we may ask: Is this condition due, perhaps to the blindness per se? Arnold Gesell[3] concluded from a careful observation of one case of congenital anophthalmia that blindness in itself does not produce a serious degree of retardation. This is further substantiated by Franz Kallman, Eugene Barrera, and Harriet Metzger,[4] who reported normal mental development in a girl totally blind with bilateral microphthalmia. She, however, had identical twin brothers with the same condition associated with mental deficiency. It would appear that oligophrenia associated with this eye condition has a genetic basis as demonstrated by other workers, e.g., Torsten Sjögren and Tage Larsson.[5] Kallman's, Barrera's, and Metzger's description of the behavior, especially the motility patterns of the above-mentioned twins, is strikingly similar to that present in the children of the present series. This speaks in favor of the argument that the condition is due to a combination of severe blindness coming on very early plus brain pathology and mental deficiency. In addition, this is against the notion that the syndrome is specific to retrolental fibroplasia. From a comparison of those cases congenitally blind (very mild symptomatology) and those cases with retrolental fibroplasia (severe symptomatology), it would appear that blindness which comes on very early is not an all-important or exclusively acting factor. However, comparison of the children blinded postnatally from other causes (practically no symptoms) with those whose blindness is due to retrolental fibroplasia (severe symptomatology) suggests that very early blindness is possibly a contributory factor.

A further question presents itself: Do psychological factors perhaps play a role in the production of this disorder? Many aspects of the clinical picture favor this as does the presence of apparently considerable early emotional neglect in all the psychiatric cases (five in this series) and the apparent absence of this factor in the nonpsychiatric children (i.e., those blinded very early—congenitally blind), the other children with retrolental fibroplasia without this syndrome, and those blinded postnatally owing to other causes.

One may postulate that the condition is due to a combination of a total or extremely severe blindness occurring in the first few weeks of life with an emotional neglect which acts as an inhibitory force to the potential development of the immature ego of the infant. This is further suggested by many similarities between these blind children and those emotionally deprived children described by John Bowlby,[6] René Spitz,[7] Jenny Aubry,[8] and others.

In many ways, however, the cases in the present study are much more similar to those of early infantile autism, which, at a phenomenological level, we also describe as involving a faulty ego development. For example, there is in these blind children severe autism and the lack of differentiation between themselves and outside world, i.e., between the I and the not-I, as evidenced by their referring to themselves in the third person. One can also explain the echolalia and the repetition of the meaningless words seen in these children on this basis. For example, Jean Piaget[9] states, "But from the point of view of personality and from the social point of view, imitation would seem to be, as Janet and Baldwin maintain, a confusion between the I and the not-I, between the activity of one's own body and that of other people's bodies." However, one may see such referring to oneself in the third person, echolalia, and the repetition of meaningless words in certain 'organic' states and extreme degrees of mental deficiency also.

Many other symptoms are remarkably similar to those of the autistic schizophrenic child, e.g., the autoerotic activity of body rocking and especially the choreoathetotic posturings of the hands with arm waving. One might raise the question of the possibility that these children suffer from two conditions: schizophrenia and blindness. Lauretta Bender states that prematurity itself may be a feature of childhood schizophrenia. However, the absence of a family history of mental illness, the differences in the clinical picture, and the prevalence of this disorder in its milder form among most children with retrolental fibroplasia, speaks against this possibility.

Margaret Mahler[10] has pointed out that in the child with early infantile autism, the mother, as representative of the outside world, never seems to have been perceived emotionally, and this first representative of outside reality seems not to have been cathected. In a later paper[11] she postulates an autistic stage in the development of normal children in which there appears to be nothing but a self. She considers that in the child with early infantile autism there is a fixation at this stage of development. Might not such a state of affairs exist in the children of the present study, in this case, however, being brought about by a different mechanism? It was Paul Schilder[12] who emphasized the importance of the visual apparatus in enabling the young infant to differentiate between himself and the outside world and thereby to build up his body image. By deduction it appears possible that the absence of visual cues in itself is perhaps important in the production of this disorder. Willie Hoffer,[13] in a paper on the development of the body ego, points up the role of the visual as well as the olfactory and auditory apparatus in the early ego development of the child. Psychoanalysts have pointed out, in this regard, the role of the infant's visualization of the mother's breast. René Spitz,[14] on the other hand, has emphasized the role which the child's visualization of the face of his mother plays in his ego development. We are reminded here of the persistent activity of the young infant touching his mother's face and scrutinizing his own hands. We see the latter activity in the older schizophrenic child who is apparently trying to define more clearly his own body image. There is certainly no opportunity for this sort of thing in the totally blind infant. It is of interest here to mention the fact that a blind child with just the slightest amount of vision will often preoccupy himself for long periods of time by holding his hand up to his eyes. By deduction, therefore, it would seem that the absence of visual cues in itself is a traumatic blow to the potential development of the immature ego of the blind infant. Such a child would therefore theoretically require numerous additional sensory data of other types from his environment in order to make up for the loss in the visual area. This we see him doing in the physical sphere, e.g., by sound, touch, and smell. In the emotional area, we may postulate that such a child, as compared to the normal, requires more warm, close, emotional contact with his mother by such means as close physical contact, hearing her voice, etc., elements which have been shown to be very important in the early mother-child relationship and in the formation of the ego of the normal infant. For example, in addition to sight, Margaret Ribble[15-18] has stressed the role of the senses of touch, pressure, warmth, and kinesthesia along with those of sound, taste, and smell through such means as feeding, bathing, fondling, caressing, rocking, holding, speaking and singing to the baby, etc. She further points out [17] that automatic activity such as body-rocking and head-rolling, seen in the children of this study, is a result of the infant or child not being adequately stimulated. The blindisms and other more severe motility mannerisms of the children in this study could also be accounted for on this basis. Paul Schilder[19] has emphasized the very important role of clinging by the primitive grasp-reflex in order to maintain equilibrium and the very closely related sucking by the primitive sucking-reflex in the nuclear formation of the ego. Charlotte Wolff,[20] too, has emphasized the important role of touch to the very young infant. In all of these instances it is difficult and actually incorrect to separate the early physical or biological and the psychological needs of the infant. Observation of animal behavior, likewise, has emphasized the very important role of adequate sensory stimulation to the new-born infant. Frederick Hammet[21] pointed out the important role of "gentling" (stroking and handling gently) rats in terms of lowering their postoperative mortality rate. Milton Greenman and Louise Duhring[22] and Otto Weininger[23,24] have shown the effects of gentling on the future physical and psychological state of rats. James Reyniers[25] has shown that animals brought up in germ-free laboratories without adequate sensory stimulation died from lack of functioning of their genitourinary and gastrointestinal systems. Stroking them, particularly in the perineal and genital regions, obviated this condition. Other experimentations by Hebb,[26] Nissen, Chow, and Semmes,[27] Bingham and Griffiths,[28] Forgays and Forgays, [29] Beach and Jaynes,[30] Thompson and Heron,[31, 32] and Thompson,[33] among others, have shown the importance of sensory as well as motor stimulation on the future intelligence and behavior of infant animals. More recent studies on experimental sensory isolation in humans by Bexton, Heron, and Scott[34] and Heron, Bexton, and Hebb[35] have shown the importance of adequate sensory stimulation on the functioning of the adult ego. It would appear that perhaps the blind children of this study who manifested the characteristic psychopathological syndrome of faulty ego development did not receive the above sort of stimulation in sufficient therapeutic dosage, or putting this another way, their special psychological needs were not catered to and they, being especially vulnerable in this regard, were affected adversely.

In further support that psychogenetic factors may possibly play a relatively large role in the production of this disorder, Jane Hallenbeck[36] has reported on 18 children with retrolental fibroplasia whom she classified as suffering from a pseudomental retardation. She indicated that there had been emotional neglect and showed that marked spurts in maturation could be produced by supplying these children with an intensive program of close, warm emotional contact.

If psychogenetic factors do play a considerable role in the production of this psychopathological syndrome, then we may say it is quite possible that if these children blinded at such an early age were to receive a special type of favorable mothering care and psychological environment of the kind mentioned above, we might expect that this syndrome would not occur, at least not to such a severe degree. Certainly, from the research and therapeutic standpoints, provision of such an environment for these children from the onset of their blindness would be well worthwhile in order to determine whether this might allay or perhaps even completely alleviate the condition. For the older preschool children who already demonstrate this syndrome this approach might also be tried, i.e., in a pilot study to determine what might be the therapeutic effect of a specialized type of day nursery program, along with detailed counselling and guidance for the parents and other adults who care for and have contact with the child, sharing with them our knowledge and insight concerning the child's problems and special needs and methods of meeting them, helping to change adverse attitudes and ways of handling them, along with giving support in their difficult task. This should be done at both individual and group levels.

The pathological role of early isolation in the potentially normal child has been pointed out by many workers, some of them previously mentioned in this paper.[6-8] Lauretta Bender,[37] working originally with children suffering from organic disturbances of the cerebellum, emphasized the importance of understanding their special psychological needs and hence the necessity of providing them with a specific type of psychological environment in order that they may develop as nearly normally as possible, i.e., without serious psychopathology. Later she extended this fundamental concept to include children with deviations in any aspect of their somatic, and especially their neurologic make-up. With regard to the topic of this paper she has pointed out the importance of not institutionalizing the blind child[38] or for that matter hospitalizing, institutionalizing, or otherwise separating from the mother or mother-substitute for any period longer than is absolutely necessary the sick or deviant infant.[39]

On the basis of the premise that psychological environmental factors, especially those present very early in the child's life, play an extremely important role for any normal child and particularly for the handicapped child, be it blind, brain-damaged, or otherwise disabled, the special measures which have been outlined above, i.e., close, warm, mothering care, etc., should, I believe, be used in the case of all blind children regardless of whether or not they demonstrate pathological behavior. Certainly the blind infant or preschool child should not be institutionalized.

One should guard against the psychiatric syndrome of the over-protected or over-indulged child, catering to the special psychological needs of these blind children only as long as is necessary, which in their case is longer than for normal children. Helping them in their normal drive towards independence in the motor, intellectual, social, and emotional fields should always be our goal in the case of the blind or otherwise handicapped as well as in normal children.

From the preventive aspect one should not of course lose sight of the medical problem involved. With our increasing knowledge of the etiology of many of the conditions which may cause blindness very early in life, we are now coming to a point of preventing many cases. For example, our knowledge regarding the role of excessive oxygen in the causation of retrolental fibroplasia has almost done away with new cases of this disorder.

From what has been said it may be speculated that perhaps the psychopathological condition outlined in this presentation is due either to brain damage, to the very early blindness, to lack of adequate emotional stimulation, especially in early infancy, to other factors not yet determined, or to any combination of these. The combination of total or nearly total blindness from birth and emotional neglect appears, perhaps, to be the most likely, since these two factors appeared to be those which most obviously differentiated the children with this syndrome from the other blind children, although other unknown factors, e.g. brain damage, might actually be operative. It is odd that this syndrome was not seen in any of the congenitally blind children.

In conclusion, it may be stated that there has been outlined a psychopathological syndrome characterized by autistic patterns of behavior, defective communication, primitive modes of perception, and delays in certain areas of maturation, which occurs in children blind from early infancy with retrolental fibroplasia. This syndrome simulates in several ways early infantile autism, and to a lesser extent the syndrome of emotional deprivation. The most prominent feature appeared to be a lack of adequate ego maturation. The exact etiology of this disorder remains to be further explored. The fairly marked similarity between this syndrome and early infantile autism may also shed some further light on the etiological mechanisms in this latter disease. Some ideas have been presented regarding the possible prevention of this condition and its treatment from the psychological standpoint. Some speculations regarding these basic issues and perhaps some important leads for future research have been presented.

REFERENCES

1. Bender, Lauretta: Schizophrenia in children. Its recognition, description and treatment. (Childhood Schizophrenia Symposium, 1955.) Am. J. Orthopsychiat. *26*: 499-506, 1956.
2. Kanner, L.: Autistic disturbances of affective contact. Nerv. Child *2*: 217-250, 1943.
3. Gesell, Arnold: Development and guidance of the blind infant. *In* Berthold Lowenfeld, Ed., The Blind Preschool Child. New York, American Foundation for the Blind, 1947, pp. 123-125.
4. Kallman, Franz J., Barrera, S. E. and Metzger, Harriet: The association of hereditary microphthalmia with mental deficiency. Am. J. Ment. Def. *45*: 25-36, 1940.
5. Sjögren, Torsten and Larsson, Tage: Microphthalmos and Anophthalmos with or without Coincident Oligophrenia. Acta Psychiat. et Neurol. (Suppl.) 56, 1949.
6. Bowlby, John: Maternal Care and Mental Health. Monograph Series 2. Geneva, World Health Organization, 1952.
7. Spitz, René: Hospitalism. An inquiry into the genesis of psychiatric con-

ditions in early childhood. Psychoanal. Stud. Child *1*: 53-74, 1945.

8. Aubry, Jenny: The effects of lack of maternal care: Methods of studying children aged one to three years, placed in institutions. *In* Gerald Caplan, Ed., Emotional Problems of Early Childhood. New York, Basic Books, 1955, pp. 293-306.
9. Piaget, Jean: The Language and Thought of the Child. London, Routledge & Kegan Paul, 1955, p. 11.
10. Mahler, Margaret S.: On child psychosis and schizophrenia, autistic and symbiotic infantile psychoses. Psychoanal. Stud. Child 7: 286-305, 1952.
11. —— and Settlage, Calvin F.: The classification and treatment of childhood psychosis. Paper presented at meeting of the American Psychiatric Association, May, 1956.
12. Schilder, Paul: The Image and Appearance of the Human Body. New York, International Universities Press, 1950.
13. Hoffer, Willie: Development of the body ego. Psychoanal. Stud. Child *5*: 18-23, 1950.
14. Spitz, René A.: The primal cavity: A contribution to the genesis of perception and its role for psychoanalytic theory. Psychoanal. Stud. Child *10*: 215-240, 1955.
15. Ribble, Margaret, A.: The significance of infantile sucking for the psychic development of the individual. J. Nerv. & Ment. Dis. *90*: 455-463, 1939.
16. ——: Disorganizing factors of infant personality. Am. J. Psychiat. *18*: 459-463, 1941.
17. ——: The Rights of Infants; Early Psychological Needs and Their Satisfaction. New York, Columbia University Press, 1943.
18. ——: Infantile experience in relation to personality development. In J. McV. Hunt, Ed., Personality and the Behavior Disorders, New York, Ronald Press, 1944, vol. 2, pp. 621-651.
19. Schilder, Paul: The relation between clinging and equilibrium. Internat. J. Psycho-Analysis, *20*: 58-63, 1939.
20. Wolff, Charlotte: A Psychology of Gesture. London, Methuen, 1948, p. 49.
21. Hammett, Frederick S.: Studies of the thyroid apparatus. Endrocrinology *4*: 221-229, 1922.
22. Greenman, Milton Jay and F. Louise Duhring: Breeding and care of the albino rat for research purposes. 2nd. ed. Philadelphia, Wistar Institute, 1931.
23. Weininger, Otto: Physiological damage under emotional stress as a function of early experience. Science *119*: 285-286, 1954.
24. ——: Gentling and weight gain in the albino rat. Canad. J. of Psychol. *8*: 147-151, 1954.
25. Reyniers, James A.: Germ-free studies. Lobund Reports, No. 1, 1946, No. 2, 1949. University of Notre Dame, Indiana.
26. Hebb, D. O.: The effects of early experience on problem-solving at maturity. Am. Psychol. *2*: 306-307, 1947.
27. Nissen, H. W., Chow, K. L. and Semmes, Josephine: Effects of restricted opportunity for tactual, kinesthetic and manipulative experience on the behavior of a chimpanzee. Am. J. Psychol. *64*: 485-507, 1951.

28. Bingham, W. E. and Griffiths, W. J.: The effect of different environments during infancy on adult behavior in the rat. J. Comp. Physiol. Psychol. *45*: 307-312, 1952.
29. Forgays, D. G. and Forgays, J. W.: The nature of the effect of free-environmental experience on the rat. J. Comp. Physiol. Psychol. *45*: 322-328, 1952.
30. Beach, F. A. and Jaynes, J.: Effects of early experience upon the behavior of animals. Psychol. Bull. *51*: 239-263, 1954.
31. Thompson, W. R. and Heron, W.: Effects of restriction early in life on problem-solving ability in dogs. Canad. J. Psychol. *8*: 17-31, 1954.
32. —— and ——: The effects of early restriction on activity in dogs. J. Comp. Physiol. Psychol. *47*: 77-82, 1954.
33. ——: Early environment—its importance for later behavior. In Paul H. Hoch and Joseph Zubin, Ed., Psychopathology of Childhood. New York, Grune and Stratton, 1955, pp. 120-139.
34. Bexton, W. H., Heron, W. and Scott, T. H.: The effects of decreased variation in the sensory environment. Canad. J. Psychol. *7*: 70-76, 1953.
35. Heron, W., Bexton, W. H. and Hebb, D. O.: Cognitive effects of a decreased variation to the sensory environment. Am. Psychol. *8*: 366, 1953.
36. Hallenbeck, Jane: Pseudo-retardation in retrolental fibroplasia. New Outlook *48*: 301-307, 1954.
37. Bender, Lauretta: The psychology of children suffering from organic disturbances of the cerebellum. Am. J. Orthopsychiat. *10*: 287-293, 1940.
38. ——: The influence of institutionalization on the young child. In Berthold Lowenfeld, Ed, The Blind Preschool Child. New York, American Foundation for the Blind, 1947, pp. 3-4.
39. ——: Psychopathology of Children with Organic Brain Disorders. Springfield, Ill. Charles C. Thomas, 1956.

7

VERBAL BEHAVIOR ANALYSIS—PSYCHODYNAMIC, STRUCTURAL AND TEMPORAL CORRELATES OF SPECIFIC VARIABLES

By GOVE HAMBIDGE, JR., M.D.,

AND LOUIS A. GOTTSCHALK, M.D.*

RECENT YEARS HAVE SEEN an increasing interest in the accurate specification and quantification of the interaction processes between people in the interview situation. Our attention was drawn to this area, and the result of our discussions four years ago was a research project designed to determine whether psychodynamic patterns are qualitatively reflected in the choice and frequency of use of various classes of words and sounds made in speech.

In our previous paper we reviewed the literature and presented the methods and procedures used in this and allied studies reported and to be reported by us on verbal behavior analysis.† Here we shall summarize only those aspects of procedure which are necessary to follow what is being presented.

In September 1952, one of us (G.H.) began the psychoanalysis of a male patient in his mid-thirties. At the same time, the patient was asked to participate in our verbal behavior study. He contributed one pair of verbal samples at weekly intervals for the next fifteen months. These samples were all collected under rigidly standardized experimental conditions by the same investigator (G.H.). All material was faithfully tape-recorded and then transcribed to paper. The incidence of unclear

* Department of Psychiatry, University of Minnesota School of Medicine; Department of Psychiatry, University of Cincinnati School of Medicine. Prepared with the technical and statistical assistance of Peter Schonbach, Ph.D.

† Gottschalk, L. A., and Hambidge, G., Jr.: Verbal behavior analysis. I. A systematic approach to the problem of quantifying psychologic processes. J. Proj. Tech. *19*: 387-409, 1955.

words on the tape which introduced distortion in the typewritten protocol was of the order of approximately one in one thousand.

Two types of verbal behavior samples were recorded in each experimental session. Each was of five minutes' duration. In one, the patient was visually stimulated, being handed in each experimental session the same set of four TAT cards with simplified instructions. In the other the patient was stimulated verbally by being asked to tell of some interesting or dramatic life experience. Thus, the former was a relatively structured stimulus situation, the latter relatively unstructured. The first was modelled after a projective test situation, the second after a psychiatric interview situation. During the recording an inaudible electronic interval timer introduced a time signal onto the tape every five seconds. The typewritten record was divided into sections of a minute's duration, and each minute of material was further subdivided into five-second periods marked off by a diagonal (table 1).

TABLE 1.—*Verbal Behavior Samples**

Speaker: —— *Date:* July 30, 1953

Investigator: *G.H.* *Method:* Visual

Sample No.: 180.69

F T ^{v}D T O^{m} O^{m}

Ah this is / a / // picture of a man who /

^{v}D F ^{y}D A C ^{sx}D C

has ah just come home from a / ah trip.

O^{m} ^{v}D A ^{sy}D ^{ty}D

He's ah // ah / gotten in late.

O^{f} ^{v}D ^{a}D O^{m} ^{v}D

Ah his ah / wife is asleep. He's ah //

^{a}D ^{a}D O^{m} ^{v}D ^{a}D

ah hot / and tired and he's thirsty and

O^{m} ^{v}D

he / has ah //

* A few words are codified for illustrative purposes.

Every word in the protocol was then categorized by a system of codification of language largely derived from psychodynamic principles rather than those of grammar and syntax (table 2). One class of words includes all those which refer to environmental objects. These are in

TABLE 2.—*Some Classes of Words*

- Environmental objects (0)
    - Self (S)
    - Other human objects (0)
    - Inanimate objects (T)
- Concepts or abstractions (C)
- Processes between objects or concepts
    - Neuromuscular action (A)
    - Motivation (IA)
    - Perception (P)
- References to measure (M)
    - Time (t); space (s); quantity (q)
- Qualification: words which differentiate
    - Differentiate objects (^{a}D)
    - Differentiate processes (^{y}D)

turn differentiated into self and non-self. Non-self is broken down into other human objects, animals, flora, and inanimate objects. A second class of words is concepts or abstractions. A third class has subgroups of words expressing neuromuscular actions, motivation, perception, and thought, all of which represent types of processes between objects or concepts. Other rubrics are references to measure, qualification, gender, part-whole, etc. Measure references are words that indicate some relativity in time, space, or quantity regardless of the part of speech or context in which they are used. After we had codified the words in each sample, we then transferred the total number of words in each category for each minute to a scoring sheet.

Our previous paper has detailed some of the techniques we developed and results we obtained from the study of up to ten samples given by any particular subject. In this paper, we are reporting on the extensive study of 80 samples from a single subject obtained once a week over a period of one year. After many complicated and unsuccessful attempts to discover a method of analysis which would permit us to work *from* the word categories *to* the dynamic-thematic content, we finally discovered a technique which has been consistently productive (table 3). We have studied the first 80 samples, 40 visually induced and 40 verbally induced. For each variable, we arranged each of the two sets of 40 samples in order according to the incidence of that variable, sample by sample. We subtracted the number of fills (F), i. e., "er's," "ah's," "um's," etc., from the total output (W), to obtain a corrected output (W minus F). From

TABLE 3.—*The Isolated Variable Technique*

1. Select variable for study.
2. Calculate incidence/1000 words for each sample.
3. Rearrange samples in order of incidence of variable selected.
4. Arrange 5 highest by decreasing scores.
5. Arrange 5 lowest by increasing scores.
6. Prepare careful summaries of samples.
7. Enumerate separately the common dynamic and other factors in each group.
8. Note any consistent quantitative variation (continua).
9. Specify these by pro-mille (incidence per 1000 words) scores of variable.

this, we calculated the incidence of each variable per thousand words spoken for each sample. We thus corrected not only for F contamination, but also for variation in output per unit time.

We now had a series of tables, one for each variable, listing the samples from highest to lowest incidence per thousand words (pro-mille score) for that variable. The samples in each table were then divided arbitrarily into groups of 5 samples. The highest and the lowest groups of 5 samples were chosen for study.

Experiment 1

We used this procedure in order to isolate those samples which showed the highest and lowest incidence of each variable. We hypothesized that the dynamic concomitants of a particular variable would (1) also be present in purest form in these samples, and (2) might be found to be ordered quantitatively along a continuum parallel to the decreasing or increasing incidence (pro-mille score) of the variable from sample to sample.

Since we knew from gross inspection of the samples that each one exhibited multiple dynamic factors, we further hypothesized that the dynamic factor or factors which were common to all five samples would represent the concomitant of the high or low incidence of the specific variable under study. In the first experiment we were interested in the qualitative isolation of dynamic concomitants.

Results. The following results all refer to the verbally induced samples. Individual variables in the verbal samples of this patient have certain consistent implications when the incidence of the variable is either unusually high or unusually low.

a. Total verbal output (corrected as total words, W, minus fills, F) very low: Of the several dynamics in each sample, there is one which is common to all, namely, the mistreatment of a person either by another or by self. In four of the samples there is an angry reaction to this mistreatment. In four of the samples this mistreatment is of a dependent person by an authority figure. The mistreatment is not always seen as hostile.

b. Total verbal output (corrected as W minus F) very high: These samples are characterized by lack of inhibition, but beyond this the dynamics vary. Some examples are given in table 4.

TABLE 4.—*Some Examples of Verbally Induced Samples (Total Output Very High)*

Sample no.	W - F Raw score	Content
60	594	Pleasures of raising a hunting dog
42	580	Resenting wife's interest in promoting a compost heap
54	576	Adventure in Louisiana bayou
16	543	How he killed spiders as a child
64	543	Swimming-hole fun

c. Incidence of references to self (S) very low: The verbal output is group- or other-oriented, wherein the group is attempting to solve a problem (table 5).

TABLE 5.—*Self* (S) *References Low (Verbally Stimulated Samples Only)*

Sample no.	Pro-Mille Score	Summary of sample
14	7	Activity of a large professional and community group working on a public health research project
18	10	Activity of a smaller professional group organizing and giving a farewell party to one of its members
64	11	Activity of a personal group—a family—on a recreational outing
70	19	Activity of self and a friend on a research trip to another city
44	25	Activity of self and two sons in a mutually undertaken project

d. Incidence of references to self (S) very high: These samples consistently reflect self-orientation to the neglect of the environment, i. e., self-concern and curiosity with and without anxiety, details of bodily sensations and feeling states (table 6).

TABLE 6.—*Self* (S) *References High* (*Verbally Stimulated Samples Only*)

Sample no.	Pro-Mille Score	Summary of sample
30	131	Self-concern and curiosity about a recent personal illness
34	118	Self-concern and curiosity about his recent reaction on visit to a town where he previously had a lot of anxiety
20	100	Self-concern and curiosity over his emotional and bodily reactions to stopping smoking
48	100	Self-concern and curiosity regarding his feelings and performance in amateur painting in present as compared with past
38	95	Self-concern and curiosity regarding a smashed finger at age of five and how he and others reacted

e. Incidence of references to objects (O) very low: The samples are characterized by problem-solving activity on problems which cannot be resolved by S (self) alone, but without any direct request for such help.

f. Incidence of references to objects (O) high: These samples are tied together by one consistent dynamic dependency. They emphasize the object-orientation of craving for dependency gratification, the person or animal to be gratified being a relatively passive recipient.

g. Incidence of references to concepts (C) low: The dynamic content of this series is dramatically similar throughout; each sample tells of the patient's own active, successful mastery of a problem-solving situation completed in the time sequence of the immediate story. The situations are all anxiety-provoking. Effort is sustained and ego mastery of both inner conflict and outer challenge characterizes all samples, thus reflecting an active as opposed to a passive attitude.

TABLE 7.—*Low Incidence of Words* ([a]D) *Which Differentiate Objects* (*Verbally Stimulated Samples Only*)

Sample no. [a]D	Pro-Mille Score	Summary of sample
80	52	Ten years ago as an intern he drew the wrong blood and was about to transfuse his patient, when he became anxious, re-checked, discovered his error, drew the correct blood, and transfused the patient (original error a memory slip).
72	53	Two years ago he found a snake which had swallowed two rats. Feeling grateful, he wanted to preserve the snake, yet was anxious not to have it around his baby. To protect baby he put a wash-tub over the snake.
66	66	A couple of weeks ago he built a dog-house to shelter his dog. It turned out much too large, so he got joking criticism from his wife. He felt embarrassed (suppressed fear-anger over rejection) and answered (retaliation) that it was for him and his sons when they were in the dog-house (muted but direct retaliation).
74	77	Last night he planned different stories. Today, when handed the TAT cards, they did not feel right. (Sample No. 73, companion sample, is in [a]D high group.) Stories were to have been of a man who killed his loved one and was now free; of a farmer planning a piece of tail away from his pregnant wife; of a guy shot because he was an s.o.b.
78	77	Right now he is angry for having to help in this experiment. He has to come in, wait around. Criticizes self for wanting to impress therapist. And therapist needles him on purpose. He reluctantly concedes experiment may be a good idea, reluctantly decides to continue to cooperate.

h. Incidence of references to concepts (C) high: While these samples express in general a passive attitude, more careful examination reveals that the speaker is *not* either effectively passive or effectively active. Rather, the samples speak for either an impasse between these impulses or an alternation between activity and passivity. Understanding of the dynamic base here is considerably increased when the quantitative variation is explored (not discussed in this paper).

i. Incidence of verbs (total verbs, grammatically defined) low: All of these samples involve a threat to either physical or mental well-being; the person or animal being damaged is a passive recipient. Dynamically speaking, defense is limited to repair and does not show active prevention. The samples are all characterized by a lot of descriptive material. Time-wise in the samples, neuromuscular and physical activity is limited to brief bursts, and when it occurs it is dramatic (crushing spiders, a gasoline explosion).

j. Incidence of verbs (total verbs, grammatically defined) high: While this group of samples is homogeneous in terms of an over-all nondramatic narrative style and freedom of self-expression, we did not discover any other dynamic trend which occurred throughout all the samples. (Visual low-verb samples are very different, but not discussed in this paper.)

k. Incidence of differentiators (mostly adjectives, ^{a}D) low: This variable correlates with the assumption of responsibility for the care of another or for the performance of various activities. The dynamics become clear only when studied quantitatively (see *Experiment 2*).

l. Incidence of differentiators (^{a}D) high: The dynamic is fear of wanted but dangerous dependency with various illustrations of the consequences of dependency on another (see *Experiment 2*).

m. Incidence of measures (M) low: Correlates with need for external help or guidance to achieve a pattern of behavior which will produce personal success in pleasing others. Speaker does not ask directly for help. In two samples the speaker is active, in the other three passive.

n. Incidence of measures (M) high: This group of samples is characterized by an active observational-exploratory-orientative activity (reality-testing) through the cataloging of similarities and differences. In all samples there is a wish to orient self in relation to self and environment in terms of a comparison of past known events with present relatively non-understood events or situations. This is carried out actively, the main stimulus to activity being satisfaction of curiosity.

o. Incidence of male sex references (corrected by subtracting total references to self from the total number of male references, m-S) low: The dynamic is absence of masculine self-assertion and an attempt to comply with and/or ingratiate an outside authority.

p. Incidence of male sex references (corrected as m-S) high: These samples all exhibit self-assertion by males.

q. Incidence of female sex references (f) high: An insufficient male struggles to escape the feared and resented domination by a female by various means, e. g., ingratiation, physical attack and destruction, extramarital affair, maintaining an impasse, getting help from others.

Experiment 2

This experiment was specifically designed to test in a preliminary way our hypothesis that the dynamic concomitants of a variable might be ordered quantitatively along a continuum parallel to the decreasing or increasing incidence of that variable in the sequence of samples. We again worked with the five samples of highest and lowest incidence of each variable. We arranged the data and abstracts of the data for each set of five samples on a special work sheet to facilitate this study. On the far right we wrote out a condensed outline of each of the samples for a particular variable. These outlines were placed in order. For the high incidence samples, the arrangement from top to bottom of the page was in the order of highest to lowest score. For the low incidence samples, the arrangement was the the reverse of this, going from lowest to highest, top to bottom. In the next column to the left we noted opposite each outline what we called the "elements" of the sample. These were abstractions of themes, elevations of expression of fear or anger, methods of approach to material, characteristic psychological maneuvers, balance of description versus action, etc. In the third column to the left, again opposite each sample, we noted the dynamics of the sample. After these procedures had been carried out, it was a simple matter to write out a summary of the common elements and dynamics. At this point, any quantitative continuum became clear. We made a clear distinction between what we have called a *quantitative continuum,* in which the dynamic quantitative variation is stepwise and without any exception identical to the order of the five samples according to *pro-mille* (incidence of variable) score, and a *tendency to quantitative ordering,* in which one or more samples are out of order.

Results. The following results all refer to the verbally induced samples. The examination of the visually induced samples will be considered under *Experiment 3*. Some of the variables studied so far give an absolute quantitative continuum, others a tendency to quantitative ordering, and for still others we have discovered no evidence either for a quantitative continuum or for a tendency toward such ordering.

a. Samples in which the total verbal output is very low: This sequence is a good example of lack of quantitative orientation. In sequence the object being mistreated is self, other, self, other, inanimate object. The amount or direction of anger expressed is not sequentially ordered. The amount or kind of mistreatment is not so ordered, nor is the acting out which is described.
b. Samples in which the total verbal output is very high: There is no quantitative orientation.
c. Samples in which the incidence of references to the self is very low: These samples are a good illustration of a quantitative continuum. Qualitatively speaking, all samples describe group activity. Group solidarity is implied. All samples are relatively nonconflictual. The themes are nondramatic. However, in an invariant stepwise progression the samples exhibit increasing "personalization" or closeness of the members of the group (see table 5), a finding which we have noted under "elements" rather than as dynamics. This type of finding has forced us to revise our hypothesis to include elements as well as dynamics as important concomitants of the variables.
d. Samples in which the incidence of references to the self is very high: All samples with scores above 100 are introspective without reference to reaction of others to himself, the speaker. The last sample (score 95) shows a sudden incursion of a new element, the reaction of others to him (see table 6).
e. Samples in which the incidence of references to objects (0) is very low: There is a tendency toward quantitative ordering going from the lowest sample, in which the problem is merely described, to the next, which shows solution in fantasy, then active trial-and-error solution and, lastly, a firm decision and consistent working on the problem (see *Experiment 1*).

f. Samples in which the incidence of words (aD—mostly adjectives) which differentiate objects is low: Here we find a closely integrated and complex triple continuum (see table 7): (1) *the speaker's impulse to help another,* or actual helping activity, results in defiant reluctance expressed in a quantitative continuum from pure acting out (in lowest sample, the speaker, who is a physician, tells how he nearly perpetrated an accidental medical death) to directly expressed rebellion toward the experimenter for "making" speaker help in the experiment by giving these samples; (2) *recognition of dependency* goes from complete denial (by describing self as anxiously independent) in the lowest sample to open recognition in the highest, while simultaneously acting upon the impulse to help another goes from very active (dependency denied) to almost complete repudiation—another way to state this would be to say that the speaker accepts the other's dependency in the lowest sample and from this through the highest sample shows increasing rejection of the other's dependence on him; (3) *the location of the stories on a time continuum* goes from the remote past through the recent past to the immediate present with no exception in the 5-sample sequence.

g. The aD high samples demonstrate an equally interesting quantitative dynamic continuum: The basic dynamic is fear of wanted but dangerous dependency out of a fear of domination by and hostility toward the self (S) by another (O). Here we find that dependency results in an emergency response of fear and rage followed by a resentful attack by self on the other person, resulting in fear of counterattack. The quantitative sequence is shown in decreasing physical violence and expressed turbulence of feeling from a maximum of overt fight with intent to injure to a minimum of an objective statement of a particular form of sociocultural deprivation of dependency in which the same dynamics are clearly present.

h. Samples in which male sex references (m), corrected by subtracting references to self, are low: All five samples have an m-S score of zero and exhibit absence of masculine self-assertion.

i. Samples in which male sex references (m), corrected by subtracting references to self, are high: Here again we found a perfect continuum in terms of masculine self-assertion. These samples go from irresponsible self-assertion with possible unwanted consequences through joyful freedom without unwanted consequences to mature, responsible self-assertion.

Experiment 3

This experiment was set up in order to continue our study of the similarities and differences in findings from the two stimulus situations. We studied the visually stimulated samples in the same manner that we had the verbally. The visually stimulated samples were obtained in a situation which was a miniature representation of the projective test technique. The verbally stimulated samples in turn were obtained in a situation which was similar to the psychiatric interview. On the basis of our previous studies we hypothesized that some of the variables should show clear-cut differences in dynamic correlates under these two sets of conditions.

Results. Our findings can be divided into two categories: (1) those variables for which we observe only small differences between visually and verbally stimulated samples in terms of the dynamic correlates, and (2) those for which there is a striking difference. We shall illustrate both types.

1. Samples in which references to objects (O) are low in incidence: There is a very close parallel between visual and verbal samples. The major difference is that the visual samples portray the problem-solving activity in a depressive atmosphere which is not present in the verbally stimulated samples (cf. *Experiments 1* and *2* in regard to this variable).
2. Samples in which references to concepts (C) are low in incidence: These show a striking contrast. *Visually stimulated*: The common dynamic is an unsuccessful struggle or attempt at mastery against superior forces. *Verbally stimulated*: Here the common dynamic is active and successful mastery completed in the time-sequence of the immediate story.

Samples in which references to concepts (C) are high in incidence: These also show a striking contrast under the two different stimulus conditions. *Visually stimulated*: These are characterized by passive avoidance of or not really coming to grips with a problem. *Verbally stimulated*: These samples express a conflict between passive, dependent turning to others for help and an inhibited impulse to do it alone, the conflict being expressed either as an impasse or as an alternation between the two forms (passive-active) of behavior.

Discussion. In our previous work we found various consistent differences between visual and verbal samples. When we studied the dynamics of the two types produced on any one day by a subject, we found that unpredictably the basic dynamics of the day might be expressed in one type of sample, the defenses or reparative maneuvers appearing in the companion sample. Now, however, when each of the two sets of samples is chosen according to the high or low incidence of certain critical variables, we find consistent dynamic differences reflected. This observation will bear further study, as its implications for projective testing in relation to the clinical interview are extensive.

Experiment 4

This experiment was designed to provide findings pertinent to the hypothesis that the high or low incidence of certain variables in the experimental samples would show an intimate temporal correlation with the events and changes observed during the course of the patient's psychoanalysis. This material is in the process of study at the present time, so we can sketch in only preliminary observations:

1. The 80 samples were divided originally into two groups of 40, 20 visual and 20 verbal in each group. Group I (samples 1-40) was collected between 9/24/52 and 3/18/53. Group II (samples 41-80) was collected between 3/25/53 and 9/16/53. They cover the first and second six-month periods of the patient's analysis.

2. Some variables increase in incidence while others decrease as the treatment progresses. We occasionally find that for one variable the low incidence samples fall primarily into one group while the high incidence samples fall into the other. For instance, the visually stimulated samples in which male sex references (corrected as m-S because speaker is male) are low in incidence are numbers 19, 25, 7, 5, and 11 when arranged according to increasing pro-mille score. In the passage of time, the last sample of this sequence is number 25. The m-S high incidence (visually stimulated) samples are numbers 39, 71, 35, 53, and 55. In the passage of time, the first sample of this sequence to appear is number 35. There is thus a hiatus between the low and high m-S samples represented by samples 27 through 33. We also noted a clustering of high f (female sex) reference samples between numbers 27 and 32, with the exception of sample 30. All of these findings made us suspect that there might be a natural breaking or turning point in the analysis at this time. Examination of the psychoanalytic hours showed

that the patient had for the previous month been dealing with a major depression with strong latent castration fears (he had slept with his mother for the first 12 years of his life, while father slept in the living room). The day preceding sample 27, he brought in a dream of nakedness, expressed an exhibitionistic urge to be recognized as a man, and saw treatment as dangerous self-exposure. On the following day, the day on which he gave sample 27, he broke into an overt, poorly controlled, self-pitying, and self-punitive depression. His lack of control was temporarily broken on the day he gave sample 30, when he presented a controlled, intellectualized approach to the discovery of his lack of self-discipline and irresponsible impulses (he was referred for treatment as the result of having seduced a little girl). From this point, his analysis was dominated by a latent fear of genital damage (castration anxiety) at the hands of a woman until this finally broke into the open two days before he gave sample number 37. The major source of his acute fear was his seeing girls as jealous of his genital organs. His masculine self-assertion was considerably freed in his job performance from this time on.

Summary

We have reported four experiments designed to study the psychodynamic correlates of verbal communication at the level of individual word choice expressed in terms of the choice and frequency of use of certain word categories. Our findings strongly support the thesis that such word choice and frequency of use is related to the dynamic state of the patient both qualitatively and quantitatively. These findings further show consistent differences between the visually stimulated and the verbally stimulated samples in that they measure or study different aspects of the same person. This points to a specific method for examining the relationship between the psychiatric interview and the projective test situation. Finally, we believe that we have beginning evidence to indicate that the psychoanalytic experience and state of progress at the time of giving the sample influence the way the patient expresses himself in terms of the choice and use of language variables in these two experimental situations.

8

STABILITY AND MODIFIABILITY OF PERSONALITY PATTERNS MANIFESTED DURING A STANDARDIZED INTERVIEW

By JOSEPH D. MATARAZZO, Ph.D., GEORGE SASLOW, M.D., RUTH G. MATARAZZO, Ph.D., AND JEANNE S. PHILLIPS, Ph.D.*

NUMEROUS STUDIES reported during the past several years seem to indicate that assessment of personality by use of the various well-known objective and projective methods leaves much to be desired. The results with these techniques, while sometimes positive, have been, in the view of many investigators, less than encouraging.[14] There is increasing evidence that to attempt (through the use of ink blots, etc.) to assess fixed or unchanging intrapsychic traits, such as levels of anxiety, the presence or absence of "defenses" of various kinds, etc. by employing these instruments is to commit what MacKinnon has called the "organism error."[15] This error involves the assumption that personality characteristics are stable and invariant and will be present independently of the stimulus situation or "field" in which one is attempting to observe or record these traits. Rorschach's *extratensive* and *introversive* types,[22] as well as the various TAT *needs* and *presses*,[19] represent for the most part examples of these stable "traits." Some recent workers in the field of assessment have attempted to overcome this difficulty; for example, conceiving of the associations to the Rorschach cards as potential responses to what might be thought of as 10 representative samples of different stimulus situations in which the individual might find himself.[23] However ingenious this interpretation may be, it still seems not to have fully overcome the "organism error" since there is no independent evidence of even a minimal correlation between the 10 ink blot stimulus cards and real life situations, let alone "representative" ones.

This is one major reason why many research workers and practicing

* The authors are now at the University of Oregon Medical School, Portland, Oregon. Prepared with the assistance of research grants from the National Institute of Mental Health, United States Public Health Service.

clinicians such as H. S. Sullivan[27] have used the equally unreliable (in the sense of unstandardized) "interview" as their instrument of assessment. One alleged advantage of the interview is its flexibility which allows one to explore unique areas of behavior for each individual. Also, the interview presents a real-life, interpersonal, or "dynamic" stimulus situation so that every individual is given an opportunity to manifest his unique and presumably learned social behavior patterns.

Notoriously low inter-interviewer agreement in assessment of personality patterns[1, 21] has made the interview subject to criticism also. It is important, therefore, if the interview is to be an instrument of research, to ask what could be achieved if this stimulus situation were standardized. Chapple,[2-9] working primarily in applied anthropology, has been developing just such a standardized interview during the past several years. A review of the development and present status of the instrument (the interaction chronograph) used for making measurements of the interaction between interviewer and interviewee during the standardized interview may be consulted for a more thorough description than is possible below.[17]

Essentially the interaction chronograph is a device which allows an observer to record, with a high degree of precision, the behavioral interaction* of two individuals in terms of some 12 time-unit variables. These variables are objectively recorded by a series of electrically controlled counters which are connected to two keys, one for the interviewer and the other for the subject. Whenever the designated individual is talking, nodding, gesturing, or in other ways communicating (interacting) with the second person, the appropriate key is depressed by the observer, who is on the other side of a one-way mirror. Values for the variables are cumulative and can with little difficulty be abstracted from the printed record of the complete interview.

More complete definitions of these 12 interaction variables can be found in our earlier reports.[17, 24] Briefly they are: (1) *A's Units,* the *frequency* of the patient's actions. (2) *Action,* the average *duration* of A's actions. (3) *Silence,* the average *duration* of A's silences. (4) *Tempo,* the average *duration* of each action of A *plus* his following inaction as a single measure. (5) *Activity,* the average *duration* of each action of A *minus* his following inaction as a single measure. (6) *A's Adjustment,* the average *duration* with which A "interrupted" B *minus*

* Records include only such behavior as number of utterances, number of interruptions, their durations, etc., and not the "content" of the verbalizations.

the duration with which A "failed to respond to" B. (7) *B's Adjustment,* the average *duration* of the other (usually the interviewer) person's adjustment. (8) *Initiative,* the *relative frequency* with which A initiated to B following a double silence, as in period 2. (9) *Dominance,* the *relative frequency* with which A dominates B in a double action (interruption), as in period 4. (10) *A's Synchronization,* the *frequency* with which A failed to synchronize with B either by failing to respond to B or by interrupting B. (11) *B's Synchronization,* the *frequency* of the other (usually the interviewer) person's failure to synchronize with A. (12) *B's Units,* the *frequency* of the interviewer's actions. In addition to containing individual counters for each variable, the interaction chronograph has a "signal" counter which functions as a marker to record the start of different periods of the interview. These periods will be described below.

Chapple[4] and Goldman-Eisler,[10-13] working independently in England, have found that the use of this instrument for the objective assessment of patient personality patterns is made more difficult by the differences in "interaction patterns" (or "personalities") of different interviewers. These studies have shown that the differences in inter- and intra-interviewer interaction patterns have a subtle but demonstrably marked effect on the interviewees' interaction patterns when these are carefully and objectively recorded. These experimental results thus have helped to define some of the uncontrolled variance which in the past has made the interview, including the interviewer's behavior, a less than adequate research tool. Experimenters have attempted to use the interviewer as an *independent* variable in their efforts to measure various interviewee characteristics (the *dependent* variables). But experience has indicated, and the results of Chapple, Goldman-Eisler, and a recent study by Saslow, Goodrich and Stein[25] confirm, that the interviewer is not an objective scientific instrument. In fact, these studies have shown that interviewers are themselves dependent in the sense of uncontrolled variables.

Saslow, Goodrich, and Stein found a number of statistically significant differences (for the interaction variables described earlier) in the interaction patterns of a single experienced interviewer when the latter interacted in his habitual (i.e., unstandardized) manner with a normal and a patient group.[25] Thus it was shown that a *single* interviewer behaves differently with different subjects. As might be expected, a corollary of this finding was that the two populations of subjects manifested different mean interaction patterns with this interviewer. Raines and Rohrer[21] investigated the effect of using *different interviewers* with the same population of subjects. They found extremely low agreement among their interviewers for the personality variables being assessed by use of these interviews and found it necessary to conclude: "The results of this study support a 'projection' hypothesis to account for the variance between psychiatrists observed here; that is, that one of the major variables responsible for variation between psychiatrists in impressions of patients is the differing personalities of the psychiatrists themselves."[21] When the research "instrument" has been the demonstrably unreliable interviewer, it is no wonder that so little headway has been made in the areas of personality assessment and evaluation of psychotherapy.

In recent years Chapple has developed a *standardized interview* designed to make the interviewer (and the conduct of the interview) an independent variable, and thereby to permit comparison of results in the same or different settings obtained by different interviewers, or results obtained by the same interviewer at various times. Chapple's standardized method involves certain "rules" for the interviewer to follow in his own interviewing behavior and in the over-all conduct of the interview itself. The standardized interview is divided into five periods with periods 1, 3, and 5 free give-and-take periods, and periods 2 (silence) and 4 (interruption) *stress* phases of the interview. In tables 1 and 2 will be found a description, taken from several sources,[4, 5, 8] of the standardized interview and the "rules" governing the interviewer's behavior during the five interview subperiods.

TABLE 1.—*Characteristics of the Standardized Interview*

Period	Type of interviewing	Duration of period	
		Fixed duration	Variable duration
I	Free	10 minutes	
II	Stress (silence)		12 failures to respond or 15 minutes, whichever is shorter
III	Free	5 minutes	
IV	Stress (interruption)		12 interruptions or 15 minutes, whichever is shorter
V	Free	5 minutes	
Total		20 minutes	plus a maximum of 30 more minutes

TABLE 2.—*Standardized Interviewer's Behavior: Rules For Interviewer*

Periods 1 to 5 (All Periods)

a. Interviewer introduces each period by a five-second utterance (following his signal to the observer).

b. All interviewing must be nondirective. No direct questioning, no probing or depth interviewing. Interviewer can reflect, ask for clarification, ask for more information, introduce a new topic area, etc. In general, interviewer's comments should be nonchallenging and open-ended and related to the patient's past comments or to some new, general topic.

c. All interactions must be verbal only, or verbal and gestural at the same time; i.e., interviewer cannot use head nods and other gestures alone. This rule simplifies the observer's task.

d. All of interviewer's utterances must be of approximately five seconds' duration.

e. After patient finishes a comment or other interaction, interviewer must respond in less than one second, except as otherwise noted in periods 2 and 4.

f. Each time that the patient interrupts interviewer, the latter must continue to talk for two more seconds. This rule insures more explicit definition of a patient's ascendance-submission pattern than would be possible if interviewer "submitted" immediately.

Periods 1, 3, and 5

a. Interviewer must never interrupt patient.

b. If after interviewer makes a comment patient does not respond, interviewer must wait fifteen seconds and then speak again for five seconds.

Period 2 Only

a. Interviewer must "fail to respond" to last interaction of patient a total of twelve times or period 2 should last for fifteen minutes, whichever is shorter.

b. After interviewer has been silent for fifteen seconds (and patient has not taken initiative) interviewer makes another five-second comment.

Period 4 Only

a. Each time patient acts, interviewer must interrupt patient for five seconds for a total of twelve times.

b. Interviewer's interruption should begin about three seconds after patient has begun his interaction.

c. After having interrupted patient, if the patient continues through the interruption (does not submit), interviewer will not interrupt again until patient has finished his utterance, i.e., interviewer will interrupt patient only once during each utterance of the latter if patient does not "yield."

d. The period is ended after twelve interruptions or fifteen minutes of attempting to obtain these.

Chapple's standardized interview thus provides a means of eliciting samples of patients' behaviors (dependent variables) in a miniature, molar, interpersonal situation, certain characteristics of which are objective and predefined (independent variables). Such a controlled "field" situation would seem to hold promise for more reliable and potentially more valid assessment of personality.

Using the interaction chronograph and Chapple's standardized interview, our group planned a series of three studies which had the following two aims: (1) to investigate for the interview as a whole the test-retest stability of the interaction pattern for any given individual (that is, could we obtain higher assessment reliabilities than those typically reported for psychiatric interviews?); and (2) if our first aim were successful, to investigate another major problem in personality research, namely, is personality relatively stable and invariant or is it a function of changes in environmental or stimulus conditions?

Procedure

Two different interviewers, one for test and the other for retest, were used in two of the studies, while in a third study the same interviewer conducted both the original and retest interviews. In order to evaluate the influence of length of interval between test and retest interviews, two of these studies employed an *immediate* retest (with a test-retest interval of a few minutes) while the third used a *seven-day* interval between test and retest.

Specifically, the *first study* employed two different interviewers; one a young internist* and the other an older psychiatrist. Twenty clinic outpatients were interviewed independently in experiments conducted a few minutes apart by these two experienced interviewers. A counterbalanced design was used to control interviewer-order effects and each interviewer thus interviewed every other patient first; an AB order with the first patient and a BA order with the second, etc. In this way each interviewer came first in the sequence for ten patients and second for the remaining ten. Statistical evaluation of these "interviewer-order" effects on patients' behavior was therefore possible.

So that patient smoking would be discouraged, ash trays were removed from the interviewer's desk. No mention of the experiment was made and it began when the interviewer opened the interview with a

* We acknowledge with gratitude the participation of Dr. Samuel B. Guze, who collaborated in two of the three reliability studies herein described. The second interviewer served in all three of the studies reported here. The same observer was used for both test and retest in all three studies.

5-second statement such as "My name is Dr.——. Can you tell me how you happened to come to the clinic at this time?" The interviewer pressed a concealed button for a light signal to the observer. The latter was seated in the next room on the other side of a five by two foot one-way mirror and recorded the interaction by pressing designated buttons for the interviewer and the patient. A high-fidelity microphone was hung from the ceiling and connected to both an audograph on the observer's desk and earphones which were worn by the observer. Verbatim recordings of the interview were transcribed the next day for subsequent content analyses.

The second interviewer was always in another building when the first doctor was conducting his interview, thereby assuring independence; both began with no knowledge about the patient. After finishing his interview, the first interviewer would say, "Mr(s). ——, I'd like another doctor in our clinic to talk with you now, and if you will wait here a minute or two I will go to get him." Upon his arrival, the second interviewer signalled the observer and began the retest half of the experiment. For the 20 patients, the test-retest interval between these two independent interviews averaged about three minutes, with a range from about one to five minutes.

The aim of the first study was to investigate, over a *brief* test-retest interval, the stability of patient interaction patterns *across two different interviewers*. Should the reliability (stability) coefficients prove high enough, we could then investigate what changes, if any, occur in patient interaction patterns across the five predefined and relatively standardized subperiods of the interview. We saw this latter as a means of investigating the question of stability versus modifiability of interaction variables as a function of controlled changes in stimulus conditions. It was realized that the interaction patterns herein studied were but one aspect of "personality."

A *second study* with another group of 20 patients was started concomitantly with that mentioned above. The design was identical in all respects but two: (1) only one interviewer (the older psychiatrist) was used, and (2) his second interview with each of the 20 patients was conducted a week later, thus changing the test-retest interval from a few minutes to seven days. This change in design allowed us to investigate, for the interview as a whole, the stability of interaction patterns *in time*. The use of the standardized interview on both occasions, one week apart, also allowed us to evaluate the reliability over seven days of the behaviorial *modifications* produced within a single interview as a function of the predefined shifts in the interviewer's behavior through the five subperiods.

At the completion of the first study, and at a time when the second study was approximately half finished, a *third study* with still another group of 20 patients was begun. This last was an *exact replication* of the first study. It was an attempt to *cross-validate* the findings of the first study, since the stability coefficients obtained therein were unusually high for such complex measures of psychological variables as one finds in the interview.

The 60 subjects for all three studies were unselected and were interviewed in the order in which they were referred to the psychiatric clinic of a large urban medical center. They were all white and ranged in age from approximately 16 to 62 (median ages for the three studies being 32, 34.5, and 33 respectively). Each study included approximately one half males (11, 9, and 8) and one half females (9, 11, and 12. The presenting complaints were typical of outpatients at any psychiatric facility.

At this point it should be mentioned that neither the subjects themselves, nor "uninitiated" through experienced professional interviewers (a dozen or more psychiatrists and psychologists) who observed the interview, were aware that the standardized interview, when conducted by the experienced interviewers, was different from other psychiatric interviews.

Results

From table 1, which was presented earlier, it can be seen that 20 minutes of the standardized interview are *fixed* and that, depending upon the subject's behavior in periods 2 and 4, which are *variable*, up to 30 more minutes, totalling 50 in all, are possible to complete the standardized interview. The actual *mean length* of the interview was surprisingly similar in each of the three studies, being 32.8 minutes and 31.5 minutes in the original and replication series respectively, and 31.94 minutes in the study employing the seven-day interval. There were no differences between the mean lengths of first and second interviews in any of these three studies. That there was considerable *individual* variation in length of interview, however, can be noted from the fact that the *range* of the 60 pairs of interviews extends from 24.5 minutes for one patient to the full 50 (50.3) minutes for another. Thus it can be seen that the standardized interview has the following characteristics: (1) despite its standardization along certain dimensions, it still allows considerable freedom for individual differences among patients (as evidenced by the appreciable range); (2) it lasts *on the average* about 32 minutes; (3) for any given individual, the length of time required for the completion of the interview on initial test is very nearly identical with the length of time required for completion of the second or retest interview; and (4) except for one presumably chance difference, which was not cross-validated, there are no statistically significant differences in the means of interaction variables measured for the interview as a whole as a result either of differences in the *doctors* as interviewers or of the *order* (first or second) per se in which they interviewed. These results for length of interview indicate that, for this variable at least, one interview is comparable to another and interviews on the same individual can thus be directly compared.

In table 3 are shown results bearing on the question of the stability of interaction patterns (dependent variables) when the stimulus (interviewer's behavior during the standardized interview) is controlled and thereby kept relatively constant (independent variable). Included in this table are both test and retest means, ranges, and stability coefficients (rho) for each of the nine interaction chronograph variables. These values are given individually for the original, replication, and seven-day interval studies.

In the first of these studies (reading across), values are shown for Doctor 1 with all 20 patients and for Doctor 2 with the same 20 patients. Doctor-order effects are purposely *confounded* here since an analysis of covariance revealed no *doctor* or *doctor-order* effects; that is, there were no differences between the means of the 10 patients interviewed first by Doctor 1 compared to the 10 he interviewed second relative to a similar comparison for Doctor 2. Values for the replication study (presented in table 3) were derived in the same manner. As the use of a single interviewer eliminated the possibility of doctor effects in the third study, only the (first versus second) interview-order analysis was necessary. For this third study, as for the others, there were no differences in the interaction variables which could be attributed to this order effect. Thus, in each of these three investigations the stability of interaction patterns can be examined without further consideration of these two potentially contaminating variables.

In table 3 the values of the test-retest coefficient of stability (rho) for each of the variables studied indicate a very striking *stability* for these interaction variables.* All but one of the 27 stability coefficients (9 variables times 3 studies) are significant at the .01 level of confidence; the one exception (*Dr.'s Units,* seven-day study) is still significant at the .05 level. Furthermore, as can be seen from the means and ranges for any given variable, this stability is *absolute* as well as *relative.*

This latter point is demonstrated throughout table 3. However, one example purposely selected from the seven-day study shows this very clearly. This variable is *Pt.'s Units.* The test-retest stability coefficient (rho) with a value of .765, which is significant at the .01 level, indicates considerable stability for this variable over a time interval of seven days. However, since correlations of this magnitude are possible even when the values obtained in the second interview are considerably different from those in the first, provided of course that they always are approximately some *multiple* of the values obtained in the first, this value of .765 indicates only *relative* stability. For example, one could get a perfect correlation on *Pt.'s Units* if, in the second session, the *interviewer* always got double or some other multiple of the number of units from the same patients; i.e., if from three patients he obtained 30, 40, and 50 units during the first interview, and 60, 80, and 100 respectively in the second, the value of rho would be 1.00. This would indicate perfect relative but definitely not absolute stability. The latter would obtain only if the units for these three patients for the second interview were again 30, 40, and 50. Thus the obtained rho of .765 for *Pt.'s Units* over a seven-day period indicates by itself only a rather striking *relative* stability for this variable. Evidence for a similarly significant *absolute* stability comes from inspection of the marked similarity in the means and ranges for the first and second interviews. Thus, for example, individual inspection of the ranges for the 20 patients for *Pt.'s Units* shows that during the same standardized interview *one subject* interacted 43 times during the first interview and 48 times during the second interview one week later, whereas a *second subject* interacted 118 times during the first interview and 131 times during the second. The slight, though statistically insignificant, difference in the two group means (72 and 78) and the rho of .765 indicate that this stability, both relative and absolute, is

* Use of the Coefficient of Correlation, Pearson *r*, yielded results essentially similar to those in table 3. Occasional skewing and restricted range made rho a better statistic for further analyses of these data which will be presented in other tables.

TABLE 3.—*Test-Retest Means, Ranges, and Stability Correlations (Rho) of Interaction Variables for Total Interview in Three Patient Series*

Series		Pt.'s Units		Pt.'s Action**		Pt.'s Silence**	
		Mean	Range	Mean	Range	Mean	Range
Original	Dr. 1	72.20	25 to 127	48.20	13 to 154	9.10	4 to 19
	Dr. 2	69.85	29 to 112	43.90	9 to 136	8.20	4 to 13
	Rho	.807 †		.847 †		.854 †	
Replication	Dr. 1	68.30	39 to 132	44.15	12 to 93	9.10	5 to 18
	Dr. 2	76.65	41 to 133	39.35	12 to 93	9.00	6 to 15
	Rho	.917 †		.945 †		.859 †	
Seven-day	First	72.30	43 to 118	34.55	5 to 86	9.75	6 to 24
	Second	78.30	48 to 131	34.05	9 to 73	9.30	6 to 15
	Rho	.765 †		.597 †		.582 †	
		Pt.'s Tempo		Pt.'s Activity		Pt.'s Adjust.	
		Mean	Range	Mean	Range	Mean	Range
Original	Dr. 1	57.20	24 to 159	39.55	−2 to 150	−1.53	0 to −5
	Dr. 2	52.85	26 to 142	36.20	2 to 131	−1.28	0 to −4
	Rho	.805 †		.874 †		.716 †	
Replication	Dr. 1	53.65	19 to 100	35.00	4 to 87	−1.08	+.50 to −6
	Dr. 2	48.55	19 to 100	30.35	3 to 85	− .66	+.88 to −5
	Rho	.941 †		.910 †		.821 †	
Seven-day	First	46.00	27 to 96	28.00	8 to 76	− .89	+.58 to −3
	Second	44.40	22 to 84	25.75	3 to 62	−1.15	+.88 to −5

Series		Dr.'s Adjust		Pt.'s Synchron.		Dr.'s Units	
		Mean	Range	Mean	Range	Mean	Range
Original	Dr. 1	−1.83	−3.6 to +1.0	.84	.63 to .99	62.79	21 to 109
	Dr. 2	−1.53	−3.0 to + .14	.84	.76 to .98	59.74	27 to 93
	Rho	.668 †		.691 †		.782 †	
Replication	Dr. 1	−2.24	− .77 to −4.8	.84	.69 to .97	58.75	28 to 119
	Dr. 2	−1.93	− .88 to −3.0	.85	.77 to .98	63.45	32 to 115
	Rho	.780 †		.717 †		.880 †	
Seven-day	First	−2.09	− .98 to −3.3	.86	.76 to .93	59.65	37 to 96
	Second	−2.17	− .95 to −3.7	.88	.73 to 1.01	66.25	37 to 118
	Rho	.558 †		.544 †		.528 *	

* Significant at the .05 level of probability.

† Significant at the .01 level of probability.

** Unlike the erroneous procedure first used in these studies,[18, 24, 26] the means for *Action* and *Silence* shown here for all three studies were computed from the raw data of the total interview rather than by averaging the means of the five subperiods.

rather strikingly high. Similar comparisons can be made for each of the other variables in table 3, although it is apparent from the magnitude of the correlations that for some variables, unlike the case just described for *Pt.'s Units*, the extremes of the range need not necessarily represent the same individual for test and retest in every case.

Taking individually the three studies presented in table 3, one notices several interesting findings. The first of these is that the stability coefficients in the study employing one interviewer and a seven-day interval between the initial test and retest interviews were somewhat lower relative to the other two studies. For the nine variables in the original study, the range in the stability coefficients (reading across) was from .668 to .874, all significant at the .01 level of confidence. Upon replication (again reading across in table 3), these values were not only cross-validated but increased somewhat; the range for the nine stability coefficients was now .717 to .945. Thus the use of two *different interviewers* and a test-retest interval of a *few minutes* was associated in both studies with rather high stability coefficients for these interaction patterns.

While nearly all variables (8 out of 9) still reached the .01 level of confidence when one interviewer and a test-retest interval of seven days were used, the range (.528 to .776) indicates that these values, relatively speaking, are lower than those of the other two studies. A single index* of this lowering can be derived by computing the *average* rho for the nine variables in *each* of the 3 studies. In the first study this *average* rho for the nine variables is .783; for the replication it is .863; while for the seven-day study it is .641. Corresponding *median* values are: .805, .880, and .597, respectively. These results, and those presented in table 3, would indicate that: (1) there is a fairly high stability in interaction patterns (whether one or two interviewers are used and whether the test-retest interval is a few minutes or seven days), and (2) these stability coefficients drop slightly, relative to the two interviewers-few-minute-interval conditions when one interviewer *and* a seven-day interval are used.

There are many possible factors associated with this slight lowering of stability in the seven-day study. Four factors at least may be involved: (1) an *habituation* effect as any given patient "gets used to" the same interviewer on the two occasions; (2) the patient's "set" may be different

* For our purposes it is possible to think of each of the nine rho values for each study in table 3 as a *raw score*, thereby making averaging possible. Use of the z-transformation statistic is unnecessary as we are interested in demonstrating a point which is crudely apparent by inspection.

in still another way on the two occasions, e.g., as manifested by a difference in what he talks about (differences in patient's "content" in the two interviews); (3) extra-interview influences may have occurred in the life of the patient during the seven-day interval, e.g., major life changes such as a decision to leave one's spouse, change jobs, etc.; and (4) a slight but true lowering of stability in time simply as a function of "random" or "unknown" life factors, such that one would expect progressively lower stability coefficients as the retest interval was increased to one month, six months, one year, etc.

Each of the four possibilities seems amenable to experimental investigation. The "habituation" factor could be explored by employing for test-retest, as in our two other studies, two different interviewers with the same patient (in counterbalanced order) for interviews seven days apart. If stability coefficients higher than those of the present seven-day study were obtained, the "habituation" hypothesis would be tenable. Our group is currently investigating the hypothesis that the "content" of the two interviews may be more dissimilar in interviews seven days apart than in two interviews conducted on the same day. The third possibility, that important "extra-interview influences" may modify behavior during the seven-day test-retest interval, could be investigated by using any of a number of devices (a specially designed questionnaire, an open-ended interview, etc.) at the end of the retest session. The fourth possibility, that of progressive "decay" in stability coefficients as a function of time, could be investigated by using in counterbalanced order two interviewers two weeks apart in one study, one month apart in another, six months apart in a third, etc. Of course if the "habituation" factor were also of interest here, one still could employ the latter approach but use only one interviewer for both test and retest.

In contrast to the four factors just discussed, there is an *alternative hypothesis* for explaining the lowering of stability coefficients in the seven-day interval study. Although these are not presented in table 3, the standard deviations of *all nine* of the interaction variables shown in this table for the first interviews of the seven-day study are *smaller* than their counterparts in the original and replication studies. (To take one example, while the average number of patient units in *all three* studies is approximately 72, the standard deviation of 15 for the seven-day study is considerably smaller than the value of 25 found in the two other series.) The smaller standard deviations indicate that this sample of patients is *more homogeneous* with respect to all the interaction variables studied. The lowering of stability coefficients from initial test to retest over an interval of seven days thus may be merely a reflection of the *narrower range of variability* in this group for each of these nine variables. A choice among these hypotheses must await further research.

There is another interesting finding which can be abstracted from the data presented in table 3. This has to do with the relative as well as absolute variation (or stability) in the magnitudes of the rhos of any *single variable* across all three studies. If one places in rank order from 1 to 9 the rho of each variable in each of the three studies, these ranks will indicate approximately how stable a variable is relative to the other eight variables, and also how well it maintains this relative rank in each of the three studies.

Thus, for example, the rho for *Pt.'s Units* attains ranks of 6, 7, and 8 in the 3 studies. The rhos for the variable, *Dr.'s Units,* on the other hand, are ranked 4, 5, and 1, respectively, and thus this variable shows more variability (or less stability) in its rank position. Summing up the three ranks of the rhos for each variable yields this order, from most to least stable: (2) Pt.'s Units, (4) Pt.'s Tempo, (1) Pt.'s Activity, (3) Pt.'s Action, (6) Pt.'s Adjustment, (5) Pt.'s Silence, (7) Dr.'s Units, (8) Dr.'s Adjustments, and (9) Pt.'s Synchronization. This analysis thus indicates that an individual's amount of interaction (Activity) is the most stable interaction variable. Genetic factors may be involved here but further research is, of course, necessary in this area.[6]

Comparison of the ranks of each variable among the three studies shows the degree to which the nine variables retained their relative positions. For example, while *Activity* (ranks 9, 6, 7) maintained its high rank through the three studies, to what extent did all nine variables, *taken as a group,* maintain their respective positions? For purposes of gross comparison we computed a rank-order correlation, rho, across these nine ranks to compare the original and replication series. The obtained value of rho is .650, and indicates that the relative stability of a variable in the *original* study was fairly predictive (.650) of its relative stability in the *replication* series. When rank position of the variables in the *original* study are compared to the ranks in the *seven-day* study, it can be seen that the stability in rank position became much lower (.350) when the interviews were a week apart. This rho of .350 indicates considerable reordering in relative stability of rank position. Confirmation of this reordering obtains in the comparable rho value (.367) when the *replication* study is compared to the same *seven-day* study.

Thus, whether one averages *across* table 3 for any one study or compares one variable with itself *vertically* in the same table, a similar observation is made; namely, that predictions from test to retest are somewhat less reliable under the conditions of the seven-day study than they are under the conditions of the original and replication studies. It should be emphasized that this is only a relative lowering, however, since 26 out of 27 test-retest correlations (including 8 out of 9 in the seven-day study) reach the .01 level, indicating considerable stability for the interaction variables under both conditions. The first aim of our research program was thus accomplished. The stability coefficients in table 3 are a demonstration that high inter-interviewer agreement (as well as intra-interviewer agreement) can be accomplished if one brings certain relevant aspects of the interviewer's behavior under experimental control.

We shall now discuss the second question of the research program: Is personality, or at least that aspect of personality measured by these interaction variables, relatively stable and invariant, or is it more a function of changes in environmental or stimulus conditions? The above results indicate that *for the interview as a whole* an individual's "personality" as reflected in these variables is relatively constant from one situation to another *similar* situation. However, since the stimulus conditions (the interviewer's standarized behavior) were *identical* with respect to the aforementioned "rules" in both test and retest situations, the results in table 3 do not allow one to draw any conclusions regarding the question being asked. Investigation of this question requires *changing* stimulus conditions.

Since Chapple's standardized interview, containing as it does two stress and three non-stress phases, was designed primarily to present subjects with just such changing stimulus conditions, an *intra-interview* analysis (as distinct from the inter-interview analysis presented in table 3) across these five subperiods will provide information relevant to the problem of stability versus modifiability of behavior patterns. Chapple obtains scores for the interaction variables individually for *each* of the five subperiods. By dividing the obtained value of a variable for any given subperiod by the number of patient units in that period, Chapple derives an *average* score for that variable for each of the five subperiods. For example, a patient whose units for the five subperiods were 20, 12, 10, 12, and 10, and whose corresponding actions were 800, 288, 400, 144, and 400, would be scored as having *average actions* of 40, 24, 40, 12, and 40. These last figures, being averages, are thus relatively independent of differences in the number of units obtained by this patient during the five subperiods.

These subperiod averages for single individuals were combined for the 20 subjects comprising each of the three studies. Results for the interview *as a whole* are presented in table 3. The group results *by subperiods* are presented for one interaction variable, *Pt.'s Silence,* in table 4. Test and retest values for each of the three studies are also presented in this table. Comparable results for another variable, *Pt.'s Action,* are shown in table 5. Because of the present design of the instrument used in these studies, these two were the only variables available for examination of the question of stability-modifiability (dependent variables) as a function of planned modifications in the interviewer's behavior (independent variable).

TABLE 4.—*Means, Standard Deviations, and F-tests for Individual Periods of Patient "Silence" Variable in Three Patient Series*

	Original		Replication		Seven-day	
Period	Dr. 1	Dr. 2	Dr. 1	Dr. 2	First	Second
I Mean	7.40	8.65	9.15	9.05	8.30	8.25
S. D.	2.44	2.50	2.22	2.44	1.58	2.05
II Mean	12.70	11.55	15.05	13.10	14.75	15.00
S. D.	8.24	6.33	9.06	4.50	5.88	5.62
III Mean	10.70	9.30	9.40	9.30	8.85	8.90
S. D.	4.52	2.72	4.21	2.90	2.71	2.78
IV Mean	6.45	5.80	5.65	6.20	5.40	6.40
S. D.	3.10	1.78	1.28	2.25	1.74	3.23
V Mean	8.40	7.40	8.50	8.05	8.45	8.60
S. D.	2.60	1.80	1.80	2.22	1.78	2.18
F-test	7.89	11.49	14.80	23.44	26.06	26.30
Significance Level	.001	.001	.001	.001	.001	.001

TABLE 5.—*Means, Standard Deviations, and F-tests for Individual Periods of Patient "Action" Variable in Three Patient Series*

Period	Original		Replication		Seven-day	
	Dr. 1	Dr. 2	Dr. 1	Dr. 2	First	Second
I Mean	74.45	65.25	68.40	54.60	72.80	50.70
S. D.	68.02	45.92	46.16	31.32	110.80	40.85
II Mean	60.90	69.40	44.25	48.80	45.55	43.30
S. D.	59.40	81.60	29.46	31.97	37.88	25.43
III Mean	67.75	79.25	87.40	53.05	53.10	48.85
S. D.	44.70	127.76	87.30	37.52	53.74	28.56
IV Mean	21.00	8.85	11.25	9.50	9.35	8.60
S. D.	49.74	3.47	5.71	2.38	4.02	2.38
V Mean	75.90	59.30	62.50	42.80	48.05	37.50
S. D.	124.12	67.82	49.35	31.44	22.94	18.03
F-test	3.28	3.91	9.52	16.75	3.22	10.79
Significance Level	.05	.01	.001	.001	.05	.001

The first stress (period 2) of the standardized interview consists of the interviewer's failing to respond to the patient's last utterance. The interviewer's "silence behavior" thus represents a change from his habitual pattern of responding within *one* second after the patient's last utterance (periods 1, 3, and 5) to a new pattern of not responding to the patient's last utterance for *fifteen* seconds (see "rules", table 2). Table 4 indicates that the effect of this increase in the interviewer's silence behavior in period 2 is to *increase* correspondingly the average silence of the patients taken as a group.

Reading down through the five subperiods for either test or retest in all three studies there becomes apparent a marked and completely consistent increase in length of patient silence per unit in period 2 as a function of increases in length of doctor silences and a drop in patient silence due to doctor's interruption in period 4. This finding is repeated six times in all. Thus, for example, reading down under Doctor 1 in the original study reveals an increase from 7.40 to 12.70 hundreths of a minute in the group's average silence behavior as this interviewer increased his silence from one second per unit in period 1 to 15 seconds per unit in period 2. The average silence falls back to 10.70 in period 3 as the interviewer resumes his one-second silences, and falls further in period 4 (6.45) when his silences are, in effect, "negative" ones; i.e., he does not wait for the patient to finish, but interrupts, instead. Following this interruption period, the average silence value returns approximately to its baseline in period 5 (8.40) as the interviewer resumes his one-second silence behavior.

In the last two rows of table 4 it can be seen that this phenomenon, *modification* in patient interaction patterns as a function of changes in stimulus conditions, is statistically highly significant for the group. In *each* of the six observations, the value for F across these five correlated silence means[16] is significant at the .001 level of confidence. These results indicate that "silence behavior," as one dimension of "personality," *can be modified by changing stimulus conditions.* That "silence behavior" is, at the same time, a *stable or invariant* "personality" pattern *when stimulus conditions are the same* can be seen from the rather strikingly high test-retest stability coefficients (.854, .859, and .582) shown for this variable in table 3.

The results for *Action* shown in table 5 are essentially similar to those for *Silence*. However, it is the second stress, *interruption in period 4,* which seems to have its greatest effect on this variable. Relative to the patient's average length of action in each of the other four periods, the average action drops *markedly* when the stimulus *changes* to interrupting behavior in period 4. The phenomenon is consistent in all three pairs of studies, although the significance level varies slightly, reaching the .001 level in three of the six group observations, the .01 level in one, and the .05 level in two. Interestingly, there is also a fairly consistent though not significant trend for *Action* to become shorter under conditions of interview silence in period 2. (Analysis by t-test reveals that for *Action,* period 4 differs significantly from all other periods, while for *Silence,* periods 2 and 4 differ from all other periods. The results are consistent in all three studies.) Table 5 thus seems to indicate that patients' actions tend to become shorter when the interviewer increases his silence and become strikingly shorter when the interviewer is interrupting. The extremely short actions in period 4 appear to be due to the fact that patients "submit," "quit talking," or "terminate their utterance" when the interviewer suddenly begins to interrupt them. Evidence for this lack of "dominance" on the part of the patients is presented in other publications (18, 24, 26). Nevertheless, table 5 presents evidence that like "silence," "action," as a "personality" variable, is also *modifiable* by *changes* in environmental or stimulus conditions. Its *stability* under *constant* stimulus conditions is evidenced in table 3, where the test-retest correlations are shown to be .847, .945, and .597.

However, tables 4 and 5 present only *group trends,* i.e., the results when the twenty subjects in each study are considered as a group. It is of interest to ask how representative are these results for the 20 patients in each group taken *individually*. The three groups of 20 patients were combined into a total of 60 individuals, yielding the following results. The group pattern for "Action" shown in table 5 is almost universal, as evidenced by the fact that independently of each patient's own baseline 58 out of the 60 individuals showed this drop in *Action* in period 4. Two patients in the original series failed to show it with Doctor 1, although these same two did show it with Doctor 2. Thus, for the 60 pairs of test-retest interviews, making 120 interviews in all, the group pattern shown in table 5 was manifested individually 118 times and failed to show itself only twice.

The results are less consistent for the *Silence* pattern shown in table 4. Again, independently of each patient's own baseline, 37 of the 60 individuals showed an increase in silence during period 2 as the interviewer increased his own duration of silence. Twenty-three individuals either did not show this increase at all or showed it with one interviewer but failed to show it with the other. This lower uniformity is seen more clearly from the fact that, out of 120 interviews with these 60 patients, the increase in silence during period 2 occurred 81 times (67.5 per cent) and failed to occur 39 times (32.5 per cent). Thus it occurred about two times out of three, whereas the drop in action occurred in almost 100 per cent of the instances. Finally, the decrease in silence in period 4 was *absent* in only 10 per cent of the 120 individual interviews.

This analysis by individuals, as well as the group results shown in tables 4 and 5, would seem to provide evidence that the particular "personality" patterns studied by the present method are *modifiable* as a result of subperiod *changes* in stimulus conditions. On the other hand, the markedly high stability coefficients in the presence of the rather wide individual differences (as reflected in the ranges) shown in table 3 seem to indicate both that individuals are "*unique*" and that they also will "be themselves" (show this same "uniqueness" relative to all the other individuals) when they are once more exposed to the same stimulus conditions (the standardized interview).

MacKinnon's prediction thus seems to be confirmed by our data. After reviewing numerous theories and studies on personality, MacKinnon expressed his views as follows: "No longer can there be any doubt that there is both specificity and generality of behavior. Both personal consistency and inconsistency must be recognized . . . A field theory which sees behavior and personality as functions of a total field of which they are subparts is the form of theory which today seems best suited for the conceptual representation of personality."[15] It is our belief that the results presented in table 3 are evidence of "generality" or "personal consistency" in behavior, while the results in tables 4 and 5 are evidence of "personal inconsistency" or "specificity" of behavior.

These findings seem to raise more questions than they answer. For example, what are the limits of this *generality* and *specificity?* Will generality still be shown for test and retest when one of the interviewers is a woman? How about changes in other parameters of the stimulus (while maintaining the standardized interview) such as age of the interviewer, his experience and "confidence", variations in socioeconomic differences between patient and interviewer, degree of "authority" conveyed by the interviewer, degree and kind of illness of the patient, and numerous other "set" variables? Can specificity (modifiability) be increased still further by making changes in the present standardized subperiod variations? Are there limits to this specificity relative to each individual's own baseline? That is, are there experimental situations which will be associated with an *increase* in action under the condition of interruption in period 4 in contradistinction to the universal *decrease* found under the present conditions? Use of drugs, singly or in combination, may produce just such a reversal of action behavior in period 4. These are but a few of the many questions which the present findings raise.

By standard psychological test methods we are currently investigating a number of measurable "organismic" variables (such as I.Q., level of anxiety, etc.) which might be correlated with the wide individual differences in interaction patterns suggested by the large standard deviations and ranges shown in tables 3, 4, and 5. We hope to obtain data which may help us to understand which other variables characterize, for example, a patient who interacts 25 times under standardized interview conditions as opposed to a second patient who interacts 127 times under the same conditions (see Dr. 1, original study, table 3).

TABLE 6.—*All Sixty First Interviews: Dr. 1 plus Dr. 2*

Variable	Females	Males	F	e
1. Mean Pt.'s Units	69.38	75.00	.864	
Range	40 to 130	25 to 132		
2. Mean Pt.'s Action	47.74	50.78	.018	
Range	13 to 143	12 to 243		
3. Mean Pt.'s Silence	8.48	9.74	3.530	
Range	3 to 14	6 to 19		
4. Mean Tempo	50.69	50.96	.002	
Range	23 to 104	19 to 159		
5. Mean Activity	33.81	31.89	.079	
Range	3 to 94	5 to 150		
6. Mean Pt.'s Adjust.	—.78	—1.51	5.459*	.274*
Range	—3.00 to +.63	—4.95 to +.50		
7. Mean Dr.'s Adjust.	—1.90	—1.96	.543	
Range	—3.34 to —.28	—4.82 to +.12		
8. Mean Pt.'s Synchron.	.84	.85	.000	
Range	.74 to .98	.69 to .99		
9. Mean Dr.'s Units	58.35	63.00	.700	
Range	32 to 112	21 to 119		
10. Mean Initiative	.75	.70	.857	
Range	.38 to 1.00	.17 to .92		
11. Mean Dominance	—.33	—.49	5.650*	.261*
Range	—.75 to +.29	—1.00 to +.13		

* Significant at the .05 level of probability.

At present it is possible to evaluate the effects on interaction pattern of one "organismic" variable, *sex* of the patient. Tables 6 and 7 show a comparison of the interaction patterns of the 28 males and 32 females who comprised the 60 subjects in the aforementioned three studies. Table 6 shows the data by sex for the *first* interview, while table 7 presents the same analysis for the *second* of the two interviews. Doctor 1's 20 first interviews and Doctor 2's 40 first interviews are combined in table 6. (Doctor 2 has 40 first interviews to Doctor 1's 20 because the latter did not serve in the seven-day study. In that series all 20 first and

TABLE 7.—*All Sixty Second Interviews: Dr. 1 plus Dr. 2*

Variable	Females	Males	F	e
1. Mean Pt.'s Units	69.56	78.79	2.447	
Range	41 to 133	29 to 133		
2. Mean Pt.'s Action	50.19	44.86	.256	
Range	15 to 178	11 to 257		
3. Mean Pt.'s Silence	8.72	9.75	2.533	
Range	5 to 14	6 to 17		
4. Mean Tempo	52.34	47.82	.498	
Range	25 to 143	19 to 142		
5. Mean Activity	35.03	28.89	.833	
Range	4 to 134	2 to 131		
6. Mean Pt.'s Adjust.	—.85	—1.37	2.392	
Range	—5.24 to +.89	—5.36 to +.88		
7. Mean Dr.'s Adjust.	—1.94	—2.08	.286	
Range	—3.35 to +1.00	—3.71 to +.14		
8. Mean Pt.'s Synchron.	—.85	.86	.000	
Range	.63 to 1.00	.73 to .98		
9. Mean Dr.'s Units	60.16	66.14	1.110	
Range	32 to 106	27 to 118		
10. Mean Initiative	.72	.72	.000	
Range	.31 to .94	.23 to 1.00		
11. Mean Dominance	—.26	—.53	12.500†	.405*
Range	—.75 to +.83	—.92 to —.07		

* Significant at the .01 level of probability.

† Significant at the .001 level of probability.

second interviews were conducted by Doctor 2.) In table 6 it is seen that *sex* as an organismic variable is associated with differences in only two of the interaction variables, *Pt.'s Adjustment* and *Dominance. Mean Pt.'s Adjustment* is the *average* length of time during which the patient "interrupted" the interviewer *minus* the length of the time during which the patient "failed to respond" to the interviewer. A positive Patient Adjustment score indicates that on the average the patients interrupted for longer durations than they were silent. A negative adjustment score indicates that the patients were silent more of the time than they were interrupting. Thus, the two negative means shown in table 6 for Patients' Adjustment indicate that when both females and males fail to adjust to our two *male* interviewers this lack of adjustment is largely due to longer durations of failures to respond, relatively speaking. However, the "higher" mean for the females (-.78 compared to -1.51 for the males) indicates that despite the fact that both groups "failed to respond" for longer periods than they "interrupted," the females failed to respond less and, conversely, did more interrupting than males.

Since Chapple's *Patient's Adjustment* variable represents a *single* algebraic sum of these two possibilities, one cannot be certain which the females did more of relative to the males. However, the second sex difference presented in table 6, greater *Dominance* shown by females relative to the males, would indicate that the "higher" adjustment mean of the females is probably a reflection of longer interruptions by them relative to the males. The two negative dominance averages (-.33 and -.49) indicate that under conditions of interruption in period 4 both females and males "submit to" more than they "dominate" the two male interviewers. The "higher" mean value for the females (-.33) indicates, however, that as a group they submit *less often* than do the men (-.49). Thus female *patients* as a group may be considered "more dominant" than men patients under conditions of interruption. There are considerable individual differences in both groups, however, as indicated by the large ranges. It will be of interest to investigate whether non-patient ("normal") males and females show the same or different "dominance-submission" patterns.

When these *same* 60 female and male subjects are interviewed a second time, only the sex difference in dominance pattern is *cross-validated.* The difference in dominance shown in table 7 is even more marked on this occasion. Thus it can be seen that the mean *difference* for dominance is larger in table 7 (.27) than in table 6 (.16). This difference is seen to be the result of the females' becoming somewhat *more* dominant (their mean went from -.33 "up" to -.26) while the males become *less* dominant or more submissive (from -.49 to -.53). A comparison of the "strength" of the relationship between sex and the dominance pattern in the first versus the second interviews reveals this stronger relationship between dominance and sex in the second interview in still another way. The differences in female and male means were shown by F-test to reach the .05 and .001 levels in tables 6 and 7, respectively. However, a significant F-test tells only that a statistically reliable difference exists. It provides no index of the *strength* of this relationship. A correlation measure (epsilon) does provide this information, however.[20] The values for this index are given in the last column of both tables 6 and 7. Table 6 reveals that the correlation between sex and dominance score was .261 (.05 level) in the first interviews and that this relationship went up to .405 (.01 level) in the second interviews (table 7).

It is not clear why the sex difference for *Patient Adjustment* was not cross-validated in the second interview series. The trend is nevertheless in the same direction as can be seen from the difference in means for females and males for this variable in table 7.

Preliminary analysis of the influence of a second "organismic" variable, *age*, on the interaction patterns of the 60 patients indicates that some of the individual differences noted in tables 3, 4, and 5 may well be associated with this factor also. Separate analysis of the three series of 20 patients indicates that patient *Initiative* especially, but also patient *Dominance* and *Adjustment* patterns, may vary as a function of differences in age. Confidence in this conclusion will, of course, have to await completion of the analysis of the total sample of 60.

In view of the various findings reported in this paper it might be of interest to examine the intercorrelations among the eleven interaction variables measured by the interaction chronograph method. Since these intercorrelations have not previously been computed or published they are presented in table 8. The matrix of intercorrelations presented in this table is based on the data for all 60 patients and represents the *first* interview results only. There is, however, little reason to suspect that these relationships will vary when replicated in the second interview. The replication is, of course, necessary and will be completed for purposes of cross-validating the results shown in table 8. It is apparent from the very high intercorrelations that some of the eleven variables reflect common variances. Thus a factor analysis which will reveal the smallest number of variables necessary to describe the interaction patterns studied by the interaction chronograph will be one of our next steps.

Summary

The research program described above had two aims. The first was to determine whether certain temporal characteristics of interaction patterns manifested during a psychiatric interview remain *stable* if the test-retest stimulus (interview) conditions are standardized and controlled along certain dimensions. The second aim was to determine whether these interaction patterns *change* or *become modified* as one introduces planned changes in the stimulus conditions through the use of a standardized interview containing two stress and three non-stress subperiods.

TABLE 8.—*Intercorrelations* Among IC Variables Based on First Interviews For a Sample of 60 Patients*

	1	2	3	4	5	6	7	8	9	10	11
1. Pt.'s Units		—.946	.289	—.958	—.948	—.098	.086	.668	.980	—.108	—.047
2. Action			—.247	.952	.947	—.038	.086	—.665	—.953	.286	.058
3. Silence				—.162	—.385	—.529	—.748	.571	.350	—.633	—.558
4. Tempo					.950	.028	.055	—.600	—.858	.201	—.051
5. Activity						.208	.241	—.604	—.865	.403	.114
6. Pt.'s Adj.							.391	—.183	—.135	.326	.359
7. Dr.'s Adj.								—.352	—.141	.662	.389
8. Synchr.									.738	—.729	—.230
9. Dr.'s Units										—.411	.014
10. Initiat.											.338
11. Domin.											

*These are rank-order correlations. The value of rho necessary to reach the .05 level of probability is .28; while it is .37 for the .01 level.

Chapple's standardized interview was the stimulus and the interaction chronograph was the instrument of measurement. The results indicate that both of the questions studied could be answered in the affirmative with a high degree of assurance. The findings of strikingly high reliabilities (stability coefficients) across two different interviewers for interviews conducted *independently* on the same day, and for two interviews on the same patient conducted by a *single interviewer* seven days apart, are unusual in personality research. These results, as well as the finding of modifiability in interaction patterns as a function of controlled stimulus conditions, are an indication that this instrument (the standardized interview) may have considerable use for investigating such problems as changes in behavior as a function of interpolated psychotherapy, drug administration, differences in rapport or other "set" factors, etc. The finding of relationships between two "organismic" variables *(age* and *sex)* and the interaction patterns studied here indicates that some research currently under way may reveal still other "organismic" variable correlates to account for the large individual differences in interaction patterns observed. Finally, a factor analysis of the matrix of intercorrelations among the 11 variables presented here may reveal several "factors" which would better describe the characteristics of these interaction patterns. This factor analysis is now being made.

REFERENCES

1. Ash, P.: The reliability of psychiatric diagnoses. J. Abnorm. Soc. Psychol. *44*: 272-276, 1949.
2. Chapple, E. D.: Quantitative analysis of the interaction of individuals. Proc. Nat. Acad. Sci. *25*: 58-67, 1939.
3. ——: "Personality" differences as described by invariant properties of individuals in interaction. Proc. Nat. Acad. Sci. *26*: 10-16, 1940.
4. ——: The interaction chronograph; its evolution and present application. Personnel *25*: 295-307, 1949.
5. ——: The standard experimental (stress) interview as used in interaction chronograph investigations. Human Organiz. *12*: 23-32, 1953.
6. ——, and Arensberg, C. M.: Measuring human relations: an introduction to the study of the interaction of individuals. Genet. Psychol. Monog. *22*: 3-147, 1940.
7. ——, and Lindemann, E.: Clinical implications of measurements of interaction rates in psychiatric interviews. Appl. Anthrop. *1*: 1-11, 1942.
8. ——, and Donald G., Jr.: A method for evaluating supervisory personnel, Harvard Bus. Rev. *24*: 197-214, 1946.

9. ——, Chapple, M. F., and Repp, J. A.: Behavioral definitions of personality and temperament characteristics. Human Organiz. *13*: 34-39, 1954.
10. Goldman-Eisler, F.: The measurement of time sequences in conversational behavior. Brit. J. Psychol. *42*: 355-362, 1951.
11. ——: Individual differences between interviewers and their effect on interviewees' conversational behavior. J. Ment. Sci. *98*: 660-670, 1952.
12. ——: A study of individual differences and of interaction in the behavior of some aspects of language in interviews. J. Ment. Sci. *100*: 177-197, 1954.
13. ——: On the variability of the speed of talking and its relation to the length of utterance in conversations. Brit. J. Psychol. *45*: 94-107, 1954.
14. Kelly, E. L.: Theory and techniques of assessment. Annu. Rev. Psychol. *5*: 281-310, 1954.
15. MacKinnon, D. W.: The structure of personality, vol. 1. In J. McV. Hunt, Ed., Personality and the Behavior Disorders. New York, Ronald Press, 1944, pp. 3-48.
16. McNemar, Q.: Psychological statistics. New York, Wiley, 1955.
17. Matarazzo, J. D., Saslow, G., and Matarazzo, Ruth G.: The Interaction Chronograph as an instrument for objective measurement of interaction patterns during interviews. J. Psychol. *41*: 347-367, 1956.
18. ——, —— and Guze, S. B.: Stability of interaction patterns during interviews: a replication. J. consult. Psychol. *20*: 267-274, 1956.
19. Murray, H. A., et al.: Explorations in Personality. New York, Oxford, 1938.
20. Peters, C. C., and Van Voorhis, W. R.: Statistical Procedures and Their Mathematical Bases. New York, McGraw-Hill, 1940.
21. Raines, G. N., and Rohrer, J. H.: The operational matrix of psychiatric practice. I. Consistency and variability in interview impressions of different psychiatrists. Am. J. Psychiat. *11*: 721-733, 1955.
22. Rorschach, H.: Psychodiagnostics. New York, Grune & Stratton, 1942.
23. Sarason, S. B.: The Clinical Interaction: With Special Reference to the Rorschach. New York, Harper, 1954.
24. Saslow, G., Matarazzo, J. D., and Guze, S. B.: The stability of interaction chronograph patterns in psychiatric interviews. J. consult. Psychol. *19*: 417-430, 1955.
25. ——, Goodrich, D. W., and Stein, M.: Study of therapist behavior in diagnostic interview by means of the interaction chronograph. J. Clin. Psychol. *12*: 133-139, 1956.
26. ——, Matarazzo, J. D., Phillips, Jeanne S., and Matarazzo, Ruth G.: Test-retest stability of interaction patterns during interviews conducted one week apart. J. Abnorm. Soc. Psychol. *54*: 295-302, 1957.
27. Sullivan, H. S.: The Interpersonal Theory of Psychiatry. New York, Norton, 1953.

9

CHANGES IN LANGUAGE DURING ELECTROSHOCK THERAPY

By ROBERT L. KAHN, PH.D., AND MAX FINK, M.D.*

IN RECENT YEARS Weinstein and his associates have described patterns of symbolic adaptation in patients with cerebral dysfunction.[1] The main emphasis in their work has been placed on altered language patterns. Their observations have shown the similarity and relationship between various kinds of behavior which were previously regarded as disparate phenomena. Instead of being isolated defects due to focal brain lesions, these phenomena can be understood as unified aspects of an altered pattern of adaptation under the conditions of a diffuse disturbance in brain function. Some of the factors which determine the particular type of adaptation shown include the premorbid personality and the nature of the environmental stresses.

This emphasis on language has been shown to be a useful method of study. For example, the presence of certain characteristic changes in language under the influence of amobarbital sodium, such as disorientation for time and place, denial of illness, and reduplication, has been standardized as a diagnostic test of brain disease in neurological patients.[2, 3]

This technique has application in the study of other conditions of altered brain function, as in the somatic therapies. The electroshock population is of interest for two reasons. It is possible in these patients, as it is not in those with neurological diseases, to manipulate experimentally the stimulus causing changes in brain function. Secondly, the mode of action and the psychological changes associated with electroshock treatment remain poorly understood. In a previous study we have shown that a favorable clinical response to electroshock treatment is related to early and persistent manifestations of language changes with amobarbi-

* Department of Experimental Psychiatry, Hillside Hospital, Glen Oaks, New York. Prepared with assistance from the National Institute of Mental Health, Public Health Service and the Dazian Foundation for Medical Research.

tal sodium characteristic of altered brain function.[4] This finding was considered to support the hypothesis advanced by Weinstein and Kahn[1, 5] that the mechanism of therapeutic action of electrically induced convulsions lay in the creation of a condition of altered brain function in which the patient might express his problems in a new symbolic fashion, particularly in the form of denial.

The present investigation is a further attempt to test this hypothesis by studying changes in language that occur with treatment. The following questions specifically were studied:

1. Are there characteristic identifiable changes in language which develop in the course of electroshock treatment?
2. Are these changes related to the clinical response?
3. Are these changes related to the degree of alteration of brain function?
4. Does the administration of amobarbital sodium prior to treatment produce any changes in language which have prognostic value for the eventual clinical response to treatment, the development of altered brain function, and the development of language changes during treatment?

Method

Population: Sixty-five consecutive referrals for electroshock treatment at the Hillside Hospital were studied. The Reiter electrostimulator was used on 49 patients, while 16 were treated with the Medcraft. There were 20 men in the series and 45 women and ages ranged from 21 to 68.

Each patient was tested prior to treatment and retested during the second week of treatment after having received 4-6 convulsions, and during the third week after having received 7-9 convulsions. On each of these occasions the patient was first tested clinically and then after amobarbital sodium had been administered at the rate of .05 grams per minute until nystagmus, slurred speech, drowsiness, and errors in counting backward were noted.[2]

The test consisted of a standardized series of questions concerning orientation and awareness of illness. This study is based, however, on the response to only three of the questions used: (1) What is your main trouble? (2) Why did you come to this place? (3) If you could have one wish, what would you wish for? All responses were recorded verbatim. Observations were also made on such nonverbal aspects as smiling, laughing, gestures, and other bodily movements.

Results

Patterns of Language Change Noted Clinically During Treatment

In evaluating the changes in language, the original responses to the three questions given clinically prior to treatment were used as the baseline. The evaluation of what constituted a change was based on explicit objective changes in grammar rather than on subjective or interpretative changes as to affect, mood, feeling, pitch, voice quality, *etc.* In this manner the following types of language change were noted clinically during the course of treatment: (1) alteration in the syntactical use of person, (2) evasion, (3) verbal denial, (4) qualification, (5) change in tense, (6) displacement, (7) stereotyped expressions and cliches, and (8) smiling and laughing.

Alteration in the syntactical use of person. Instead of using the first person singular as in the pretreatment period, 28 patients used the second or third person and, occasionally, the first person plural. To the question concerning main trouble such responses were given as, "It's what they call a depression," "They told me I was emotionally and mentally sick," "We're having a lot of trouble with my mother-in-law," "My cousin brought me; she said I was nervous," "What's *your* main trouble, or don't *you* know?" and "My Mrs. is sick and I would appreciate it if they would let her in here as soon as possible." The reason for coming to the hospital was variously given as, "My wife brought me," "My father told me to come here," or "My doctor said this was a good hospital." The wish was given as "Perfect health for my family," "My children, my husband, and all my good friends should be healthy and happy," and "There should be peace in the world."

Evasion. Evasion in answering the question about their illness was shown by 27 patients. This commonly took the form of answering this question with another, as, "What do you mean by my main trouble?," "What do you expect me to say?," "Well, what it it?," and "What did I say last time?" Other language patterns considered evasive included such responses as, "I don't know how to tell you," "I don't get what you mean," "Let me think," "It's hard to say," and "I just don't know how to express it.' One patient asked the examiner to give her a hint.

Verbal denial. Explicit verbal denial of illness was shown by 23 patients. They either said they had no main trouble, were well or else, after giving evasive 'I don't know" responses, denied their illness and symptoms when specifically questioned about them.

Qualification. Qualification of a response in the direction of less commitment was shown by 19 patients. This language pattern was characterized by the use of such words as "guess," "kind of," "sort of," "think," "apparently," "probably," "possibly," "might be," "seem," "assumed," and "perhaps." Thus such responses were given as, "I guess I have been jittery," "I seem to be very much depressed," "Probably that I'm nervous," "I suffer from anxieties, apparently," "Possibly worry about the future," "I have sort of gotten frightened," "Mentally upset, I assume," and "I think I'm a little insecure."

Change in tense. In 18 patients there was a change in tense in describing their illness. In most cases the patient used the past tense: "I was depressed when I came here" or "I had been nervous." In other cases the patient answered the question about his main trouble by putting it in the future tense as a wish.

Displacement. In 20 cases there was a displacement of the complaint to something other than originally given prior to treatment. This was invariably less serious than the original complaint. Sometimes the displacement was in the form of a somatic complaint, as saying the main trouble was "diarrhea," "headaches," "pain in the feet," "I slammed the finger in the door," and "I've got an itch." In other cases the displacement was to some concrete aspect of the hospital situation, as "My main trouble is getting these treatments," or "I'm upset because I was transferred to another ward."

Stereotyped expressions and cliches. The use of stereotyped expressions and cliches was shown by 11 patients. They gave such responses as "It seems to me under the proper circumstances I'd be all right," "[My trouble is] monetary problems with people that are honorary and sincere," "That's the root of the whole thing," "The only thing certain is death and taxes," "Learn my lesson and be a good boy," "To be a person of pep and reliability," and "I just want to stop being a lazy lout." One woman responded to a question of her one wish with, "I think I should consult my husband before I make a wish because he's a lawyer and the father of my children."

Smiling and laughing. In 20 cases the patient was noted to smile or laugh either immediately preceding or following his response to the question concerning his illness.

Language Changes Shown with Amobarbital Sodium During Treatment

The language patterns after amobarbital sodium during the second and third weeks of treatment were similar to those noted clinically. With the drug, however, the changes appeared earlier in the course of treatment. A given language pattern might be noted in the second week of treatment with the drug, but would not occur clinically until the third week. In addition, the reactions to the drug took more extreme forms, which are described as (1) cryptic responses, and (2) withdrawal reactions.

Cryptic responses. These were shown by 23 patients. Responses were classed as cryptic when they had no obvious relevance to the test question or when their meaning was obscure, representing a very personalized expression. Thus one patient, when asked his main trouble, said, "Nightmare of the afternoon of the evening of the nightmare." Others gave such responses as "I didn't know the problems—couldn't do the problems," "Getting my husband to write down what he does," or "What could I say—you don't get the crossword."

Withdrawal reactions. Some pattern of withdrawal was noted in 33 patients. This behavior was characterized by incomplete sentences, incoherent mumbling, neologisms, perseveration, the use of a foreign language by bilingual patients, and delay or failure to respond to the questions. These patients would characteristically lie with their eyes open, would smile or turn their heads when the examiner spoke, and would speak clearly and promptly and in English when asked questions not pertaining to their illness.

Other Changes in Language

Other changes in language were noted both clinically and with amobarbital sodium in response to the other questions of the test battery but not as a part of this study. There was frequent misnaming of the examiner or reference to him as "Mister." With the drug those patients who had a "positive reaction," *i.e.*, one characteristic of altered brain function, showed the characteristic patterns of disorientation for place and time and confabulation described in previous communications.[(2)]

Relation of Language Changes to Clinical Response

The evaluation of clinical response to treatment was made independently of this study. The patients were rated by the supervising psychiatrist in charge of the treatments, by the patient's own therapist and supervising psychiatrist, and by the medical director. On the basis of these ratings the patients were classified into three groups: 28 patients were considered much improved, no longer showing the symptoms which had brought them into the hospital; 22 patients were rated as moderately improved, showing some symptomatic relief but still showing disturbing features; and 15 were regarded as unimproved, having shown only equivocal or transient changes at best. The ratings were short term evaluations, being made within two months after completion of treatment.

For quantitative purposes the language changes shown during both the second and third weeks of treatment have been grouped together as though the patients had been tested only once. If a particular pattern was shown during both periods, the item was scored only once. Altogether, 89 per cent of the patients showed at least one of these patterns of language change clinically during treatment. Such changes were found in all of the much improved patients but in only 73 per cent of the unimproved group. It was apparent that there was a relation between the degree of clinical improvement and the number of changes in language patterns. When the data are analyzed for the patients who showed three or more language pattern changes, there is a significant difference between the groups (table 1). While 68 per cent of the much improved patients showed three or more language changes, only 20 per cent of the unimproved patients showed this degree of language change. Using Chi-square, the over-all difference is significant at better than the 1 per cent level of confidence.

TABLE 1.—*Relation of Language Changes Shown Clinically to Response to Treatment*

Change	No.	Three or more patterns *		Fewer than three patterns *	
Much improved	28	19	68 per cent	9	32 per cent
Moderately improved	22	7	32	15	68
Unimproved	15	3	20	12	80
Total	65	29	45 per cent	36	55 per cent

* $X^2 = 11.26$; $P < .01$

When each language pattern is analyzed individually (as shown in fig. 1) it becomes apparent that not all patterns discriminated equally between the groups. In all but one case, a greater percentage of the much improved group was most likely to show denial, use of the second or third person, evasion, and displacement of complaint. The only language pattern on which little difference was found between the much improved and unimproved patients was the incidence of smiling and laughing.

Analysis of the changes shown by the different groups under amytal is shown for the cryptic and withdrawal reactions only in figure 1. While the crytic responses did not vary much with the different groups, the showing of a withdrawal reaction differentiated the three groups significantly,* occurring in 71 per cent of the much improved, 45 per cent of the moderately improved, and only 20 per cent of the unimproved patients.

Relation of Language Changes to Electroencephalographic Response

In a previous communication a method of quantitatively evaluating electroencephalographic records was described.[6] Criteria were established for rating records as showing relatively high, middle or low degree of slowing according to five criteria: average per cent time delta waves (waves of six or fewer cycles per second), the highest per cent time delta waves at any one lead, the lowest frequency in the record, the highest amplitude of delta waves, and the longest duration of a burst of delta waves. In the present study, an electroencephalogram was obtained prior to treatment and in the second and third weeks of treatment. Each record was evaluated according to the dichotomy of showing a relatively high degree of delta activity or not, using these criteria.

In table 2 the relationship is shown between electroencephalographic slowing and changes in language. Those patients with the highest degree of cerebral dysfunction, having high degree delta in both the second and third weeks of treatment, show a greater number of language changes both clinically and with amobarbital sodium. Using the withdrawal reaction as an index of the drug effect, however, the difference just fails to be statistically significant.

Pretreatment Language Patterns

The language patterns described in this study were considered as changes only when they occurred after the original pretreatment clinical test which was used as a baseline. Seven patients, however, showed some

* $X^2 = 10.72$, significant at better than the 1 per cent level of confidence.

TABLE 2.—*Relation of Language Change to High Degree Delta on the Electroencephalogram During the Second and Third Weeks of Treatment*

Change	No.	Three or more changes clinically *		Withdrawal reactions with amobarbital sodium †	
Both weeks high Delta Activity	25	16	64 per cent	15	60 per cent
One week high Delta Activity	16	8	50	9	56
No high Delta Activity	24	6	25	8	33

* $X^2 = 7.62$; $P < .05$
† $X^2 = 4.87$; $P < .10$

form of these language patterns in the initial clinical test. The manifestation of these same patterns by these patients at any other time was accordingly not scored as a change.

When given amobarbital sodium prior to treatment, however, 30 patients (or 46 per cent of the total) showed some language change comparable to that noted during treatment. Table 3 shows the relation between such changes at this time and the eventual clinical response. These changes were found in 68 per cent of the much improved patients, in 36 per cent of the moderately improved, and in 20 per cent of the unimproved groups.

TABLE 3.—*Relation of Pretreatment Language Changes with Amobarbital Sodium to Eventual Clinical Response*

Change	No.	Change with amobarbital sodium *	
Much improved	28	19	68 per cent
Moderately improved	22	8	36
Unimproved	15	3	20

* $X^2 = 10.30$; $P < .01$

In table 4 it is demonstrated that the pretreatment change with the drug was also prognostic of the eventual physiological response to treatment as measured by the degree of electroencephalographic slowing. The over-all distribution just falls short of statistical significance, although when those who showed high delta activity in both periods are compared with all the other cases as a group, the difference is significant at the 5 per cent level of confidence.

TABLE 4.—*Relation of Pretreatment Changes with Amobarbital Sodium to High Degree EEG Delta Activity During the Second and Third Weeks of Treatment*

Change	No.	Change with amobarbital sodium *	
Both weeks high Delta Activity	25	16	64 per cent
One week high Delta Activity	16	6	38
No high Delta Activity	24	8	33

* $X^2 = 5.27$; $P < .10$

Finally, the initial response to amobarbital sodium was also prognostic of the degree of language change shown clinically and to the manifestation of withdrawal reactions with the drug during treatment (table 5).

TABLE 5.—*Relation Between Pretreatment Language Response to Amobarbital Sodium and Clinical Changes and Withdrawal During Treatment*

	No.	Three or more clinical language patterns *		Withdrawal reactions to amobarbital sodium †	
Pretreatment response to amobarbital sodium	30	18	60 per cent	21	70 per cent
No pretreatment response to amobarbital sodium	35	11	31	12	34

* $X^2 = 4.26$; $P < .05$
† $X^2 = 6.88$; $P < .01$

Discussion

The relationship of the language changes to the development of altered brain function and to the clinical response is consistent with our original hypothesis concerning the mode of action of electroshock treatment. In previous studies[4, 6] we have shown that the clinical outcome is related to the presence and degree of alteration in cerebral function. Using the "amytal test"[2] and the EEG as indices, it has been found that those patients with the earliest and most persistent manifestations of cerebral dysfunction were most likely to have a favorable response. Such physiological changes create the milieu which facilitates behavioral change.

The present study, analyzing language patterns, clarifies the nature of the behavioral changes that occur with treatment.

The language shown originally (prior to treatment) may be summarized in the statement, "I have this particular illness." The subject of this sentence answers the question "who," the predicate refers to "what," and the verb describes the relationship, including the temporal and intensity aspects. During treatment the subject of the sentence may be modified by changes in the use of person, so that the sentence might read, "You [or he, she, or they] have this particular illness." Changes in the predicate are shown by such patterns as displacement or evasion. In displacement the sentence might read, "I have some other kind of illness," while, with evasion, it would be, "I have something, but I don't know what." Changes in the verb are shown by denial, qualification, or alteration of tense. In denial the statement would be, "I don't have this particular illness;" a qualified sentence would read, "I might have this particular illness;" while with alteration of tense the sentence would be, "I *had* this particular illness."

Some language patterns modify the sentence as a whole. If the patient smiles, or if he introduces his statement by saying, "The doctors tell me that . . . ," any part or all of the sentence may be modified. In other reactions, particularly those noted under amytal, the patient avoids giving any meaningful statement at all. In the withdrawal reaction he says nothing or omits part of the sentence. In the use of cliches or cryptic expressions no specific referential meaning can be drawn from the language.

It is evident from this analysis that the language changes are not random or bizarre, but form a patterned reorganization of communication characterized by an alteration in the patient's attitudes to his problems and his illness. The patient either says he is not now and never has been ill, displaces his illness temporally, spatially, or personally, is less committed to his awareness of his illness by the use of qualifications, or avoids the whole problem by evasion and noncommunication.

These patterns are comparable to those noted previously by Weinstein and Kahn[1] in patients with cerebral disorders, and referred to by these authors as the "language of denial." Similar language changes have also been described following other somatic therapies. Frank[7, 8] reports that lobotomized patients avoid talking about the operation, and he states that "the facility and glibness with which they say 'well I had an operation for my nerves, I guess' contain the quality of unconscious denial." Legault,[9] working intensively with post-lobotomy patients, found persistent attitudes of denial. One patient, when asked why she came to see the doctor, said it was her relatives' idea. Many gave qualified responses, saying they "supposed" they had had an operation. Others doubted that the operation was on the brain, or used an evasive, stereotyped expression as "some nerve in there," or displaced the procedure as in, "Oh, yes, I went to the hospital and got two black eyes." When asked about the symptoms that led up to the operation, patients gave such response as, "It seems to have gone." In studying patients who showed clinical improvement following prolonged coma reactions in insulin coma therapy, we have noted similar changes in language. In a case report[10] we noted the appearance of reduplicative phenomena, evasion, verbal denial, displacement, increased use of stereotyped expressions and cliches, cryptic responses, and much smiling and laughing, at a time when clinical improvement was most marked.

Since these language changes occur most frequently in patients who are clinically evaluated as improved, may not the language patterns themselves be the critical cues that give a favorable clinical impression? There is traditionally much difficulty in rating patients after treatment. Such evaluations are highly variable because of the lack of suitable objective criteria. While there are other objective cues which can be used, such as the amount of sedation required or the quantity of food eaten, the appearance of these language patterns may constitute an operational basis for clinical evaluation in the psychiatric interview.

Not all patients, however, who showed at least three of the language changes were regarded as much improved, and not all of the much improved patients showed this degree of change. There may be other aspects of language and communication not covered by this study which are significant. Another explanation is that the use of these language patterns may vary in time or in different situations. On the basis of our previous observations of the "Amytal test" and the electroencephalogram in electroshock patients, we should predict that unimproved patients would show these language changes only transiently, while improved patients would show them persistently. Future work should also be directed toward comparison of language patterns shown when the patient is speaking to a physician with those used when he is with his family or friends. The degree to which members of the patient's family are made more comfortable by the changed language, and even their inclination to use similar language, may explain the variability in the duration of improvement following treatment. Both Weinstein and Kahn[1, 11] and Legault[9] have indicated a relationship between the patterns of communication of the patient and those of his family.

Finally, our results demonstrate the prognostic usefulness of amobarbital sodium administered prior to treatment. The prognostic value of the drug in the somatic therapies has been noted previously by Hoch[12] and others,[13, 14] who felt that patients who became more normal in speech, ideation, and behavior under the influence of barbiturates were most likely to improve with treatment. In the present study the manifestation of a change in language with the drug was related not only to the development of altered brain function and to the clinical outcome, but to the eventual manifestation of these language patterns clinically. On this basis, an operational definition of the goal of electroshock therapy might be described as enduring clinical manifestation of those language patterns which occur initially only with amobarbital sodium.

Summary and Conclusions

1. Sixty-five consecutive patients referred for electroshock treatment were studied prior to and during the second and third weeks of treatment. Each patient was tested at these times both clinically and with amobarbital sodium with a standard series of questions concerning attitude toward illness.

2. The results showed that characteristic changes in language occurred both clinically and with amobarbital sodium during treatment. These changes were significantly related to the clinical response to treatment

and to the degree of alteration of brain function as measured by the electroencephalogram.

3. The presence of these language patterns with amobarbital sodium prior to treatment was related to the eventual clinical response, the development of altered brain function, and the development of language changes clinically during treatment.

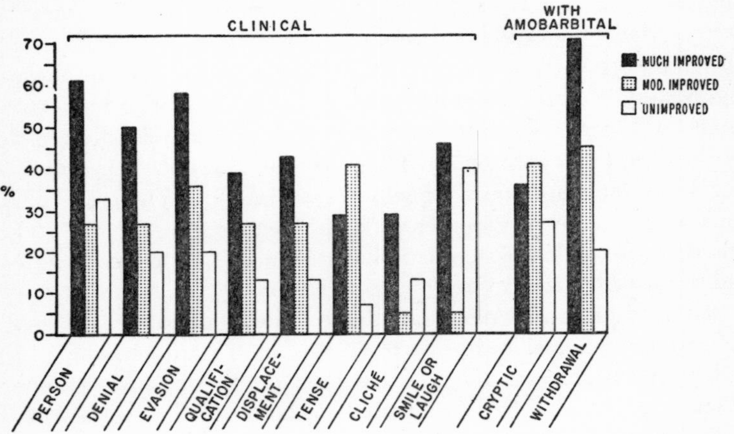

FIG. 1. Relation of each language pattern to response to treatment.

4. It is felt that these language changes constitute an operational basis for the evaluation of the clinical response.

5. The results support the hypothesis that the therapeutic mechanism of electroshock treatment is the development of different patterns of symbolic adaptation to the patient's problems and illness under the conditions of altered brain function.

REFERENCES

1. WEINSTEIN, E. A., AND KAHN, R. L.: Denial of Illness: Symbolic and Physiological Aspects. Springfield, Ill., Charles C. Thomas, 1955.

2. ——, ——, SUGARMAN, L. A., AND LINN, L.: Diagnostic use of amobarbital sodium ("Amytal Sodium") in organic brain disease. Am. J. Psychiat. *112*: 889-894, 1953.

3. ——, ——, AND MALITZ, S.: Serial administration of the "Amytal test" for brain disease: its diagnostic and prognostic value. Arch. Neurol. & Psychiat. *71*: 217-226, 1954.

4. KAHN, R. L., FINK, M., AND WEINSTEIN, E. A.: Relation between altered brain function and denial in electroshock therapy. Arch. Neurol. & Psychiat. *76*: 23-29, 1956.
5. WEINSTEIN, E. A., LINN, L., AND KAHN, R. L.: Psychosis during electroshock therapy: its relation to the theory of shock therapy. Am. J. Psychiat. *109*: 22-26, 1952.
6. FINK, M., AND KAHN, R. L.: Quantitative studies of slow wave activity following electroshock, Electroencephalog. Clin. Neurophysiol. *8*: 158, 1956.
7. FRANK, J.: Clinical survey and results of 200 cases of prefrontal leucotomy. J. Ment. Sci. *92*: 497-508, 1946.
8. ——: Some aspects of lobotomy (prefrontal leucotomy) under psychoanalytic scrutiny. Psychiatry *13*: 35-42, 1950.
9. LEGAULT, O.: Denial as a complex process in post lobotomy. Psychiatry *17*: 153-161, 1954.
10. KAHN, R. L., GRAUBERT, D., AND FINK, M.: Delusional reduplication of parts of the body after insulin coma therapy. J. Hillside Hosp. *4*: 134-137, 1955.
11. WEINSTEIN, E. A., AND KAHN, R. L.: Personality factors in denial of illness. Arch. Neurol. & Psychiat. *69*: 355-367, 1953.
12. HOCH, P. H.: The present status of narcodiagnosis and therapy. J. Nerv. Ment. Dis. *103*: 248-259, 1946.
13. HARRIS, M. M., HORWITZ, W. A., AND MILCH, E. A.: Regarding Sodium Amytal as a prognostic aid in insulin and metrozol shock therapy of mental patients (dementia praecox). Am. J. Psychiat. *96*: 327, 1939.
14. GOTTLIEB, J. S., AND HOPE, J. M.: Prognostic value of intravenous administration of Sodium Amytal in cases of schizophrenia. Arch. Neurol. & Psychiat. *46*: 86-100, 1941.

Discussions of Chapters 5-9

By JOSEPH ZUBIN, PH.D.*

THIS MORNING we were treated to a series of experimental studies dealing with the normative aspects of communication. This afternoon has been devoted largely to experimental studies in the psychopathology of communication, especially concerning the interview. In reviewing this afternoon's papers, the following points of agreement may be noted:

1. The communicative act is at the very heart of psychopathology.
2. The interview technique is one of the most important tools for eliciting communication in psychopathology.
3. Very little is known about the mechanism of the interview and its controls.
4. Nevertheless, the interview is enjoying a rather wide popularity.
5. It appears in a variety of forms.
6. It certainly needs more research.

Regarding the points of disagreement, the following may be noted: First, the same or similar phenomena are often interpreted in dynamic terms by one group and in organic terms by another, reflecting the schism in current psychopathology. It is, however, becoming quite apparent that this schism is really unnecessary and that since words and drugs can bring about similar changes in behavior there must be a common link between the so-called dynamic explanation and the biochemical explanation.

Certain questions permeated all of the papers and we might point these out as the transcending problems in this field at the moment. Why are communication and its chief tool, the interview, so important? Why was it necessary to devote an entire symposium to this problem? Apparently, the measurement of attitudes, feelings, self-evaluation, and other private events is still not attainable through objective techniques. While intelligence and certain other aspects of personality have yielded before the onslaught of the psychometrician and his measurement techniques, the personal world of the patient as well as of the normal person—in which

* Biometrics Research, New York State Department of Mental Hygiene; Professor of Medical Psychology, Columbia University.

values, attitudes, feelings, emotions, self-evaluations are included—has lagged in scientific development. At the present time only the interview, with all its shortcomings, is a tool of choice for the detection and measurement of this area of behavior. The interview has been defined as a face-to-face conversation between two individuals for a definite purpose with a nonreciprocal relationship existing between the two interlocutors, i.e., the interviewer and interviewee. Each of these elements in the definition, the face-to-face situation, the use of conversation as the medium, the presence of two individuals, the presence of a definite goal and a nonreciprocal relationship, is an essential factor in the totality of the interview and any alteration in these factors will tend to change the interview to a degenerate form.

In view of the importance of the interview, why has it been neglected so long by scientists? The only available answer is that like the air about us it has been with us since childhood and we have never really been able to detect its presence until the problem was forced upon us through observing individuals who fail to communicate or who communicate badly with their fellows. The strategy and the tactics of conversation are so inbred within us that it takes an herculean effort to disengage these factors. For this reason, there have been few if any scientific models proposed for the interview. However, this lag is fast being compensated. One model deals with the application of reinforcement theory to verbal behavior, following Skinner's work. The second involves drawing an analogy to physical motion following Newtonian laws; the third draws its elements from information theory.

It should be noted at this point that the interview is the sole criterion we now have for validation of tests in the general area of feelings, attitudes and emotions and that such instruments as the projective techniques, when analyzed into their components, merely become standardized interviews. When they are treated as interviews they yield interesting information about personality that can be validated through other sources, but when they are looked upon as tests and scored in orthodox fashion they fail to reveal any significant relations with other methods of measuring behavior. Thus, the projective techniques must be supplemented with interview approaches in order to find their usefulness.

There are now two approaches to the evaluation of the communicative act between patient and interviewer. The first gives complete freedom to the interviewer to explore whichever area he may be interested in and to utilize such techniques as free association to probe with the patient areas of interest to them both. Only after such an interview is completed can the tape recording be used for analyzing the content of the interview and, of course, the comments of the interviewer upon reviewing the taped interview might be added to explain the results of this content analysis. At the opposite end of the continuum we have experimental interviews in which definite attempts are made to control the interview procedure in an objective manner with certain definite purposes in mind. For example, there is the focused interview in which definite areas of interest are brought up, e.g., affect; and certain experimental techniques are utilized for reinforcing certain previously defined aspects of the response so as to elicit as much of that type of response as possible. The latter interview too can be analyzed for content. Generally speaking, there are two varieties of content analysis. First there is the formal analysis, exemplified by Goldfarb, et al., Matarazzo, et al, and Hambidge. In this analysis certain formal aspects such as number of words, ratio of adjectives to verbs, total time taken in speaking, etc. are the primary variables for analysis. A content analysis, on the other hand, may devote itself primarily to the meaning of the words spoken, as is exemplified in Keeler's chapter. Both of these techniques are useful in bringing out the essential variables involved in the interview.

As for the methods of manipulating the variables underlying the interview, the following varieties are available: We have the interviews dealing with focused approaches in which specific material is elicited as, for example, in the Kinsey interview and as Kahn does to some extent. This focuses primarily on the content. One may also focus on the formal aspect, namely the silences, the various other characteristics of the communicative act, as is done by Matarazzo et al. Finally, there is a technique utilized in our own approach to interviewing, in which we respond to every affective utterance that the patient makes by saying "Unh-hunh" to determine whether there would be more affective utterances elicited during the "reinforcement" period than during the periods in which no "reinforcement" is given. This study is largely a result of our attempt to obtain a measure of flatness of affect in our prognostic studies. Thus far it seems that such measures of the ability to emit affective utterances are useful in differentiating between patients and in indicating their individual differences with respect to this important prognostic variable.

In general, the approach to the interview which is free and open and does not involve any experimental controls can lead to a content analysis which is useful in understanding how the therapeutic process moves at the present time, but which is not as valuable for providing new insights into the communicative act itself. This uncontrolled approach has led to the accumulation of many tape recordings but has not yielded any scientific progress because no basic hypothesis was involved in the experimental design, and without such hypotheses no evaluation of the results is possible.

The controlled interviews discussed this afternoon were as follows: Goldfarb et al. indicated that an experimental variation of the speed of auditory feedback influences speech communication in a very definite way. (The rest of this chapter is to be discussed by Dr. Sutton.) Matarazzo, et al., have given us a fine example of the use of the Chapple interaction chronograph with mental patients. This technique presents essentially the skeleton of the interview interaction between the two interlocutors; that is, it indicates the relative amount of time taken up in speaking by each person, the silences that each engages in, the submissiveness or dominance exhibited when both attempt to speak at the same time, etc. In their analysis of their results they indicate that there is a high degree of stability with reference to the overt behavior of the patient during the interview. Some of these reliability coefficients are quite remarkable. However, in some only 36 per cent of the variance is controlled, and one wonders whether some of this variability may not be a reflection of changes in the subject during the course of the interview rather than of an instability of the technique itself. It may very well be that the patients who show this change in their stability are yielding information far more important than are those who go through the process in an invariant manner.

As yet there is no validity demonstrated for this technique, though evidence does exist for covariation between what the interviewer does and how the interviewee responds. There is still need to relate this behavior to life behavior. One wonders whether, despite the stability of the technique, we have any evidence that important personality variables are being measured with it at the present time. The fact that interviewer silence will produce corresponding interviewee silence and that some patients, when interrupted, will yield the floor, should come as no surprise. However, what individual differences in this behavior mean requires further investigation. Another factor which seems rather noteworthy is the mechanical nature of the procedure—the stresses, the interruptions. The opportunity to observe the patient's behavior in response to silence is mechanically injected into the situation and one wonders whether a method utilizing reinforcement rather than the techniques of the interaction chronoscope might not make for a more natural setting.

Turning now to the chapter by Kahn and Fink, dealing with changes in language in electric shock therapy, several questions might be raised. First, the phenomena which have been described as denial might very well represent a loss of familiarity due to the shock. Since denial invokes a definite dynamic assumption while loss of familiarity may be regarded as a phenomenon demonstrably produced by electric shock, one wonders which of these two possible explanations is the more parsimonious. Another question arises from the fact that there was no control group in this study. This raises the question of what a repetition of the interview in untreated patients might have brought about. Would similar phenomena be elicited? The relation of the characteristics of the patient to outcome is interesting but it should be remembered that there was only a two-month follow-up and, furthermore, that the type of patient treated was not fully specified. However, the prognostic value of pretreatment language behavior certainly is an interesting phenomenon to observe and to note later in relation to outcome. Another factor which has been studied and which perhaps might bear further scrutiny is the relation between the so-called organic syndrome following the third or fourth shock treatment and the final outcome. The dynamic interpretation of interview content certainly indicates that we need more basic criteria for our evaluation.

Such terms as "evasion" and "denial" represent inferred rather than objective categories of classification. It would have been better to use a more neutral term. It is also interesting to note that the proportion of cases not showing any change in linguistic behavior was rather impressive, about two-thirds.

Hambidge and Gottschalk have presented a most interesting contrast between the use of verbal and visual stimulation (presentation of a TAT card) for the evocation of a story. They find significant differences between these two methods of eliciting a story. The interpretation of story content in terms of life experience is always hazardous since the relation between fantasy and reality has never been worked out fully. In some cases fantasy is merely an extension of reality; in other cases it is a compensation for reality, but one never knows which direction the story will take. All in all, this group of papers has demonstrated the great need for conceptual models for the interview and for hypotheses emanating from these models. When these are provided, research can take firmer root in communication.

By SAMUEL SUTTON, PH.D.*

AN INDIVIDUAL'S SPEECH can be radically modified by altering his sensory reception of that behavior. This suggests that auditory feedback normally acts as a monitoring mechanism for regulating ongoing speech behavior. Differences in the degree and kind of speech alteration among individuals or groups may be due to a variety of causes acting singly or in combination.

One possible explanation of these differences is that they may be a function of the degree to which the individual uses different feedback channels in monitoring speech behavior. Thus, if an individual is more dependent on kinesthetic feedback from the vocal apparatus, his speech may be very little disturbed by distorted auditory feedback. Also, we do not know what differences exist between individuals in their degree of utilization of any sensory feedback to control their speech productions. If individuals do vary with respect to their dependence on sensory feedback for the regulation of speech, the degree of alteration of their speech behavior may only reflect this differential dependence.

A different kind of possibility arises from the fact that individuals seem to differ in the delay time which produces greatest alteration of a particular aspect of speech. This may be a function of the individual's normal speaking rate. Until the factor of delay time is systematically investigated, it will be difficult to interpret the meaning of differences between groups in the degree of speech alteration arising from the use of a single delay time.

Whatever the mechanisms underlying individual and group differences, delayed speech feedback gives an unusual opportunity for studying fairly complex behavior under highly controlled conditions. The effect of delayed feedback on speech does not seem to be dependent on

* Director, Prognosis Project, Research Foundation for Mental Hygiene. Biometrics Research, New York State Psychiatric Institute, and Lecturer, Psychology, Columbia University.

motivational and attentional factors. As long as the individual is willing to speak, the effect is compelling. The speech productions are automatically recorded and are available for extremely objective analysis.

In our own work with normal children we used an actual count of specific speech alterations rather than a gross judgment of speech disturbance. Older children prolonged more syllables, repeated more words and were slowed more in rate of speaking than were younger children. However, older children also had a greater decrease in the number of intrusions such as "uh" and "um." While the older children had a greater disturbance on the first three speech measures, we can hardly consider a decrease in the number of intrusions as constituting more disturbance. Thus, it seems less useful to work with the concept of total speech disturbance than to work with specific aspects of speech.

10

Presidential Address

THE PSYCHOPATHOLOGIC FOUNDATION OF PSYCHIATRY

By OSKAR DIETHELM, M.D.*

PSYCHOPATHOLOGY HAS A HISTORY of less than a century and has only recently been recognized for its importance in clinical psychiatry. It has not yet, however, reached the place which pathology occupies for the field of medicine in general. A brief review of the development of psychopathology and pathology may illustrate where we are now and what the future outlook will be.

In the beginning, i.e., in the middle of the last century, psychopathology was synonymous with abnormal psychology, limiting itself to abnormal psychologic functioning. The advent of physiologic psychology broadened the field and finally led to the concept of the psychobiologically integrated person. Psychopathology became the science of abnormal personality functions. Further development led to the recognition that the disturbed person must be considered in his relation to other people, to his environment, and to cultural influences. A biosocial concept replaced the psychobiologic one and forced the psychopathologist and the psychiatrist to study pathologic personality functions, including not only the psychologic but also the biologic, social, and cultural aspects. All these aspects are inherent in the investigation of a psychopathologic observation.

A psychopathologic study must include that which is directly observable as well as all the dynamic factors involved—factors which may be primarily psychologic, biologic, social, or cultural. As with pathology, it must obtain its questions from the normal structure and functions and therefore maintain a close relationship to anatomy, physiology, psychology and cultural anthropology. In addition, as with pathology, it must

* Department of Psychiatry, Cornell University Medical College; Payne Whitney Psychiatric Clinic, New York Hospital.

find its problems in the clinical field, i.e., psychiatry, and its answers in the study of patients and in animal experiments. The same principles apply to both pathology and psychopathology, as psychopathology might well be considered an intrinsic part of a pathology which concerns itself with the pathologic phenomena of the whole patient.

Psychopathology, like pathology, studies findings which are unusual in degree or occur within the wrong age period. This definition of "pathologic" includes unusual and disturbing behavior in relation to other people and to the expectancy and demands of the culture to which the individual belongs. As there is no essential difference between pathology and psychopathology, a further historical comparison is justified.

Pathology obtained a sound position in medicine when, in the eighteenth century, through the work of Morgagni, careful observation of details was recognized and it was no longer considered permissible to omit any details in the examination, and when all observations had to be clearly described. Pathology still subscribes to these requirements. To this morphologic phase might be compared the psychopathologic studies in the nineteenth century, climaxing the excellent studies of the Heidelberg school under the leadership of Kraepelin. In one way, however, Kraepelin was far ahead of this phase when he brought into psychopathology the concept of experimental verification of these observations. As did their predecessors in pathology, he and his group developed suitable methodology for the study of the individual by introducing methods of adequate clinical observations. It became accepted that examinations must be regulated in order to obtain adequate results and comparable observations from different observers. Facts must therefore be carefully described, and subjective impressions were not acceptable. Terms must be specific and generalities avoided; for example, a hallucination must be described in all details with regard to sensory experiences and content.

The results of this phase of psychopathology became as far-reaching in the clinical field as the morphologic studies of pathology, resulting in excellent descriptions of psychopathologic states. However, just as it had been in pathology, the contribution to etiology remained meager.

The next historical phase of pathology came with the introduction of the histological studies of Bichat at the beginning of the nineteenth century. He demanded a study of the different textures of an organ. A fundamentally similar development occurred in psychopathology in the latter part of the nineteenth century when Janet and Morton Prince studied psychodynamic aspects and Forel and the French psychiatrists utilized hypnotic investigation. These contributions also began to increase interest in etiology.

The great change in pathology took place in the middle of the nineteenth century with Virchow's proposal of cellular pathology. The title of his new journal, *Archiv für pathologische Anatomie und Physiologie und klinische Medizin,* demonstrates the inclusiveness of his concept of pathology. In the opening paper he stated that diseases "represent the course of appearance of life under changed conditions." He demanded of scientific medicine the study of these changed conditions, the determination of the influence of definite conditions, and the finding of means to abolish them. In psychopathology a similar fundamental progress occurred with Freud's contribution. As did Virchow, he proposed a new theory. In addition, he offered suitable methodology. Psychodynamic psychopathology with emphasis on the genetic approach came forcefully into the field of medicine. The study of etiology became as important to psychopathology as it had become to pathology. Progress continued in both fields. Pathology expanded its interest into bacteriology and immunology and then into chemistry; psychopathology into social psychology and cultural aspects. The methods of study and experimental approaches became enriched through the development of the projective techniques.

When we turn to the present status of psychopathology, we can see difficulties which arose in pathology and have found their adjustment in the evolution of this science. Virchow deplored the mistake of drawing "arbitrarily general conclusions from investigations of isolated details" —a mistake which "the systematic mind of the Germans" often committed. The founder of the revolutionary cellular pathology, a believer in scientific evolution, Virchow warned that if one destroys historical bridges they must be restored. Modern pathology demands that the causes and effects of all possible factors present be studied—a multifactorial approach which is now accepted in psychopathology. The historical similarities of pathology and psychopathology could be developed much further, but the data presented may suffice for this discussion of the psychopathologic foundations of clinical psychiatric study and treatment.

The observer's attitude is important in any scientific observation, but nowhere is bias more marked than in behavioral science. The observer's personal psychodynamics will influence him. Theories will affect his way of looking at the facts, his selection of special data, and his differentiation of the essential from the nonessential. This statement, which may appear unjustifiedly extreme, is supported unfortunately by the development of psychopathology in the last fifty years. Causality was the exclusive guiding principle for some, while others accepted just as strongly the principle of teleology. Those who stressed the need for strict objectivity often neglected to consider the subjective experience of the patient and the meaning of this experience to him. Phenomenology taught that one does not study facts but should try to understand the essential nature of an occurrence. Mechanism and determinism affected the thinking of the students at the beginning of this century, to be attacked by the adherents of a neoromantic philosophy with polarity as an inherent guiding principle. The schools of the nineteenth century which taught that brain function parallels psychologic function exerted considerable influence until recent years. At one period, ethic considerations were influential and sin and guilt became of importance and were used in varying degrees according to the conscious and unconscious attitudes of the student in psychopathology and clinical psychiatry. These remarks are made to point out the many pitfalls which threatened steady progress. None of us will be able to avoid bias, but by keeping this possibility in mind we will succeed in being constructively self-critical and avoid the danger of building up and fortifying systems.

The cultural influence upon the investigator has received little attention. The sociologist might point out that psychiatrists follow middle class standards and evaluate the normal accordingly. These standards may not apply to different cultures and not to a disorganized society in our own culture. In study (e.g., psychopathic behavior) it is not possible to compare readily the psychopathic behavior of a well-organized society with groups in which different standards and attitudes prevail. Psychopathologic considerations of historical personalities of other periods which appeared frequently in literature some years ago have suffered greatly from the fact that the writers had an insufficient knowledge of the culture of the historical period selected.

The danger of using analogies has unfortunately been illustrated repeatedly in clinical studies and theories and in the comparison of human and animal behavior. One need merely to think of the application of the concept of neuroses to unusual animal behavior to see the difficulties and obstacles which arise in experimental psychopathology by such an unfortunate use of analogies. It is to the credit of current psychopathology that analogies are used less frequently and that the data and explanations of previous observers are critically reconsidered. The same constructive attitude has appeared in ethnic studies where findings in primitive peoples are no longer equated with those of childhood or psychopathology in our culture. The need for truly comparative studies has become recognized and has led to fruitful investigations. With this has come about a changing attitude to the use of the concept of race in psychopathology.

In the historical growth of the science of psychopathology, dualism and psychophysical parallelism have been replaced by psychobiology, which now has given way to the biosocial concept. More recently, existentialism has in some countries modified the biosocial concept. All these concepts have contributed to growth, exerted stimulation, and enlarged vision for research and clinical application.

Experiments of increasing importance in recent years have been modified or altered according to a change in theories but have become steadily more refined and valuable. Difficulties peculiar to psychopathologic experimentation have been singled out and methods changed to overcome these obstacles. These problems have not all been solved but progress along this line is considerable. One is aware of the need to plan experiments of short duration to avoid the emergence of new and complicating emotions during the controlled situation. It is important to find situations which can be repeated to establish individual physiologic and psychologic responsiveness and in which relearning will not nullify the results. Students of psychopathology have stressed that in animal experimentation one must know a great deal of the biologic, psychologic and social characteristics of different strains of animals to evaluate the results of experimentation. The role of placeboes in the evaluation of pharmacologic studies, in psychopathologic and in control cases is beginning to be studied by means of psychopathologic methods and considerations. Through psychopathology a constant need for critical reevaluation of the results of modern drugs in clinical psychiatry has been accepted and has advanced the progress of drug therapy. It therefore became easy to confute the claims of having induced an "experimental schizophrenia" through administration of drugs and to point out more valid but thought-provoking explanations.

The meaning of a psychopathologic reaction according to the age period in which it occurs received first support from clinical observations and has not been included sufficiently as yet in experimental work. The concepts of disorganization versus nonorganization of a personality must obtain experimental validation, as must the older concepts of psychopathologic habit formation and regression. Clinically it has become obvious that the concept of schizophrenia as a regressive disease can hardly be maintained in its original form.

Many symptoms which were used in support of regression can now be recognized as the results of environmental influences, including hospital setting and the psychopathologic behavior of the patients around reactions of people in the patient's home. Schizophrenic and other types of deterioration observed in hospitals are now investigated by psychologic, sociologic, and biologic means, which help the clinician to recognize differentiations in apparently uniform states of apathy and thinking disorders. Scientific, as against purely empirical, therapy must be based on psychopathologic knowledge.

Further progress can be made by the study of the natural course of a psychopathologic disorder during a patient's lifetime. The final outcome must not become the decisive factor in the recognition of a disease entity, as Kraepelin postulated. On the other hand, the tendency of modern psychiatrists to neglect to consider the whole course of the illness has been shortsighted and has impeded progress. It has also permitted therapeutic claims which a long-term view of the disorder would have contradicted.

The value of a historical attitude in psychopathology cannot be emphasized too much. When observations have been made carefully and described in detail, when procedures of study and descriptions of life situations are given which permit the recognition of claimed dynamic factors, then adequate studies can be repeated in different historical or cultural phases. Thus it becomes clear which factors influenced the psychopathologic disorder and which symptoms have not been altered in changing conditions. Such studies have been made and have permitted us to see the disappearance of such well recognized patterns as hysterical attacks of various kinds and the emergence of different expressions of the same or similar dynamic factors. The change in symptoms of agitated depressions of the involutional age which thirty years ago were connected closely to endocrinologic functions illustrates the effect of changing psychologic and cultural attitudes. The occurrence of neologisms, frequently in German-speaking and occasionally in English-speaking schizophrenic patients, points to the need of language study as well as the study of psychodynamic factors.

Pathologists have recognized the role of social factors in the changing pictures of the epidemics of the middle ages and of modern times. The psychopathologist can contribute valuable knowledge in this field by adding investigations of the psychologic-cultural social conditions to those of the pathologist's physical-social conditions. The results would be a great gain for clinical psychiatry in the understanding of hysterical and other psychopathologic reactions.

Historical studies would also give the psychiatrist an understanding of the influence of current philosophies on the clinician's thinking and theories. It would oblige him to keep in mind that psychiatric investigative and clinical procedures, theories, and therapies are part of the status of medicine and science at a given period and part of the cultural development.

The outlook for the future of psychiatry is most promising because psychopathology has become the foundation upon which the clinician builds and functions. By following the progress of pathology, psychopathologists have established a sound body of observable facts and of dynamic understanding which compares well to pathologic anatomy and physiology. Broad experimentation in which other sciences are used has been started. The aid of chemistry including the administration of drugs, of individual and social psychology, and of cultural anthropology is now highly valued in all these investigations.

Psychopathology has become the basis for the study and treatment of patients and should be accepted as such. It offers the constant necessary control for treatment and thus compares well to the role which clinical and surgical pathology plays in the practice of medicine. The result of therapy must be judged from an evaluation of the psychopathologic findings and changes and in the progress of the patient in his daily life during a period of many years. It is therefore essential that catamnestic data of cases which previously were presented in detail in the literature be published. These catamnestic publications must, however, include a critical evaluation of the personal as well as critical changes which have occurred.

Psychopathologic investigation and evaluation can play this important role only if psychopathology considers the degree of change in the function of personality as well as the age period. Interest in pathogenesis and in etiology will furnish facts which will replace the many assumptions of present-day psychiatry. It will lay the foundation for the support of current well-conceived theories and suggest possibilities for their modification and replacement with the progress of knowledge. In addition, psychopathology and psychiatry must consider the biosocial functions of the individual in their broadest sense. Separate events must be studied most carefully and described minutely and there should be included investigation of all possible dynamic factors, thus presenting the internal and external life of the patient. Psychopathology includes both the carefully observed and described phenomena and the determination of the dynamic factors. The acceptance of both intrinsically inherent aspects of this science must be recognized by psychiatrists if they want to profit fully from the progress of the science of psychopathology.

11

PROBLEMS IN CONCEPTUALIZATION AND COMMUNICATION IN CHILDREN WITH DEVELOPMENTAL ALEXIA

By LAURETTA BENDER, M.D.*

THERE IS TODAY general recognition of an educational problem in children variously designated as learning disability (including reading, spelling, and writing disability), language retardation, developmental or maturational alexia, dyslexia, dyslalia, or aphasia, word deafness and word-blindness, or cortical deafness and blindness. The practical problem in terms of the number who do not acquire language skills as rapidly as others of comparable ability and schooling is enormous. It is of great importance to the child psychiatrist because of the many ramifications in deviant behavior. The scientific and quasiscientific literature is also enormous. There are many controversies as to whether the basic cause is related to method of teaching, personality problems or ego defects, or to a specific maturational lag—to mention three of the most clearly defined concepts.

These very real and important issues will not be considered here. Neither will the problems of communication arising directly from the difficulties such children have in reading, spelling and writing. Instead, some very basic and far-reaching difficulties in concept formation which appear to be primary to the difficulty in acquiring language skills will be discussed.†

Experiences with the problem children at Bellevue Hospital led to the early recognition that more than 50 per cent of boys with the kinds of problems that sent them there were nonreaders or severely retarded in

* Professor of Clinical Psychiatry, New York University College of Medicine; Principal Research Scientist in Child Psychiatry, New York State Department of Mental Hygiene.

† This author was associated with Dr. Samuel T. Orton in 1926 when he launched the first work in this country on the subject, which described reading, writing and spelling disabilities in relation to cortical dominance, reversals in reading and spelling, and coined the term "strephosymbolia."

reading, whereas such reading retardation in the general school population of this country is variously reported between 5 and 15 per cent. It was also recognized that this is one of the most common causes, and a correctable one within limits, of social or emotional maladjustment, behavior disorders, delinquencies, etc., in our young people.

Thousands of children with this problem in one or another form have been seen, studied, and followed up in the last twenty-five years at Bellevue. The accumulated data have developed into a body of knowledge which has contributed considerably to our concept of disturbed child behavior.

Our insights in child psychiatry have been influenced by (1) studies in gestalt psychology and the knowledge that perceptual motor experiences have a known genesis from motility, action and movement and a maturational pattern determined, for example, by the visual motor gestalt test (Bender); (2) Paul Schilder's teaching concerning the body image, the most specific and complete perceptual motor gestalt, the maturation of which can also be followed by the Goodenough draw-a-man test among other ways; (3) psychoanalytic material and egopsychology, which also give us an understanding of the genesis and maturational patterning through childhood; and finally (4) Paul Schilder's emphasis on the patterned postural reflexes of childhood, which also pass through maturational patterns.

Lags or disturbances in maturation of any of these areas can be readily recognized by the standards indicated. Arnold Gesell, in his *Embryology of Behavior,*[14] has shown the relationship between the tonic neck reflex attitudes of the foetal infant and all subsequent action patterns and suggests the beginnings of cortical dominance. Today, the postural reflex position which will reveal increased tone and therefore a higher position of the dominant hand is the best but still least-known test for dominant handedness.

Our understanding of childhood schizophrenia has been built upon these same maturational concepts. Additional correlates between Gesell's contributions to the embryology of behavior and what can be observed in schizophrenic children have added a great deal to the insight of childhood schizophrenia. Thus, we have arrived at a definition of childhood schizophrenia as a maturational lag at the embryonic level in every area of functioning from which subsequent behavior develops, emphasizing the vaso-visceral, homeostatic, neurological, perceptual-motor, language-ideational, and emotional-social functions and behavior. The embryonic plasticity (to use the term as embryologists do) is the common characteristic of the pathological disturbance and accounts for the specific disorder in patterning in any area of functioning at any time as well as in the longitudinal pattern; and accounts also for the great variety of symptomatology, including opposite trends in different children, in the same child at different times, or at one time in different areas of behavior. There may be regression or precociousness with accelerated development, and any function may be disturbed on the plus or minus side. Thus a child may be withdrawn, mute, pseudodefective, unrelating, extremely gifted in verbal abstractions, physically precocious, or frighteningly incorporating in his capacity to relate. In all of these different patterns of behavior the underlying process—the schizophrenia—is the same. Anxiety is the primary response to this pathology and secondary defenses of every kind occur, thereby increasing the possible number of different patterns of behavior.

Review of this concept of childhood schizophrenia, already somewhat familiar, affords comparison with the disabilities in language skills, which we also see as maturational lags but in a relatively more limited area of cerebral function and behavior. In our studies at Bellevue we recognized the maturation problems in the language lags before those in childhood schizophrenia, and it was therefore possible to arrive at this concept of a developmental lag in the more involved and difficult condition of childhood schizophrenia.

There are a number of similarities between childhood schizophrenia and developmental lags in language like dyslexia, which at times make even the differential diagnosis difficult. Children with severe reading disabilities show lags in neurological patterning or "soft neurological signs" also; they are awkward in their motor control or motility, and retain the immature tonic-neck-reflex attitude responses for a longer time than other children do. Their motor tone is more variable; electroencephalographic patterns are of the dysrhythmic, immature type, as attested to by Kennard, Klingman, Taterka and Hill; general behavior is disorganized and impulsive; motor-perceptual patterns or capacity to develop gestalten remain primitive and full of motion and fluidity; and personalities are immature, impulse-driven, and dependent, so that they are often mistaken for postencephalitic, retarded, or schizophrenic children. They also suffer from anxiety and feelings of inadequacy which lead to various symptom formations.

The basic postulates for the understanding of language lags are that those parts of the neopallium which serve the specifically human functions of unilateral cortical dominance, unilateral handedness for tool or pen and pencil usage, unilateral eyedness for close focus, auditory and visual recognition of signs and symbols, and the learning processes for the spoken and written language, show a wider range of maturation age than do parts associated with other maturation or habit patterns. As a result there are many children, mostly boys, who show a syndrome which will include some or many of the following:

1. A slower maturation of language skills with a wide variety of possible patterning but most often recognizable by difficulties in learning to read by the usual methods at the usual reading readiness age (6 to 7 years for children of average intelligence).

2. A slower maturation in neurological patterning, revealed in the developmental history of motor skills as well as by tests such as the Ossoretsky test and with "soft" neurological signs and motility awkwardness.

3. An uneven pattern of intellectual development with variability in the I.Q. if the child is tested several times and with inter-test variability. Thus, the maturational pattern of intelligence, neurological patterning, and personality is not as smooth as we expect it to be in children. This feature was noted by Gesell[13] in 1939 and by Bender and Yarnell[6] in 1941 while evaluating problems in the preschool nursery at Bellevue and the latter indicated, "Some of our problem preschool children whose hyperkinesis and infantile asocial behavior had no other explanation have since proved to be reading disabilities." They showed slight motor retardation with a motility disorder, almost unclassifiable, often but not always associated with left-handedness. They were hyperkinetic and presented a special behavior disorder with poor social development; they were always inadequately understood by those who cared for them. In the 1920's and 1930's these symptoms were mistaken for postencephalitic conditions.

4. A subsequent reading disability is predictable in the preschool period. Gesell has said, "In preschool years a discerning (nursery or kindergarten) teacher may detect evidences more or less predictive of potential reading disabilities—specific weakness in drawing and in form perception, ill-defined handedness, reduced acuity, atypical directionality in movement patterns, and so on."[17]

Katrina de Hirsch has also stated, "Clinical observation shows that it is possible to predict future dyslexias in a fairly large percentage of three-, four-, and five-year olds who are originally referred on account of motor-speech delay, developmental word-deafness and severe dyslalia." Examination of motor, perceptual and emotional performance has shown "a number of basic and specific dysfunctions which seem to underlie a variety of language disturbances . . . They frequently have difficulty in finer muscular control; some of them show a degree of dyspraxia. Many are late in establishing cerebral dominance and have trouble with right-left progression. Bender Gestalt tests show striking immaturity of visuo-motor functioning. Body image is usually very primitive. These children show disturbances in figure-background relationships, they are often hyperactive and have difficulty with patterning of motor and behavioral responses. They have, in fact, trouble at every level of integration."[21]

5. Poor establishment of cortical dominance occurs in one form or another. Left-handedness occurs often and dominance is often "mixed," i.e., master eye on one side and dominant hand on the other. This was pointed out by Orton and has been frequently confirmed and as frequently denied. Evidently there are difficulties in establishing criteria that are acceptable for all for both the language lag and the cortical dominance. At this point it would seem best to define our interest as focusing on those children who show a lag in learning language skills and have a cortical dominance problem.

Three significant studies have come from England bearing on this problem. One by McFie[27] studied children with reading disabilities which he defined as more than three years of reading retardation, representing 1 per cent of the English school children. He used the Phi phenomenon and related it to the handedness in these children to evaluate the cerebral dominance and concluded that his results suggested that "the neurophysiological organization corresponding to dominance is not normally established in either hemisphere" rather than Orton's concept of a "confusion in cerebral dominance with a failure to elide antitropic records in the minor hemisphere."

Humphrey and Zangwill[22] selected from records of 1150 cases of penetrating brain wounds incurred during World War II, ten individuals who were left-handed, of average or better intelligence, had wounds limited to one side, (five left and five right), in whom the wound was sufficient to cause dysphasia if in the dominant cortex and for whom there were records of adequate testing at varying intervals for dysphasia. In this group they found that the degree of dysphasia was variable and not related to the side of injury, all but one recovered, and handedness could be changed, when this was made necessary by paralysis, without increasing the speech difficulty. They concluded that cerebral dominance does not occur in left-handed persons or tends to be less well developed than in most right-handed persons.

Rife [33] reported that extensive comparison of the finger and palm prints of right-handers with those of left-handers showed highly significant trends toward greater bilateral symmetry among left-handers and concluded that handedness cannot depend solely upon postnatal circumstances and that heredity must be a factor. This also indicates that left-handers tend to be less dominant with the left hand than right-handers are with the right, or that dominance is less well established.

6. Right-left confusion or lack of orientation is usually present and a specific feature. This may refer to the child's own right and left hands and sides of the body or be projected to other people. It may be more evident in memory than on direct observation. It may be projected into space and be associated with extensive difficulties in spatial and directional orientation.

7. Personality development tends to be immature. Other life problems exaggerate the learning difficulties and are exaggerated by them, leading many workers to look upon the life problems as causative of the learning retardation.[7-11]

8. The number of boys affected is several times that of girls, which is true also of preadolescent schizophrenia[4, 23] and of all other disorders of childhood associated with developmental deviation.

9. Familial histories include other individuals with left-handedness, "mixed" or incomplete cerebral dominance, learning disabilities in the language skills, stuttering, left-right disorientation, and other features which we will finally sum up as indicating a lag in maturation of cortical dominance. The familial pattern was emphasized from the beginning by Orton[28] and more recently by Bert Hallgren[19] in an important monograph from Denmark.

The concept of maturational lag is itself one that needs clarifying. It is based on a concept of functional areas of the brain and of personality which maturate according to a recognized pattern longitudinally. A maturational lag signifies a slow differentiation in this pattern. It does not indicate a structural defect, deficiency, or loss. There is not necessarily a limitation in the potentialities and at variable levels maturation may tend to accelerate, but often unevenly. Again one has to use the concept of plasticity in the way the embryologists use the term, being as yet unformed, but capable of being formed, being impressionable and responsive to patterning, and carrying within itself the potentialities of patterns which have not yet become fixed. This is also characteristic of a primitive state. It is this particular characteristic of developmental lags that effects such a variety of symptoms that they defy classification and make it possible for each investigator to emphasize those factors that best fit his experience and theories. However, most significantly it is these qualities in developmental lags in children that offer us the greatest opportunities for understanding of hitherto little-understood conditions and also afford methods of training and therapy and opportunities for adaptive development.

This concept of developmental lag in relation to congenital aphasia and alexia has been suggested by a number of investigators including Gesell, Schilder, and Bender and Yarnell. Interestingly enough, something akin to it was suggested by Freud in his 1891 monograph on aphasia. He says, "There were cases of aphasia in which no localized lesion needed to be assumed and the symptoms of which could be attributed to an alteration of a physiological constant in the speech apparatus. Aphasia simply reproduces a state which existed in the course of the normal process of learning to speak and read." And again, "In assessing the function of the speech apparatus under pathological conditions we adopt Hughling Jackson's doctrine that all these modes of reaction represent functional retrogression of a highly organized apparatus and correspond to earlier states of its development."[12]

The following case is illustrative, typical, and relatively uncomplicated and brings out some individually interesting features.

Gary, a Negro boy born in New York City in 1946 to an unmarried 15-year-old high school girl, was on the children's service for the second time in the spring of 1956 when he was ten years old. After his birth he was accepted in the home of his maternal grandmother, where his mother also lived and his father visited occasionally. However, his father died when he was two years old, his mother when he was five, and his grandmother when he was seven. He attended each funeral. Of course these experiences were traumatic and contributed a great deal to his bewilderment.

His physical and motor development were said to be normal. Speech development was slightly retarded; he started to use single words at 18 months and combined them into sentences at two and a half years. He was reported to be a lovable, clinging, affectionate child. He received a lot of attention in his first years. From three years of age he wandered away from home and got lost. When he was four, his grandmother took him to a Child Guidance Clinic on account of his wandering away, over-activity, restlessness, and babyishness. She was told that he was merely slow in development and to "give him time."

After his grandmother's death, and before he was eight years old, he was again taken to a Child Guidance Clinic to help in the decision as to where he should live. Meanwhile he was in his second year of schooling and was adjusting poorly. He was not learning to read and he seemed overwhelmed by the other children, in comparison to whom he seemed to be babyish.

Testing showed he had an I.Q. of 95 on the Stanford-Binet and that aside from his immaturity in behavior no pathology was noted. Arrangements were made for him to live with an aunt.

In 1955, at the age of nine, he was referred for his first observation period on the Bellevue children's service because he had accomplished nothing in school and he wandered away so much that his whereabouts was rarely known.

At Bellevue it was found that he did not know how to get along with other children; he was afraid of fighting with boys and felt that all girls were smarter than he was. He clung to adults or escaped into corners. He appeared immature though healthy. He was right-handed but left-eyed, and these findings varied from time to time. He showed right-left confusion on both his own body and the bodies of others. He whirled clumsily in response to the postural tests, showing an excessive persistence of tonic-neck-reflex dominance, which should disappear at 6½ to 7½ years, although it persists a little longer in Negro children.[42]

At this time his I.Q. was 85 on the WISC with equal verbal and performance scores but a good deal of inter-test variability. The Goodenough drawing of a man (a projection of body image concepts) scored at 10 years, a year in advance of his age. His reading level was at a low first grade, arithmetic at grade 2.7. He was in fourth grade.

He had many primitive or inadequate concepts about time. He said there were five days in the week and three months in the year and he could not name either in sequence but knew the season and was otherwise adequately oriented for immediate time. He could not tell whether his dreams came at night or in the daytime. He was easily confused as to his own identity in the new environment. Once he said he was not sure who Gary was, himself or the boy that happened to come onto the ward at the same time, since on several occasions other people said, "Which one is Gary and which one Tom?"

His fantasy life seemed largely to be dealing with his preoccupations concerning the exploration and organization of space, with rockets shooting through the sky and submarines through the sea.

His was considered to be a typical case of maturation lag with a reading and learning disability, inadequate personal identification, and immature organization, but with an average intellectual potentiality.

We recommended a well-structured program in a good foster home and school with intensive remedial reading tutoring, and supervised recreation.

He was returned to Bellevue within a year on a children's court order as a truant from school. He had run away from the foster home to the home of his aunt where an uncle, grandfather, and two cousins lived. We should have expected this. In many ways the picture had not changed except that his truancy and running away seemed more impulsive and would occur after he had failed in some task or otherwise was frustrated, when he would turn around and leave the schoolroom or his home and walk away into limbo. It was reported, however, that he could hold his own with other children and was a little more aggressive in defending himself.

On this occasion, his global I.Q. on the WISC was 84 with a performance score of 97 and a verbal score of 76. There was a marked inter-test variability and a scatter from the sixth through the twelfth year. His verbal score was lowered by a poor score in information and social comprehension of everyday situations, both of which are concrete functions. His high performance score was in block design (very superior) and object assembly, both of which are abstract functions; the block design deals with abstract spatial relations. His fantasy material and projective tests (Rorschach) revealed an exaggeration of his previous interest in rocket ships and submarines exploring the space in the air and under the water. There was expressed a great deal of cosmic movement, especially in color, such as shooting rockets, and also a great deal of human movement.

He also said that there must be machines that made his brains work and body function. However, he related that he had seen this in an educational television show which explained physiological function with mechanical illustration. When asked if he heard things in his head, he said that there ought to be noises there since he had also learned that he had eardrums in his ears and he wanted to know if there were "eyedrums" as well.

The psychiatric and neurological examination on this occasion revealed a tall, well-developed, ten-year-old Negro boy, genteel in manner, easily submitting to physical dependence upon the examiner. Ocular convergence always resulted in left divergence. He claimed he was right-handed while his two cousins were left-handed. He wrote with his right hand. However, no form of testing could confirm a definite right hand dominance. The tonic-neck-reflex and postural tests did not show increased tone in the right arm, nor was it ever held higher than the left—on occasions it drifted down. One could not find that either his right or left grip or alternate motion rate was better than the other. Furthermore, during testing his master eye changed from his right to his left and back to his right again within a half-hour.

His handwriting was best with his right hand; however, he drew circles always in counter-clockwise direction with either hand. Dominantly right-handed people do not do this.

The effort of this boy to reduce the confusing primitive, unpatterned perceptual experiences into more concrete patterns was particularly well revealed in his gestalt drawings, which within a year had become stereotyped, rigid. He still had difficulty in producing angles in his gestalten, but a year before these problems had always been solved by primitive arcs and loops which flowed along with each other. Now, however, there were no primitive loop formations but he produced rigid, straight lines which often distorted the configuration. He verticalized all oblique lines. Thus this boy in his learning and adaptive processes was trying to replace primitive plastic formations with rigid, concrete forms, thereby sacrificing the possibilities for the higher forms of conceptualization and abstraction.

In discussing his problems he admitted truancy and "running away from home," but he said he did not intend either; he just got lost. He said at school he couldn't read, write, or spell and got into trouble with the teachers and other children; then he just walked out and wandered around and didn't know where he was or what time it was. He complained of a park in his neighborhood (a small one in downtown New York) in which he couldn't tell the direction and always got lost.

His fantasy life was rich in three elements; death (with which he had had considerable experience); his own body image, structure, and function; and the exploration of space, on and over the earth, in and under the sea, and outer space with explosive, cosmic movement. He has tried to come to some understanding of the world in which he lives by attempting to fit what he hears or sees (for example on television) about it with his own extremely diffuse and unorganized perceptual experiences.

Schilder points out that "perception means that something is going on in space. Every sense has its part in space perception. Effort and experimentation lead to more unified space experience." "The development of space parallels the development of action . . . a development towards unification of experience, since unified actions in the social world are necessary. Space and the creation of objects, of space, and of one's own body image and the body image of others are all closely related."[37] Thus it is that Gary has so much trouble with his immature, unorganized perceptual experiences, language concepts, and impulses to action, though he really tries very hard.

On this last admission to Bellevue, the staff were inclined to consider Gary schizophrenic because of the immaturity and lack of organization, his tendency to draw away from people and situations, his anxiety and feelings of inadequacy, his immature motility, his facile fantasy life dealing with space and death and body image problems, his aimless running away, and the formation of defenses and compensations in order to reduce the boundaries within which reality appeared too difficult for him to grasp. However, these features all add up to a boy with a reading disability who has not received the help he needed to control the lack of organization and the lag in maturation of specific functional areas. Of course his problems and the clinical picture have no doubt been accentuated by the bewildering and disorganizing traumatic life experiences he has had, as well as by the failure of adequate help to come forward and rescue him.

He was discharged to the home of his relatives with recommendation for intensive remedial reading tutoring and supervised recreation.

Three characteristics of the primitive plasticity of developmental lags as demonstrated in language or learning disabilities in children are of particular interest:

1. The retention of primitive experiences in perceptual motor gestalten, body imagery, and conceptualization (especially in time and space).

2. The tendency to acceleration in maturation or to precocious compensatory mechanisms.

3. Amnestic phenomena for these formative or corrective or compensatory processes and stages, regardless of the age or intellectual level of the individual.

The retention of primitive experiences in perceptual motor gestalten and concept formation, at a time in the child's life when these immature features confuse his language constructs, most specifically bears on the subject of psychopathology in communication.

Paul Schilder says, "Primitive experience is an experience concerning movement which is infinite and fills the whole field of experience. This is particularly clear in the optic field although true of every perception. Primitive perceptions have particularly the character of motion and provoke immediately tonic and motor responses."[2]

We can start with a consideration of the problem of the reversal of letters and parts of words, which is recognized by many workers as a specific feature in many reading disabilities (developmental alexias or word-blindness) and which was particularly emphasized by Orton and led to his theory of right-left confusion of the antitropic anagrams in the nondominant hemisphere. He saw this as the failure of an elision from the focus of attention of the confusing memory images from the nondominant hemisphere, which are mirror-images, or reversed in form and order from those in the dominant hemisphere. It is true that reversals of letters and groups of letters and reversals of directionality in both reading and writing occur in many children with reading disabilities and are of some diagnostic value when they occur. Gesell points to the fact that these features can often be observed in the pre-school child and are thereby predictive of later reading disabilities.

In 1935 Paul Schilder made an important study of the optic perception of children with congenital alexia or reading disabilities,[35] investigating the "nature of congenital word-blindness in relation to the aphasias and agnosias." The children were examined with a good deal of written, printed, or drawn material including letters, words, sentences, numbers, and various pictures in correct and reversed positions. Some material was presented by tachistoscope. They were asked to read, describe, or reproduce the material. They had the usual battery of psychometric tests and reading tests. They were examined for eyedness and handedness and vision was evaluated. He concluded that though left-right disorientation did indeed occur in some of his cases, this was by no means the only kind of perceptual difficulty presented, nor could even extreme difficulties in left-right orientation account for the "enormous difficulty the children have to coordinate in reading the sounds of the letters which as such are well known to the child" and, in addition, "in cases which do not show mirror mistakes, difficulties in reading single letters can only be accounted for by a primary difficulty in the optic perception."

He concluded that there was a primary disturbance concerning the sound structure of the written word. He further concluded that there was a sufficient hint in these so-called optic mistakes, in the inability to coordinate the single sounds with the whole word and to differentiate the whole word into the single sounds, and in their written expression, to indicate that we deal with a primary insufficiency with cerebral centers, which may also release the mirror tendencies which certainly increase the disturbance in learning to read. Thus it is "the insufficient development of those cerebral centers which guarantee the development of the faculty of reading". The difficulty is described as of the agnostic intellectual type concerning the inner structure of the word and its sound. "These variations are probably due to a different development of those parts of the brain which are indispensable for the process of reading . . . a dysfunction of a cortical apparatus . . . [which] expresses itself in the integrating and differentiating difficulty in optic mistakes concerning letters and in increased mirror tendencies, [all of which] increase the primary trouble, which is an isolated trouble of gnostic intellectual function."

It is of interest that Victor Rosen has described the same mechanisms (quoting Schilder) but offers psychoanalytic interpretation, indicating that his patient had identified these two ego-apparatus functions, that is, the visual and auditory percepts, with his two parents, who were in sharp conflict during the child's early developmental period especially in relation to the primal scene; and therefore the synthetic process had failed to take place, thus causing this individual to be strephosymbolic and a reading disability. The analysis did not correct the reading and spelling disability. However the author explains that "the genetic origin of the disability may be due to precocious maturation of certain ego sectors involved in visual and auditory perception so that they become involved in the oedipal conflict at a crucial stage in their development." This individual had developed into a gifted mathematician.

There is considerable other evidence pointing to the immaturity or incomplete differential development or a maturational lag in the brain centers serving language learning.

The visual motor gestalt test,[3] in which line drawings are copied, represents a scale of the maturation of the visual motor gestalt function. Experience with this test in children with reading disabilities has shown that it depicts many disorders in these children. The figures tend to be more primitive, more fluid, and full of movement of the primitive vortical, whirling type. Squared figures become rounded, dots are replaced by loops, diamonds are squared, oblique lines become vertical and sometimes even horizontal. There is disorientation on the background, usually by rotation of mobile figures or verticalization tendencies; there is also a tendency to close open figures. Also there is a tendency to convert figures, especially those that are verticalized and closed, into a "man" (body image projection) by drawing a face in the closed figure.

Many of these features have been reported by other workers. Silver has reported that children with severe reading disabilities in the child psychiatric outpatient clinic of Bellevue produced all types of primitive gestalten, especially in drawing diamond and oblique constructions and in getting around corners or forming angles. Reversals of configurations also occurred. Similar distortions were noted in the marble board test.

Fabian[10] was the first to point to the significance of verticalization as a sign of immaturity in the gestalt figure. He also pointed to it as one of the prevailing signs in reading disability but interpreted it as one of the infantile ego responses to emotional personality problems.

Arnold Gesell[17] has described the preschool child struggling against the tendency to verticalize all constructions, especially the oblique ones, and notes that when this difficulty persists together with a reading disability beyond the sixth year it is of diagnostic significance — of the seriousness of the reading retardation and evident immaturity of the growing action system.

Katrina De Hirsch[21] says that the Bender gestalt test reveals a striking immaturity in gestalt function in dyslexic youngsters and also in dyslalic and speech-delayed children. She speaks of verticalization and difficulties in synthesizing interlocking figures and concludes that the youngsters' ability to experience gestalten in terms of spatial and temporal relationships is undoubtedly below par.

It is of some interest that Taterka and Katz,[41] in their study of the disturbed children from the ward at Bellevue, concluded that the closest correlation between the high percentage (81.6 per cent of the total group according to Kennard and Willner[25]) of EEG abnormalities existed between the visual motor gestalt function as indicated by the Bender gestalt test, the body imagery shown by the drawing of a man, and other perceptual motor patterns, thereby supporting Schilder's thesis that perceptual and motility disturbances arise from cerebral dysfunction which adversely affects the body image. Unfortunately this study made no correlations with reading disabilities in the children studied. However, it was concluded that the studies "suggested the probability of a defect or developmental retardation in the cerebral function." Klingman[26] has described immature electroencephalogram patterns with reading disabilities.

Body image concepts are retarded in the developmental language lags; this has been reported by many workers, including Silver,[40], de Hirsch,[21] Fabian,[11] Schilder,[36] and Bender.[3] It is to be recalled that the body image is the most complete gestalt experience involving the integration of all sensory experiences impinging on the organism; it is genetically determined and passes through maturational stages which in the child can be followed through the human figure drawing.

Motility, too, lags in the maturation of these children, as confirmed daily by the postural reflex or tonic-neck-reflex attitude tests. It is indeed remarkable that at the same age of five, six, or seven years the tonic-neck-reflex dominance of motility should become submerged (Teicher[42]) and the hand dominance and right-left orientation, the oblique and diamond gestalt structures in visual motor performance and reading readiness should all be established. A retardation or lag in one of these is usually associated with some lag in all and is predictive of a lag in learning language skills—reading, written spelling. De Hirsch has particularly well emphasized this constellation of problems and has stated that the dyslexic youngsters have trouble at every level of integration with the structuralization and organization of all gestalten or patterned behavior. Thus maturational delays are the essential problem in language disorders. This had been recognized earlier by Paul Schilder[37] and by Bender and Yarnell.[6]

Now we can go further, however, and indicate that since experiencing gestalten is the fundamental principle of psychophysiological functioning and is the basis for all psychophysiological development as well, such lags have other profound effects upon the developing child which are of special significance in the area of communication.

There have been numerous statements to the effect that children with this problem in the organization of perceptual gestalten and in mentation are specifically defective in abstract concepts, especially in regard to space and time. This has been claimed by de Hirsch and by Rabinovitch. This would appear to be an incorrect conclusion from the data obtained.

An almost uncontrolled abstractiveness appears to be a major problem, which becomes more evident the more we are able to understand the conceptual processes in children with such a developmental lag. Concreteness in standard tests results from the inadequacy of the test situation and from limitations in the examiner's understanding of the child's mode of communication. It may represent in some children the result of over-training or a defense against the confusing and anxiety-producing abstractions. Thus the child may find a solution by compulsiveness, rigidity in patterning of language skills, and concreteness. The highly motivated or over-trained child may thereby sacrifice higher forms of abstract mentation for concreteness. Our educational programs, at least for the more gifted children, should take this problem into consideration.

In our several studies of Gary we observed this type of adaptive process going on. Early psychological testing showed a predominance of abstract functioning and the latest test still indicated that his highest scores were in tests for abstract functions.

Particularly interesting phenomena may be observed in dyslexic children in regard to conceptualization of time. The different types of experience that dyslexic children report in their effort to conform to recognized time concepts defy the imagination. Ilsa Goldberg has called attention to this interesting problem.

Since space is often interlocked with time they may have to be considered together. Time has many different gestalten itself. For one thing the dyslexic child may have difficulty in learning to tell time with a timepiece. Since for the dyslexic child there is a poorly developed unicortical dominance, laterality, or directionality; and since none of the spatial constructs are well established and have a tendency to slip back from the most mature, the oblique, to the medium level of vertical or to the most primitive, the horizontal; it also holds that the dyslexic child does not function dominantly in the clockwise directionality of movement even within the primitive vertical movement basic to all visual perception. Some settle for counter-clockwise direction since they are functionally either left- or right-handed although actually without well-established dominance.

Thus in our case Gary considered himself right-handed in all activities but on testing never showed right-handed dominance at the physiological level; also all circles were drawn with either hand in the counter-clockwise direction. Others settle for clockwise direction, but often without conviction. Still others use clockwise direction with the right hand and counter-clockwise with the left hand. But since not even handedness is well established the degree of lack of organization within the whole perceptual field is hard to imagine for someone who has not experienced the problem.

One 11-year-old boy of average intelligence could not tell time by a clock. When the mechanisms were explained to him he retorted with, "But why do the hands go that way (clockwise) rather than that way (counter-clockwise)" (He used his left hand and formed all circular movement counter-clockwise). It is almost futile to ask such children to remember directions by rote because memory fails owing to the unstable, fluid state of the perceptual background, especially under the pressure of new situations or conditions of stress or fatigue. Concrete data cannot be recalled when they go contrary to organized thought processes. For example, the question was raised by another child, 'Why isn't the long hand of the clock for hours and the short one for minutes, when hours are longer than minutes"? Here we already have three problems in time concepts. One is due to the instability and reversal of the motor impulse directionality opposite to that accepted by custom and built into all time-pieces. The second is the difficulty in accepting the size and space patterns divergent to the verbal usage. The third is the difficulty in holding onto arbitrary concrete gestalten in memory which do not easily coincide with the non-concrete, perceptual motor experience of the alexic child. Another example of the difficulty such children have and of their type of adaptation is the following. An eight-year-old boy in the third grade was observed to spend a good deal of the afternoon session in school in watching the wall clock. However, he could not tell time from the clock except at exactly 3 o'clock. He knew that was the time school was dismissed and probably learned as an isolated fact that the time was 3 o'clock.

Other examples are given by Dr. Goldberg, from her wide experience in tutoring alexic children (especially those who are also emotionally disturbed or organically impaired). Since she became aware very soon of this disabling defect in time concept, she has always started as soon as possible in helping the children with time concepts. She gives them a calendar, marks their birthday and each day of a lesson, etc. Some complain that the calendar is wrong because there are only four weeks in a month and the calendars are made so that each month spreads over five weeks and many even six weeks. Furthermore, with a calendar in front of them and asked to indicate the first day of the week, they can see no more reason for starting on the left side with Sunday than on the right side with Saturday. There are many examples of the difficulty of comprehending the meaning of a calendar or a clock face as a motile gestalt.

There are basic difficulties in understanding past, present, and future time. Memory of past events is less well organized in alexic children. A severely alexic girl of fifteen could not tell outstanding past events of her life in the correct sequence. The same difficulty arose when a story was read to her. She was capable of oral reading, having had a great deal of remedial tutoring, but her reading comprehension was five years below her oral reading score. She could not use any of this read material for her thinking or for action, such as to follow written instructions for a test.

Great difficulty arises with terms such as "now," "then," "tomorrow," and "yesterday" (also spatial concepts of "here" and "there"). These children live more in the immediate present than do non-alexic children. In the same way they cannot understand the past, present, and future tenses of verbs. They are lacking in concepts of either the immediate time about them or the immediate space about them. Gary was always just wandering off and getting lost and not knowing whether it was "too late" or not. Even so, they are often oriented in the immediate present. Thus Gary always knew the day, the season, even the month, but could not tell the days of the week, the seasons, or the months of the year. One boy, when asked, "What day is today?" would start reciting the days of the week and stop on the correct one.

Many very interesting problems have not been adequately discussed. Among these are the problems in auditory perception. The element of time is more obviously important here. This is a much more difficult field to explore than visual perception. Paul Schilder has indicated the importance in developmental alexias of forming gestalten between the auditory function in language and the visual. Paul Schilder believed that the basic problem in alexia was a gnostic intellectual disorder in integration and differentiation of the sounds of the spoken word and its parts in connection with the formation of the written word and its parts. There are many other auditory problems, also of great interest, which need exploring. Small children, learning to speak long before they are exposed to the written word or can recognize it, are known to remember and reproduce words in reverse, an occurrence which in the cases I have known has been predictive of reading disabilities. Thus an eighteen-month-old boy used the word "dog" both for furry toy animals and for live dogs, but before he was two years old, he used only "gog" and a little later "go--", and then was hesitant and confused as to the object of reference. Later he proved to be of superior intelligence but had severe problems at first in reading and later in written spelling. The words "dog" and "God" are remarkable in testing children who are potential reading disabilities. They spell "cat" correctly without hesitation and often as quickly spell "dog" as "G-O-D." The gestalt formed by this word seems to be such as to force movement into reversal upon the child who by virtue of maturational lags does not find fixed patterns easy to come by.

Connected with the problem of organization of memories of past events is the phenomenon of amnesia that engulfs the disability itself and the learning processes that attempt to correct it. The fluidity of all gestalten and experiences, their lack of concreteness and the difficulty in forming associations between concepts have been shown to be associated with an inability to recall these experiences or with difficulty in recalling them in the ordered sequence in which they occurred. There is in addition the interesting fact that children forget that they ever had any difficulties of this type and forget the often elaborate process of tutoring. One child within months after terminating a two-year period of daily tutoring commented with some heat, "I was always a good reader; I never understood what you had that guy hanging around here for." I have asked many audiences of adults and rarely find anyone who can recall the process of learning to read, whether it occurred precociously, at the usual time in the first three years of school by the sight method, or late and with special tutoring. This is an interesting phenomenon comparable to the early infantile amnesia which coincides with the period of learning to talk.

Another point of interest is that children with language lags are quite different from children with a general mental retardation or with organic defects to the extent that they have capacities for accelerated development or learning, sometimes not until a delayed stage in maturation has been reached, but always while the principle features of the disability are retained. They also have capacities for vivid compensations in related areas of cerebral function. These phenomena are further evidence that the alexic child is basically abstract and not concrete in his mentation. Rosen's patient who remained severely alexic until adulthood became a gifted mathematician. Even our ten-year-old Gary tested "very superior" in block designs. Schilder and Bender have reported the compensatory art work of children with reading disabilities, in which they show precocious capacities to explore and communicate well-organized concepts about space, perspective, time, body image problems, interpersonal relationships, social concepts, and aesthetic values.

Everyone working with these children knows how rewarding they can be and how rapidly they can overcome their disabilities if the relationship to the tutor, the motivation, and the remedial techniques at all coincide with the children's needs. On the other hand anxiety, feelings of inadequacy, inability to identify with age-level children or with authoritative teaching adults, withdrawal even with regression, antagonism, paranoid attitudes, antisocial behavior, all may be the result of failure to overcome the handicap or to find compensatory activities. Defenses against these attitudes may fall into any category of neurotic symptom formation or personality deformations. Over-rigid training, severe discipline, and excessive motivation for success lead also to compulsive, rigid, perfectionistic personality responses. It is a characteristic of the maturational lags that the slowly maturing personality, with its long retention of primitive plastic characteristics, is capable of the greatest variety of clinical responses and patterns of behavior, even to opposite extremes.

By way of conclusion, we can again compare the developmental language lags and childhood schizophrenia, since they are both maturational lags. The language lags are more strongly localized in the areas of language, dominant cerebral control, and mentation, and are therefore not as all-embracing or as severe as childhood schizophrenia. Furthermore, the language lags tend to be self-correcting and are never as malignant as childhood schizophrenia may be. However, the mechanisms are similar, the childhood reactions are similar, and the compensations and defenses are similar. It may be difficult to differentiate between a severe, uncorrected language lag and a mild schizophrenia, as in the case of Gary. An interesting and important observation that we have made is that the presence of both conditions in the same child makes the prognosis for both conditions better. Such children seem to respond to suitable remedial reading tutoring with greater rapidity and are better able to tolerate their schizophrenic symptomatology also. However, the combination of both conditions in the same child tends to exaggerate the symptoms of each condition.

They are also comparable because in both there is evidence for genetic or familial etiological factors; both show lags in maturation with primitive features in organization of this behavior; both show evidence for a basic abstractiveness in function and secondary or reactive concreteness. Significantly, the immature patterns of behavior seen in both conditions are similar in appearance, in origin, and in their capacity to respond to treatment, therapy, tutoring. The communication problems in both conditions have similar mechanisms, especially in regard to spatial, temporal, social, and personal orientation, and lead to similar forms of compensatory or defensive mechanisms.

REFERENCES

1. Bender, Lauretta: Childhood schizophrenia. Psychiat. quart. *27*: 1-19, 1953.
2. ——: A Dynamic Psychopathology of Childhood. Springfield, Ill. Charles C. Thomas, 1954.
3. ——: A Visual Motor Gestalt Test and Its Clinical Use. Res. Monog. 3, Am. Orthopsychiat. Assoc. New York, 1938.
4. —— and Grugett, A. E., Jr.: Some epidemiological factors in childhood schizophrenia. Am. J. Orthopsychiat. *26*: 131-145, 1956.
5. —— and Schilder, Paul: Graphic art as a special ability in children with a reading disability. J. Clin. & Exper. Psychopath. *12*: 147-156, 1951.
6. —— and Yarnell, Helen: An observation nursery. Am. J. Psychiat. *97*: 1158-1172, 1941.
7. Blanchard, Phyllis: Psychoanalytic contributions to the problem of reading disabilities. Psychoanal. Stud. Child. *2*: 163-188, 1947.
8. Blau, A.: The Master Hand. Res. Monog. 5, American Orthopsychiatric Association. New York, 1949.
9. Fabian, A.A.: Clinical and experimental studies of school children who are retarded in reading. Quart. J. Child Behav. *3*: 15-37, 1951.
10. ——: Vertical rotation in visual motor performance—Its relationship to reading reversals. J. Educ. Psychol. *36* 129, 1945.
11. ——: Clinical and experimental studies in school children who are retarded in reading. Quart. J. Child Behav. *3*: 15-37, 1951.

12. FREUD, SIGMUND: On Aphasia. A Critical Study, *tr. by* E. Stengel. New York, International University Press, 1953. pp. 38, 42, and 87.
13. GESELL, ARNOLD: Biographies of Child Development. New York, Harper, 1939.
14. ——: Embryology of Behavior. New York, Harper, 1945.
15. —— AND AMATRUDA, C. S.: Developmental Diagnosis, ed. 2. New York, Hoeber, 1947.
16. —— AND ILG, FRANCES L.: The Child from Five to Ten. New York, Harper, 1946.
17. ——, —— AND BULLIS, G. E.: Vision, Its Development in Infant and Child. New York, Hoeber, 1949.
18. GOLDBERG, ILSA: Use of remedial reading tutoring as a method of psychotherapy for schizophrenic children with reading disabilities. Quart. J. Child Behav. *4*: 273-280, 1952.
19. HALLGREN, B.: Specific Dyslexia. A Clinical and Genetic Study. Acta Psychiat. et. Neurol. Suppl. 65. Copenhagen, 1950.
20. HILL, D.: Electroencephalography in Psychiatry. London, Macdonald, 1950.
21. DE HIRSCH, KATRINA: Gestalt psychology as applied to language disturbances. J. Nerv. & Ment. Dis. *120*: 257-261, 1954.
22. HUMPHREY, M. E., AND ZANGWILL, O. L.: Dysphasia in left-handed patients with unilateral brain lesions. J. Neurol., Neurosurg. & Psychiat. *15*: 184-193, 1952.
23. KALLMANN, FRANZ J., AND ROTH, BERNARD: Genetic aspects of preadolescent schizophrenia. Am. J. Psychiat. 112: 599-606, 1956.
24. KENNARD, M. A., RABINOVITCH, R. D., AND WEXLER, D.: The abnormal electroencephalogram as related to reading disability in children. Canad. M. A. J. *67*: 330, 1952.
25. —— AND WILLNER, M. D.: Significance of paroxysmal patterns in electroencephalograms of children without clinical epilepsy. Res. Nerv. & Men. Disease. Proc. *26*: 308, 1947.
26. KLINGMAN, O.: Discussion. In Neurology and Psychiatry in Childhood. Res. Nerv. & Men. Dis. *34*: 390, 1956.
27. MCFIE, J.: Cerebral dominance in cases of reading disability. J. Neurol., Neurosug. & Psychiat. Brit. Med. Assoc. *15*: 1852.
28. ORTON, SAMUEL T.: Reading, Writing and Speech Problems in Children. New York, Norton, 1937.
29. ——: Specific reading disability—Strephosymbolia. J.A.M.A. *90*: 1095, 1928.
30. ——: Word blindness in school children. Arch. Neurol. & Psychiat. *14*: 581-615, 1925.
31. OSERETSKY, N.: Oseretsky Test of Motor Proficiency, *ed. by* E. A. Doll. Minneapolis, Educational Test Bureau, 1946.
32. RABINOVITCH, R. D., et al: A research approach to reading retardation. In Neurology and Psychiatry of Childhood. Res. Neurol. & Mental Dis. *34*: 363-399, 1956.
33. RIFE, D. C.: Hand prints and handedness. Am. J. Hum. Genet. 7: 170-179, 1955.
34. ROSEN, VICTOR H.: Stephosymbolia. An introsystemic disturbance of the synthetic function of the ego. Psychoanal. Stud. Child *10*: 83-99, 1955.

35. Schilder, Paul: Congenital alexia and its relation to optic perception. J. Genet. Psychol. *65*: 67-88, 1944.

36. ——: Image and Appearance of the Human Body. New York, International Universities Press, 1950.

37. ——: Mind. Perception and Thought in Their Constructive Aspects. Columbia Universities Press, 1942, pp. 54 and 376.

38. ——: The psychology of the development of language and the symbol. In Lauretta Bender, Ed., A Dynamic Psychopathology of Childhood. Springfield, Ill., Charles C. Thomas, 1954, pp. 3-15.

39. Seldowitz, Morton, and Berman, Abraham B.: Crossed laterality in children. Am. J. Dis. Child. *85*: 20-33, 1953.

40. Silver, A.: Report. Orton Bull. *1*: 3, 1951.

41. Taterka, J. H., and Katz, Joseph: Study of correlation between electroencephalogram in emotionally disturbed children. Psychosom. Med. *17*: 62-72, 1955.

42. Teicher, Joseph D.: Preliminary survey of motility in children. J. Nerv. & Ment. Dis. *94*: 277-304, 1941.

12

PHARMACOLOGIC PSYCHOTHERAPY—VERBAL COMMUNICATION IN PSYCHOANALYSIS AND PSYCHOTHERAPY

By THEODORE ROTHMAN, M.D.*
AND KEITH SWARD, PH.D.

FOR SEVEN YEARS we have been trying to investigate why it is that certain types of patients fail to benefit to any detectable degree from either psychoanalysis or psychotherapy.[34] In the present instance we are reporting a study of 31 such failures. Nineteen of the patients in question came to us after undergoing, without appreciable gain, more or less prolonged psychoanalyses. Twelve other patients came at the close of an equally unrewarding exposure to fairly long-term psychotherapy.

In our own efforts to isolate some of the conditions that either facilitate or block constructive growth in a psychotherapeutic situation, we like to think of optimal psychotherapy as a special sort of two-person relationship in which patient and therapist succeed in communicating with the least possible distortion and with a maximal degree of mutual understanding and responsiveness. All psychopathology involves disturbances of communication.[35] Since we are going to describe the trials and tribulations of verbal communication in 31 refractory patients and their therapists, perhaps we should define what we mean by "communication."

To us, communication in man is the transmission of meanings through the use of symbols.[26] It also is the medium through which social interaction always occurs.[36,37] Moreover, communication seems to involve three clearly defined systems.[40] The first and most important is language. Second is vocalization, that is, the making of various kinds of noises that lie outside of language proper. These involve the quality of the voice and are the basis of various emotionally determined com-

* Associate Professor of Clinical Psychiatry, School of Medicine, University of Southern California, Los Angeles.

municative processes such as laughing, crying, moaning, groaning, whispering, yelling, or nasalization. The third communicative system has to do with gestures and large units of body motion, such as nodding of the head or winking of an eye. In this study we propose to focus on the difficulties of verbal communication that our 31 intractable cases experienced in three separate psychotherapeutic settings:

1. During previous psychoanalysis or psychotherapy which involved therapists other than ourselves.
2. During a trial period of psychotherapy in which one or the other of ourselves functioned as the therapist.
3. During a subsequent period of interaction which involved the use of pharmacologic psychotherapy.

First, however, a word about the psychopathology and the degree of incapacitation of the 19 patients who had an earlier association with psychoanalysis. As an index of the degree of impairment at the point of original consultation with us, we followed the schema prepared by the Committee on Nomenclature and Statistics of the American Psychiatric Association.[8] We used the patient's occupational and social adaptation as a baseline for our admittedly subjective estimates of disability—the degrees of difference being "no impairment"; "minimal impairment," not to exceed 10 per cent disability; "mild impairment," 20 to 30 per cent disability; "moderate impairment," 30 to 50 per cent disability; and "severe impairment," over 50 per cent disability.

From an examination of table 1, it will be seen that all 19 of our previously psychoanalyzed patients had either moderate or severe impairment at the time we first saw them.

Of these same 19 cases, the psychiatric diagnoses revealed 12 personality trait disorders of the passive-aggressive type, one personality

---

* For nomenclature see *Diagnostic and Statistical Manual: Mental Disorders*, American Psychiatric Association, 1952.

† Degree of impairment based on estimate of patients' occupational and social adjustment. Key: X, minimal, 10 per cent; X X, mild, 20-30 per cent; X X X, moderate, 30-50 per cent; X X X X, severe, 50 per cent or more.

‡Estimates of patients' verbal communication. Degree of under-verbalization: —, slight; — —, moderate; — — —, marked. Degree of over-verbalization: +, slight; + +, moderate; + + +, marked.

§ Psychoanalysts qualified by respective professional societies, i.e., American Psychoanalytic Association, American Society of Adlerian Psychology, Society of Analytical Psychology.

Table 1.—*Status of Nineteen Refractory Patients after Termination of Psychoanalysis*

CASES	DISORDERS*	DEGREE OF IMPAIRMENT†	VERBAL COMMUNICATION‡	LENGTH OF PSYCHOANALYSIS	SCHOOL OF PSYCHOANALYSIS
1	PASSIVE-AGGRESSIVE PERSONALITY	× × × ×	+ +	7 MOS.	FREUDIAN, M.D.§
2	”	× × × ×	— — —	3 YRS.	” ” §
3	”	× × ×	+ +	2 YRS.	” PH.D.
4	”	× × ×	— — —	6 MOS.	” M.D.§
5	”	× × ×	+ + +	1½ YRS.	” ” §
6	”	× × × ×	+ + +	6 MOS.	” M.D.'S (2) PSYCHIATRISTS (3)§
7	”	× × × ×	+ + +	2 YRS.	ADLERIAN, M.D.§
8	”	× × × ×	— —	2 YRS.	” ” §
9	”	× × ×	— —	1 YR.	” ” §
10	”	× × ×	— —	1 YR.	” ” §
11	”	× × ×	—	7 MOS.	FREUDIAN, M.D.§
12	”	× × × ×	— — —	2½ YRS.	” ” §
13	OBSESSIVE-COMPULSIVE REACTION	× × ×	+ + +	2½ YRS.	” ” 2 YRS.§ JUNGIAN, M.D., 6 MOS.§
14	”	× × × ×	— — —	2 YRS.	FREUDIAN, M.D.§
15	”	× × × ×	+ + +	4 YRS.	” ” 1 YR.§ ADLERIAN, ” 3 YRS.§
16	”	× × ×	— —	1 YR.	FREUDIAN, M.D., 6 MOS.§ ADLERIAN, ” 6 MOS.§
17	ANXIETY REACTION	× × ×	+ + +	3 YRS.	” ” §
18	” ”	× × ×	— —	2 YRS.	FREURIAN, ” §
19	SCHIZOID PERSONALITY	× × × ×	+ + +	3 YRS.	” PH.D

pattern disorder of a schizoid character, and six psychoneuroses, four of which were obsessive-compulsive reactions and two, anxiety states.

It will be noted further that these 19 subjects had been psychoanalyzed over intervals ranging from six months to four years. Their therapists had been for the most part qualified psychoanalysts; that is, members of the American Psychoanalytic Association, the American Society of Adlerian Psychology, or the Society of Analytical Psychology.

For the moment we shall withhold comment on the column of table 1 (as well as on a similar column in table 2) which we labeled "verbal communication."

Now for our second group of cases, composed of 12 additional patients who had previously undergone more or less extended psychotherapy. The status of this group at the time of original consultation with us we present in table 2.

In psychopathology and degree of impairment (table 2), it is essentially the story of table 1 all over again. We have another group of patients with highly disabling psychoneuroses and personality disorders of long duration.

The therapists for this group, however, differed. They consisted of psychiatrists and clinical psychologists, all of whom have had long experience in the field of psychotherapy and all of whom, with two exceptions, have been qualified as diplomates by their respective professional societies; that is, either the American Board of Psychiatry and Neurology or the American Board of Examiners in Professional Psychology of the American Psychological Association.

We call attention to the high incidence of obsessive-compulsive traits throughout this combined series of 31 cases (fig. 1). There are,

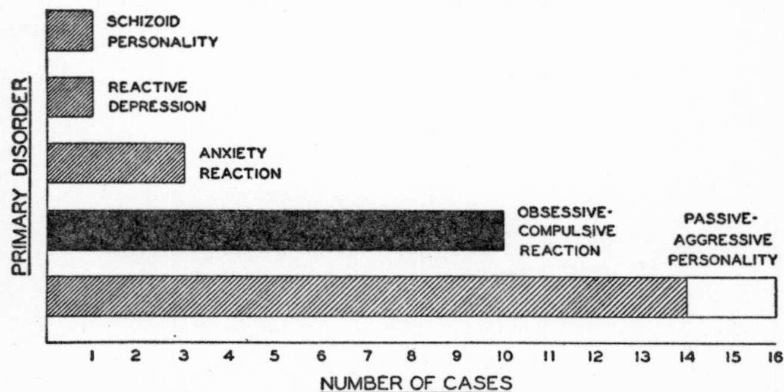

FIG. 1. Incidence of obsessive-compulsive state as the primary or secondary disorder. Shaded blocks represent secondary and black blocks primary disorder.

TABLE 2.—*Status of Twelve Refractory Patients After Termination of Psychotherapy*

CASES	DISORDERS*	DEGREE OF IMPAIRMENT†	VERBAL COMMUNICATION‡	LENGTH OF THERAPY	TYPE OF PSYCHOTHERAPY
20	PASSIVE-AGGRESSIVE PERSONALITY	× × ×	+ +	2 YRS.	PH.D.§
21	" " "	× × ×	— — —	1 YR.	PH.D.‖
22	" " "	× × ×	— —	2 YRS.	PH.D.‖
23	" " "	× × × ×	— —	2 YRS.	PH.D.‖
24	ANXIETY REACTION	× × ×	— —	2 YRS.	PH.D.‖
25	OBSESSIVE-COMPULSIVE REACTION	× × × ×	+ + +	3 YRS.	PH.D., 2 YRS.‖ PSYCHIATRIST, 1 YR.¶
26	" " "	× × × ×	+ + +	2 YRS.	PH.D.
27	" " "	× × × ×	— —	2 YRS.	PH.D.‖
28	" " "	× × × ×	— — —	2 YRS.	PH.D.‖
29	" " "	× × × ×	— —	9 MOS.	PSYCHIATRIST
30	" " "	× × ×	— — —	6 MOS.	PH.D.‖
31	REACTIVE DEPRESSION	× × × ×	+ + +	3 YRS.	PH.D.‖

* For nomenclature see Diagnostic and Statistical Manual: Mental Disorders, American Psychiatric Association, 1952.

† Degree of impairment based on estimate of patients' occupational and social adjustment. Key: ×, minimal, 19 per cent; × ×, mild, 20-30 per cent; × × ×, moderate, 30-50 per cent; × × × ×, severe, 50 per cent or more.

‡ Estimates of patients' verbal communication. Degree of under-verbalization: —, slight; — —; moderate — — —, marked. Degree of over-verbalization: +, slight; + +, moderate; + + +, marked.

§ Fellow, Division of Clinical Psychology, American Psychological Association.

‖ Diplomate in Clinical Psychology, American Board of Examiners in Professional Psychology.

¶ Diplomate in Psychiatry, American Board of Psychiatry and Neurology.

to begin with, 10 cases in which the obsessive-compulsive reaction constituted the primary disorder. In 19 of the remaining 21 cases which fell in different categories, obsessive-compulsive trends were present as related or associated states, as indicated by marked ritualistic behavior, excessive neurotic doubt, over-intellectualization, exaggerated guilt, and the presence of recurrent tormenting thoughts. In fact, obsessive-compulsive components were so conspicuous with these 19 cases that we frequently found it difficult to decide whether the obsessive-compulsive element was primary or secondary in character.

At the outset we labeled these 31 patients en bloc "psychotherapeutic failures." In so doing, we had in mind the following criteria: Nearly every one of these patients, by his own report, had terminated his prior therapeutic effort, often on his own initiative, in a state of intense dissatisfaction and with the feeling that he had "gained nothing" from the therapeutic relationship he was leaving behind. What gains, if any, had taken place during the earlier exposure to psychoanalysis or psychotherapy were not much in evidence when we first encountered this group of 31 patients. All 31 were symptom-ridden and still had rigid personality structures and severe disturbances of adaptation on every level of experience—occupational, social, and intrapsychic. And all seemed to regard their previous abortive effort at therapy as but one more "proof of failure" in a history of lifelong failure. Chief among the reasons they volunteered for "having failed again"—this time in a therapeutic setting—was the feeling, variously expressed, that they had been "unable to communicate." It is this uniformly reported difficulty of verbal communication which we now propose to analyze.

Status of Verbal Communication During Previous Psychoanalysis or Psychotherapy

The data for this study of the psychopathology of verbal communication are again these:

1. The ideas and feelings about their previous therapy which these 31 patients expressed to us during a preliminary trial period of psychotherapy and during their later experience with pharmacologic psychotherapy.

2. Our own direct observation of these same patients as we watched them respond, first to a conventional type of psychotherapy and subse-

quently to intensive psychotherapy conducted with the aid of medication.*

To begin with, it is our impression that all 31 of the patients in question had foundered during previous psychoanalysis or psychotherapy because of moderate or marked difficulties of verbal communication. These difficulties seemed to fall into two recognizable categories:

1. That of the patients whose speech was underproductive and whose total behavior qualified them as the "silent ones." These patients remained relatively blocked and emotionally constricted in the therapeutic situation. Their communications were sparse, obscure, and more or less disorganized; their vocalizations[28] frequently characterized by soft, muffled tones.

2. In what we took to be a second category were the cases whose difficulties of verbal communication lay on the side of overproduction. These patients were the "ready talkers" whose speech was characterized by over-voluble reiteration. They had flooded their previous therapists with voluminous, repetitious, ritualistic speech that seldom left the plane of pseudocommunication or the level of an almost impregnable defense against significant and revealing communication. Their vocalizations were characterized from time to time by shrill, loud, and increasingly rapid speech or even a show of tears.

We do not mean to imply that these two categories of patients—the underproductive and overproductive verbalizers—represent anything like fixed or pure types. There were previous therapeutic sessions, we are sure, when the "silent ones" became—for them—relatively expansive, as well as occasions on which the overproductive verbalizers became—for them—relatively silent. It was our inference, however, that in their earlier prolonged therapeutic operations each of these "types" of patient had run, in the general character of his verbal communications, more or less true to form.

Now a word of comment on the incidence of these designated impairments of verbal communication. The majority, 18 in number, of the cases we are considering (tables 1 and 2) were underproductive

* We are aware of the many hazards of such an undertaking. In the present instance, as in any type of clinical observation, the authors are trying to describe *objectively* a situation in which we were both involved *subjectively* as participant observers.

in their verbal communication, and all but one of these to a moderate or marked degree. The remaining 13 patients were all verbalizers of the moderately or markedly overproductive variety.

We remark in passing that there seemed to be no relationship between the degree and direction of verbal communication on the one hand and the nature of the disorder or the type of personality organization on the other. We make nothing of a further point because of the size of our samples, but by examining tables 1 and 2 in more detail it will be noted that the group that had previous psychoanalysis has a slightly larger proportion of so-called overproductive verbalizers, whereas the reverse holds true for the group of patients who had had previous psychotherapy. Here the numerical advantage lies with the "silent ones."

We shall now try to describe in more detail how these two groups of patients, each with its characteristic problems of communication, actually functioned during the earlier exposures to psychoanalysis or psychotherapy.

Behavior of the Underproductive Verbalizers During Previous Psychoanalyses

Our under-verbalizers who had had previous psychoanalytic treatment became excessively blocked in a conventional psychoanalytic setting. By their own report these inarticulate and locked-in subjects had lapsed into repeated and prolonged silences, were quite unable to put their feelings into words or adequately to recall their dreams or past experiences, and were just as powerless to free-associate when asked to do so. These "silent ones" had spoken to their analysts, as a rule, only when spoken to. When asked questions, they had replied with one- or two-sentence answers and then "run dry." Their laconic replies, we infer, had been obscure, fragmentary, and disorganized in content.

As these patients described their earlier experience with psychoanalysis: "Words wouldn't come," "I couldn't think of anything to say unless my analyst asked me a question," "I kept thinking of things I wanted to say but I just couldn't get them out," or "I often lay there saying to myself, 'My analyst must think I'm a stupid one, not even being able to talk!' " In the course of seven months of psychoanalysis, one of our under-verbalizers became so frustrated over his inability to utter more than a few words during any given analytic session that he had tried to free-associate in the privacy of his own bedroom by talking aloud to himself after turning on a tape-recorder. Even in this private situation of his own making an almost complete verbal blocking persisted.

As is customary in cases of chronic emotional disturbance, our underverbalizers had had a high degree of *psychophysiologic tension* when they first sought psychoanalytic treatment. Hence, in the therapeutic hour, they had experienced, with variations of pattern from person to person, the same alarm reactions that characterized most or all of their past and current efforts of an interpersonal nature. Accordingly, on the analytic couch as elsewhere, they reported having felt such anxiety symptoms as palpitations, dryness of the mouth, thickness of the tongue, inability to enunciate words, "feeling numb all over," sweating, flushing, tension of the facial muscles, tightness around the head, nausea, breathlessness, giddiness, headaches, abdominal cramps, precordial distress, urgency to micturate, "feeling generally sick all over," and so on. Our present concern is this: with most of these patients we gather that the longer psychoanalytic treatment lasted, the more intense these alarm reactions became. The fact that this psychophysiologic tension continued to mount, with no relief in sight, served to make the patient think of psychoanalysis increasingly as a painful if not frightening experience. It also served to make the communication barrier all the more impermeable.

With the type of case we are describing, the very experience of being unable to do what was expected in the psychoanalytic situation had produced complications in the *intrapsychic realm*. These profoundly blocked and more or less inarticulate patients, convinced that they were "not doing what one is supposed to do" in psychoanalysis, had sooner or later developed additional feelings of guilt, failure, humiliation, frustration, and hopelessness. Their ego strength, none too sturdy to begin with, fell still further. Yet for long periods of time these patients had not been able to think of terminating their therapy. Until a certain point was reached, the act of separation would have involved too much shame; it would have entailed what the patient was not ready to face, namely, the disapproval of his psychoanalyst.

Meanwhile, mounting *interpersonal difficulties* were taking their toll in the psychoanalytic framework. The doctor-patient relationship, far from ideal at the outset—like all the rest of the patient's interpersonal relationships—deteriorated at varying rates. Fearing that they could not win the approval of their psychoanalysts, these relatively constricted and uncommunicative patients had felt increasingly guilty, baffled, trapped, and helpless. Then self-doubt had gradually given way to attitudes of resentment directed at the therapist. As the majority of these patients expressed themselves later on, "He let me suffer and didn't do anything to help me," "He was so cold and impersonal," "He seemed disapproving," and "He was quiet and I felt so helpless." The impasse was broken when the patients in this category finally terminated treatment still gripped by a form of verbal paralysis and now conditioned to think of psychoanalysis in terms of punishment and lack of reward.[10]

Behavior of the Overproductive Verbalizers During Previous Psychoanalyses

In a number of particulars our overproductive verbalizers had behaved much like the "silent ones" when reacting to the psychoanalytic situation. By their own account they had experienced the same *psychophysiologic disturbances.* The same symptoms had recurred: the perspiring hand and the pounding heart along with disabling anxiety and chronic or acute mental anguish. The *intrapsychic disturbances* had followed a similar pattern. In his own right the over-verbalizer had had poor communication with the self or with his own feelings. He, too, had been caught in a rut, preoccupied with guilt, humiliation, and frustration over the fact of his inability to communicate. The over-verbalizer resembled his quieter counterpart, finally, in the *interpersonal disturbance* that characterized his earlier psychoanalytic effort. Like the underverbalizer, he ended up feeling rejected and "not understood" by his therapist; resenting his analyst, yet fearing to terminate treatment lest his analyst disapprove of him.

On two other counts, however—one intrapsychic, the other interpersonal—the reiterating over-verbalizers were a class apart from their less articulate confrères. *Intrapsychically* their verbal communications seemed to consist of obsessional, circular thoughts on the order of a positive feedback system. Normal thought processes progress from Point A to Point B to Point C to Point D, and then to goal X, acting like the negative feedback of servo-mechanisms. In these patients thoughts moved instead from Point A to B to C to D, and then back to A again in a never-ending circle. Such patients, we feel, continued to build up tension and they never reached goal X because they were flooding the lines of communication with a multitude of obscure messages in order to avoid risking the danger of self-exposure or facing the threat of any further humiliation or loss of self-esteem.

On an *interpersonal* level, as we understand his defenses in an analytic setting, the more or less garrulous over-verbalizer was engaged in a distancing or covering-up operation. His excessive verbalization was pseudocommunication which followed a repetitive, ritualistic pattern—what David Rioch[31] has neatly termed "communication without content," having the double aim of binding anxiety and of restricting the range of possible communication. This sort of verbalization calls to mind the defense mechanisms of the squid. When under attack, the squid changes from a dark color to a lighter one and moves away from the scene, leaving behind him a murky exudation which the enemy frequently mistakes for the squid himself. The overproductive verbalizer employs a similar type of protective coloration. He defends himself against "attack" by flooding or decoying the "enemy," his psychoanalyst, with a multitude of messages. In the present instance our over-verbalizing patient seems to have told his previous psychoanalyst, as he later told us, in a manner of speaking, "Here are my murky verbalizations. These I leave you. Me, you cannot touch, because I am not here."

The Behavior of the Psychoanalyst (An Interpretation of the Patient's View)

In the feelings of all these patients, the under-verbalizers as well as the over-verbalizers, the "psychoanalyst" was enshrined originally as a highly respected prestige figure and invested with all the aura that surrounds the healer who is capable of relieving mental anguish. Accordingly, when these patients began to sense that no really adequate communication or interaction was emerging from their psychoanalyses, their first inclination was to blame themselves and to exonerate the experts. However, as time wore on and the psychoanalyst failed to live up to expectations—at least in the patient's eyes—this self-punitive attitude shifted to one of growing resentment towards the therapist. The behavior of the psychoanalyst, it would seem, had something to do with the change of feeling on the part of the patient.

As we interpret the situation, this reversal of attitude—from condemnation of the self to mounting hostility toward "the other"—was less likely to occur when the psychoanalyst in any particular case was a warm human being whose techniques were somewhat flexible. Hostility was more likely to occur—and this, we feel, was the more frequent occurrence—when the psychoanalyst who was up against a psychotherapeutic stalemate remained inactive or trapped by his own therapeutic rituals. Thus the therapist who clung to a predominantly impersonal, nondirective, permissive approach came to be perceived by his patient (rightly or wrongly) as a cold, unfeeling, uninterested, or threatening spectator. As one of our more inarticulate patients remarked, retrospectively, "My analyst kept staring out of the window when I could not say a word." Still another patient who could mobilize only a few thoughts and speak only a few words over a period of several months of intensive treatment had this to say, looking backward, "I could hardly get a word out, yet my analyst acted as if he didn't care what happened to me. It was like talking to a wall. He often sat there, just staring at my face or at his empty notebook."

The psychoanalyst who tried to cope with the therapeutic impasse in a more active way usually reiterated the standard analytic instructions. That is, he continued to ask the under-verbalizer to do what he was incapable of doing: to free-associate, to bring in his dreams, to verbalize. As one such patient put it, his psychoanalyst would sometimes break the silence by urging him to "ramble on about anything that comes to mind." At other times this same therapist would hold forth on "what psychoanalysis is all about," discuss "the nature of resistance," or offer brief trial interpretations.

The standard analytic techniques seemed to be just as frustrating and in the end just as humiliating or frightening with our over-verbalizers. In fact, to invite the compulsively voluble patient to free-associate was to give his obsessional, circular, ritualistic thought processes free reign, oftentimes accompanied by mounting fear and rising psychic tension, thus conditioning the patient to associate psychoanalysis with increased anxiety.

In any event these patients met the situation for the duration of their psychoanalyses by intensifying their characteristic defenses against communication. The under-verbalizers grew increasingly miserable and ever more uncommunicative. The overproductive verbalizers increased the tempo of their circular, repetitious and tedious pseudocommunication. In the end both types of patient reacted to the helplessness and rigidity of their psychoanalysts for the most part by suddenly terminating therapy of their own accord. At this point of separation, most of the patients in question reported having felt the first real sense of relief they had experienced for months on end.

Impairment of Verbal Communication During Psychotherapy

We turn now to the prior therapeutic experiences reported by the 12 refractory patients who had failed to benefit from previous psychotherapy. We meet again the overproductive and underproductive verbalizers, each with their more or less distinctive problems of verbal communication. Reviewing their initial exposure to psychotherapy, these 12 patients could report the same unrelieved or mounting symptoms of psychophysiologic tension, as symbolized by the sweating palm, throbbing pulse, and the like. They also reported much the same initial reaction to the experience of therapeutic failure. They, too, had developed marked feelings of frustration, humiliation, guilt, and self-depreciation.

As between this group and the 19 previously psychoanalyzed cases, we feel we detected some differences worthy of comment. These observations concern an interpersonal matter—what happened to the doctor-patient relationship—and the way the average patient eventually explained his therapeutic failure to himself.

In contrast to the previously psychoanalyzed group, the 12 refractory patients who had psychotherapy seemed to retain much friendlier feelings towards the therapists with whom they had worked. Only two of these cases described their former therapists as "cold," "uninterested," "threatening," or "aggressive." The rest still thought of their previous psychotherapists as "warm," "friendly," "earnest," "understanding," and "actively interested in my welfare." Nor did these 12 unsuccessful "graduates" from psychotherapy, with perhaps two exceptions, question the competence of their earlier therapists.

In other words, with much greater frequency than was the case with the previously psychoanalyzed patient, the patient whose earlier psychotherapy had ended unsuccessfully tended to blame himself rather than his therapist for his therapeutic failure. His typical feeling ran, "I think my former therapist understood me," "He did the right thing," or "It was I who failed." In general the patient who had arrived at a dead end in psychotherapy expressed the further feeling that he had "gotten rid of a lot of emotion" and had "understood" or "accepted" many of his therapist's interpretations; yet "nothing changed," the symptoms and difficulties which brought him into therapy in the first place had remained or become even more pronounced. He would add the frequent lament, "Everything happens to me this way. I just felt surrounded by a wall or inside a barrier and that there was nothing anybody could do about it."

On the basis of our patient's report, we would note another apparent difference between unsuccessful psychotherapy and unsuccessful psychoanalysis, at least in the limited number of instances at hand. Confronted with mounting evidence of therapeutic failure, the clinical psychologist had, as a rule, referred his case to an eclectic psychiatrist. The psychoanalysts, on the other hand, perhaps more sensitive to the consideration of their status in our culture, seemed less inclined to acknowledge defeat or to refer their intractable patients elsewhere. As a result, termination of the relationship between patient and psychotherapist had occurred in most cases by mutual consent, whereas in the majority of the analytic situations the patient reported having taken flight from therapy more or less abruptly and on his own initiative.

Outcome of Trial Period of Psychotherapy

When each of the 31 patients whom we are discussing sought further treatment with one or the other of us, we had an opportunity to observe at first hand the psychopathology of communication that had defeated therapy to date. We initiated in each case a program of trial psychotherapy. The same disturbances of verbal communication that we have already described at some length recurred. Once more the patient's rising psychic tension, his disabling anxiety in a two-person relationship, and his pronounced inability to communicate in a meaningful way seemed to augur therapeutic failure. Over a period of from one to three months on the average, we could detect little or no promise of really adequate or therapeutic two-way communication. We then entertained the premise that this group of seriously incapacitated and definitely refractory cases might belong to a category of patients to whom the conventional techniques of psychoanalysis and psychotherapy have little to offer. Therefore, hoping to break through the barriers of communication that had blocked any psychotherapeutic progress up to this point, we instituted a program of pharmacologic psychotherapy.

Technique of Pharmacologic Psychotherapy

We have already described in an earlier publication[34] the technique of pharmacologic psychotherapy which we developed for the treatment of refractory psychoneuroses and personality disorders. We might epitomize the development of this technique on a pharmacologic level as follows: first of all, before treating the patients whose histories now concern us, we began using intravenous injections of sodium pentothal alone, picking up the lead suggested long ago by Bleckwenn,[4] Horsley,[19] Lindemann,[25] and Hoch.[15,17] We concluded, in time, that working with anything but minimal doses of this drug tended to hinder rather than enhance the psychotherapeutic experience. Both the doses and the methods of administration generally reported in the literature left patients in a dazed and narcotized state and produced artifacts of sedation such as excessive abreaction and an amnesia for the interview. However small the dose, it was our experience that all patients on occasion seemed to remain somewhat apathetic or somnolent or were inclined to have a partial amnesia for the therapeutic experience. Our search for the minimum effective dosage of sodium pentothal was aided by an electroencephalographic study of a group of normal subjects. These observations revealed that the doses generally reported in the literature produced high-voltage fast waves interspersed with spindles and high-voltage slow waves, and a corresponding clouding of consciousness. We concluded that the minimum effective doses for the purpose of facilitating psychotherapy ranged from 3 to 7 cc. of 2.5 per cent sodium pentothal administered intravenously at a rapid rate. An intravenous injection of 5 cc. sufficed for most patients.

Meanwhile we had been following with interest the experimental and clinical work on cortical stimulants such as Pervitin[21] and Desoxyn.[23] Our own observations led us to feel that the amphetamine-like drugs, especially when used alone, should be administered with considerable caution.

We finally decided to explore the synergistic effect of combining one of the drugs in the amphetamine series with a suitable antagonist. We seemed to achieve the desired effect by using both sodium pentothal and Desoxyn administered intravenously in the proper sequence,[34] at a rapid rate, and in minimum effective doses.*

* Described in more specific terms, the technique is as follows: First, a freshly prepared 2.5 per cent solution of sodium pentothal was injected intravenously through a 10 cc. syringe. For the great majority of our cases, 3 to 7 cc. of the drug, rapidly injected, produced the desired effect. Such an injection had as its immediate reaction a loss of consciousness or a dazed state lasting from 30 seconds to 2 minutes, as well as an abrupt stoppage of respiration, persisting from 5 to 20 seconds, gradually followed by slow, shallow, and occasionally stertorous respirations. Then, into the same needle, 5 to 10 mg. (or more in rare cases) of Desoxyn were injected rapidly from a 2 cc. syringe.

We note here, in passing, the importance of adequately preparing a patient for any experience with pharmacologic psychotherapy and the necessity of initiating the procedure cautiously and of carefully ascertaining in advance that the use of the technique is not contraindicated on either medical or psychiatric grounds.*

Frequency of treatment. The patients whose behavior we are reporting in this study had 50-minute interviews occurring on the average once or twice weekly. As they showed improvement we moved, not always successfully, toward the goal of using an increasing proportion of drugless interviews, until at the point of termination the pharmacologic agents could be dispensed with entirely.

We shall next attempt to describe what happened to the processes of communication once our 31 refractory patients could resume intensive psychotherapy with the aid of medication.

Status of Communication During Pharmacologic Psychotherapy

Here particularly, we are very much aware of the difficulties of communicating about communication. Before we begin to describe the effects of pharmacologic psychotherapy on the processes of communication and social interaction with our 31 refractory patients, we wish to underscore a number of qualifications:

1. The changes we shall describe are relative changes; they are matters of degree. They were much more apparent with certain patients than with others. They represent changes of degree within any one patient.

2. For reasons that often escaped our understanding, change for the better in a patient's total pattern of living by no means always followed the fact that the nature of his communication and interaction seemed to pick up, even radically, in the therapeutic situation.

3. The observations to follow are again clinical observations. They will deal with what we feel to be the essential behavioral changes that occur during pharmacologic psychotherapy of an intensive character.

* Intravenous injection of the drugs we employed is contraindicated, other things equal, for patients with liver, kidney, or cardiovascular disease, or for patients who are suffering from any physical involvement, such as an upper or lower respiratory disease, that produces anoxia. On psychiatric grounds, these medications should be ruled out with cases showing symptoms of agitated depression or with any gravely disturbed patient who might possibly respond to either drug with excessive abreactions or acting-out of a dangerous antisocial or self-destructive character.

Fortunately, most of these reported changes fall into categories that are highly "researchable." That is, they can be checked by others in a far more controlled manner than is possible or likely within the harried framework of private practice.[22,30,42,43,46]

With these reservations in mind, we would describe the impact of pharmacologic psychotherapy on interaction and communication as follows: A brief period of somnolence, lasting not more than several minutes, follows the administration of the drugs. At this point most patients for whom this is a new and effective experience react immediately by making statements like, "Why didn't we use this from the start?" "Why didn't someone think of this before?" "Why did I have to suffer so long?" or "What a relief!" In some instances the initial response takes the form of brief sobbing or the shedding of a few tears. Thereafter, in succeeding interviews, the majority of patients in our experience show a gradually increasing urgency to bring the self back as an object of communication or a greater readiness to verbalize about some central areas of conflict. With certain patients the resultant free flow of communication suggests flood waters that have burst a dam. With the majority the intensity and flow of communication are much less pronounced. In either case most patients tend to enter into the situation with increased enthusiasm. Without losing sight of the serious business at hand, they act on occasion as though the process of interacting with their therapist had a great deal in common with whatever it is in human nature that goes to make up "play."

Meanwhile, with expected variations, the patient reports that he "feels better" in a psychophysiologic sense. He speaks of a slight to marked falling off of tension in all its sundry forms. He begins to shed in varying degrees the feelings of frustration and hostility that had been part and parcel of his previous therapy. His vocalizations may change. He tends to drop the previously hoarse[28] and dry tone of speech for an unstrained quality of voice that is more or less full and well modulated. The facial expression becomes, as a rule, less frozen. The patient can usually express emotion with greater ease. He can make freer use of gestures and body movements in the course of "letting the therapist in" on his innermost feelings. In the majority of cases, speech that was previously sparse, obscure, or halting now tends to become more meaningful and free-flowing. It would appear that the patient-as-a-whole becomes more alive, spontaneous, and alert. His ambivalence and general psychic paralysis are reduced to the point that he becomes more decisive or better able to say "yes" or "no" to the choices that confront him both inside and outside the therapeutic situation.

With heightened self-esteem, patients undergoing pharmacologic psychotherapy usually become less fearful of self-exposure. As some put the matter in their own words, "I can talk about things without looking the other way," "It's as though the walls of self-consciousness were torn away," "Hiding my innermost thoughts from another person's scrutiny no longer seems important," or "I can let go with whatever I am thinking and feeling, in the presence of another human being." Moreover, these patients demonstrate more frequently their changed attitudes toward self-revelation by pointing the way to the hidden sources of some of their difficulties, or by making apt interpretations of their own with a great deal of delight on their part and with little assistance from their therapists. When the conditions of pharmacologic psychotherapy are suitable, the patient tends to exhibit warmer and friendlier attitudes toward his therapist. As a consequence, feelings of congruence and mutuality are more likely to suffuse the therapeutic relationship.[29] Something more nearly resembling true two-way communication comes into being. Both patient and therapist find it less difficult to exchange mutually understandable information and common frames of reference. This growing reciprocity helps the patient to grasp more readily the private roles and attitudes that have distorted and complicated a good share of his previous interpersonal experience. Social learning is now rewarded or reinforced with self-approval rather than being punished by self-hatred.[10]

What this approach seems to release, in sum, is the joy of communicating meaningfully in a two-person relationship. This, we take it, is what the social psychologist Newcomb[29] is referring to when he speaks of the "strain towards congruence" as a mainspring of the process of socialization. It fits Rioch's explanation of why a disturbed person feels so "tickled"[32] when he discovers that he and his therapist have hit on some common content of communication. *Accordingly, the patient may proceed to grow within limits, not merely because of his release from crippling anxiety, but because he has succeeded in satisfying more than ever before, or perhaps for the first time in his life, one of the most basic of all human needs—the need to communicate harmoniously with himself and with others.*

Having lived repeatedly through such an integrating experience in the two-person relationship of psychotherapy, he is now conditioned with sufficient reward or reinforcement[10] so that he can more readily benefit from extratherapeutic social interaction. With the more or less refractory and insulated patients who are our concern in this study, it is our feeling that no responsive interaction or communication of any sort might have occurred had it not been for the use of an integrated approach involving both chemical therapy and intensive psychotherapy.

In table 3 we attempt to summarize in brief and schematic form the processes of communication that obtained before and after the use of pharmacologic psychotherapy.

TABLE 3

Relative Status of Communication During Previous Psychoanalysis or Psychotherapy	*Relative Status of Communication During Pharmacologic Psychotherapy*
Fear of self-exposure in a two-person relationship	Greater readiness to face the self in the presence of another
Withdrawal of the self as an object of communication	Increased satisfaction in exchanging information
Heightened psychophysiologic tension	Reduced psychophysiologic tension
Increased defensiveness	Decreased defensiveness
Fear of loss of control	Heightened satisfaction over the release of pent-up feelings
Decreasing self-esteem	Heightened self-esteem
Inaccessibility of unrecognized motivations	Expanding awareness of unrecognized motivations
Mounting resentment toward the therapist	Readier acceptance of the therapist in a warm two-person relationship
Unresolved or rising ambivalence	Reduced ambivalence
Undiminished or aggravated distortion of two-way communication	Reduction of distortions of communication
Minimal sharing of a common content of communication	Growing consensus or mutuality of frames of reference
Persistence of private roles and attitudes	Exchanging of private roles and attitudes for those of a more mutual, nondefensive character
Feelings of despair, hopelessness, trappedness	Enhanced drive and feelings of optimism
Persistence or aggravation of inner disorder or chaos	Increased sense of order, meaning, purposiveness
Social conditioning associated with punishment	Social conditioning associated with reward or reinforcement

Results of Treatment

We appreciate the difficulties of trying to validate the effectiveness of different types of psychotherapy and our own inadequacies on this score. These difficulties were recently summarized cogently by Paul Hoch.[18] In our case we can at least define our criteria of improvement. By improvement we mean, insofar as one can judge this matter subjectively, a somewhat better life adaptation: an enhanced capacity for productive work and changes in social interaction which both the patient and those with whom he is in regular contact find more or less satisfying. When betterment of the life adaptation does occur it always involves, we feel, a heightened capacity for effective communication with the self and with others. It will be remembered that the personality difficulties under discussion include a preponderant number of moderate-to-severe obsessive-compulsive states as either the primary or secondary disorder. With such deep-seated disorders, it goes without saying that our therapeutic goal was one of achieving when possible more or less durable states of amelioration. Now for our estimated findings.

As a frame of reference for evaluating our results, we again made use of the "categories of impairment" proposed by the Committee on Nomenclature and Statistics of the American Psychiatric Association.[8] Improvement, as we define it subjectively, consists of a patient's shift from one level of disability to a less serious level of disability. For example, if a patient appeared to move on the four-step scale of incapacitation from a state of "moderate impairment" (30 to 50 per cent disability) to a state of "mild impairment" (20 to 30 per cent disability), we classified this single degree of change as one representing "slight improvement." Two degrees of change in the direction of amelioration we categorized as showing "moderate improvement," and so on.

The majority of our cases showed slight to considerable improvement, i.e., they moved from one category of impairment to categories of less severe impairment. Once more we call attention to the fact that before the initiation of pharmacologic psychotherapy all 31 of our patients had moderate-to-severe disabilities. At the point of intake, 15 of our cases showed "moderate impairment" (30 to 50 per cent disability) and 16 showed "severe impairment" (50 per cent or more disability). Thirty of these 31 cases exhibited at the same time moderate or marked difficulties of verbal communication.

More specifically, 25.8 per cent of our limited sample of 31 cases improved to a slight degree; they moved from one level of incapacitation to the next less serious level of incapacitation (table 4). Forty-five

TABLE 4—*Summary of Estimated Changes Following Pharmacologic Psychotherapy*

Degree of improvement	Cases	
	Number	Per cent
None (0)	7	22.6
Slight (+)	8	25.8
Moderate (++)	14	45.1
Marked (+++)	2	6.5
Total	31	100.0

per cent of the total group showed a moderate degree of amelioration, moving from a given category of impairment to a less serious category of impairment two steps removed. Some 6 per cent (6.5 per cent) of the sample registered considerable improvement. One-quarter (22.6 per cent) of our cases made no progress whatsoever after one to two years of treatment.

Taken at their face value our results are statistically significant. Again, 24 of our 31 cases showed improvement; seven showed no discernible change; none showed change in a "negative" direction. The so-called sign test[9,11] reveals that these changes lie beyond chance.*

In tables 5 and 6, which summarize our results in more detail, it will be seen that our treatment situations were prolonged in character. The length of care extended from six months to five years with a median treatment time of two years. It follows that with disorders of the type we are discussing—with their associated difficulties of communication—pharmacologic psychotherapy is not to be equated with brief psychotherapy.

The lasting quality of these estimated changes is another question.

* If the seven "no change" cases are counted as negative instances, the difference in favor of "improvement" is significant just at the .01 level of confidence. If the seven "no change" cases are classified as ties, the difference in favor of "improvement" lies well beyond the .01 level. These statements of probability rest on the assumption that our underlying clinical observations represent "good" data.

TABLE 5.—*Status of Nineteen Refractory Patients with Previous Psychoanalysis Following Pharmacologic Psychotherapy.*

CASES	DISORDERS	LENGTH OF TREATMENT	EXTENT OF IMPAIRMENT		DEGREES OF CHANGE
			BEFORE TREATMENT	AFTER TREATMENT	
* 1	PASSIVE-AGGRESSIVE PERSONALITY	3 YRS.	× × × ×	× ×	2^+
* 2	” ” ”	1 YR., 4 MOS.	× × × ×	× ×	2^+
3	” ” ”	2 YRS., 6 MOS.	× × ×	× ×	1^+
4	” ” ”	2 YRS.	× × ×	× ×	1^+
* 5	” ” ”	1 YR., 2 MOS.	× × ×	× ×	1^+
6	” ” ”	1 YR., 3 MOS.	× × × ×	× ×	2^+
* 7	” ” ”	2 YRS.	× × × ×	× ×	2^+
* 8	” ” ”	2 YRS.	× × × ×	×	3^+
* 9	” ” ”	1½ YRS.	× × ×	× × ×	0
* 10	” ” ”	1½ YRS.	× × ×	× × ×	0
11	” ” ”	1 YR., 7 MOS.	× × ×	×	2^+
12	” ” ”	6 MOS.	× × × ×	× ×	2^+
* 13	OBSESSIVE-COMPULSIVE REACTION	3½ YRS.	× × ×	×	2^+
14	” ” ”	1½ YRS.	× × × ×	× ×	2^+
* 15	” ” ”	4 YRS.	× × × ×	× × ×	1^+
16	” ” ”	1 YR., 7 MOS.	× × ×	× ×	1^+
* 17	ANXIETY REACTION	4 YRS.	× × ×	× ×	1^+
18	” ”	1½ YRS.	× × ×	×	2^+
* 19	SCHIZOID PERSONALITY	2 YRS.	× × × ×	× × × ×	0

* Discharged.

Table 6.—*Status of Twelve Refractory Patients with Previous Psychotherapy Following Pharmacologic Psychotherapy*

CASES	DISORDERS	LENGTH OF TREATMENT	EXTENT OF IMPAIRMENT		DEGREES OF CHANGE
			BEFORE TREATMENT	AFTER TREATMENT	
20	PASSIVE-AGGRESSIVE PERSONALITY	2 YRS.	× × ×	× ×	1+
* 21	" " "	2 YRS.	× × ×	×	2+
22	" " "	1 YR.	× × ×	×	2+
* 23	" " "	2 YRS.	× × × ×	× ×	2+
24	ANXIETY REACTION	4 YRS.	× × ×	×	2+
25	OBSESSIVE-COMPULSIVE REACTION	4 YRS.	× × × ×	× ×	2+
26	" " "	1 YR.	× × × ×	×	3+
27	" " "	5 YRS.	× × × ×	× × × ×	0
* 28	" " "	2 YRS.	× × × ×	× × × ×	0
* 29	" " "	1 YR.	× × × ×	× × × ×	0
30	" " "	3 YRS.	× × ×	× ×	1+
* 31	REACTIVE DEPRESSION	1 YR.	× × × ×	× × × ×	0

* Discharged.

Here our results are inconclusive. The record of our limited follow-up is this: with seven of the total group of 31 cases therapy failed completely; these patients were referred elsewhere for further psychiatric care. All seven probably qualify as cases of pseudoneurotic schizophrenia or of very severe obsessive-compulsive psychoneurosis.

For the remaining 24 cases, on the other hand, sustained improvement seems to be the rule to date. Of the 24 improved cases, 10 are still receiving intensive treatment; 4 are being seen once a month or at even less frequent intervals; and 10 have terminated treatment. The terminated cases, all of whom we have followed up, have functioned on their own without therapy more or less successfully for periods ranging from 6 to 34 months. Time alone will tell how large a proportion of our discharged cases or of our total group will require some form of continuing or intermittent care in years to come.[12,13]

Over so long a time-span psychotherapy alone is obviously only one of many forces that will influence the lives of these patients. Nor could one claim without being rash that pharmacologic psychotherapy alone produced the degrees of amelioration which we have recorded thus far. What we should prefer to accent at this juncture is neither the magnitude nor the durability of any therapeutic gains we think we have achieved. Our primary object, instead, is to call attention to a technique that makes effective communication and interaction possible for certain types of patients who seem to lie beyond the reach of ordinary psychoanalysis and psychotherapy. We believe that pharmacologic psychotherapy shows promise of becoming a method of choice for the treatment of refractory psychoneuroses and personality disorders that show moderate-to-severe impairment of communication.

Illustrative Cases

1. *Passive-Aggressive Personality Disorder* (*Severe Passive-Dependent Type; Underproductive Verbalization*)

The patient in question is a 30-year-old, unmarried woman whose main complaint and preoccupation centered about intense feelings of inadequacy. She found any interpersonal experience severely upsetting and fresh cause for endlessly turning over in her mind what she regarded as inappropriate or humiliating behavior on her part.

This woman reported that she had been aware of this anxious expectancy of frustration and social failure from her earliest childhood. She could show little spontaneity on any level of behavior, intrapsychic or interpersonal. The process of making decisions was by now an agonizing experience; every word she uttered, grounds for rumination and worry. Much of her discomfort or sense of panic in the presence of people she had met throughout her life by silence or withdrawal. She reported finding it extremely difficult to engage in the lightest forms of conversation with anyone. When she did find it necessary to move toward people, she had learned to do so only in the sense of a desperate striving to please. This protective reaction had had the usual consequences: chronic self-hatred and the experience of being victimized by a series of aggressors. The patient had carried the same pattern of compliance and submission into the sexual sphere. Unable to refuse any half-eligible, truly demanding lover, she had had repeated affairs. But because of the motivation involved, these experiences were relatively unrewarding. They occurred without orgasm. They led to no rounded relationships. Here, too, the patient could never be satisfied that she had performed well enough to please her partner.

The patient's father was an authoritarian character who had ruled over his wife and two daughters in a violent manner, screaming or striking out physically when crossed. He had been over-critical and impossible to please. He had allowed no show of individuality on the part of any other member of the family. For the patient, the younger of his children, he had shown little or no affection.

History of the treatment with psychoanalysis. Shortly before entering psychoanalysis, the patient had had a sexual affair with a married man, as result of which she had become pregnant and had had an illegal abortion. This experience, representing only the last of a long series of self-destructive episodes, convinced this woman that she needed mental treatment. She went to an internationally known private mental hospital where a more or less Freudian type of psychoanalysis is practiced. Since she would have had to wait for one year before being admitted for treatment at this hospital, she accepted a member of the hospital staff as her private psychoanalyst and continued to work with this same therapist when he later entered private practice. The report this patient gives of her treatment is this: At the beginning she felt somewhat over-awed by her psychoanalyst. She regarded him as a more or less omnipotent figure. She felt sure of being helped. Her interviews, conducted vis-a-vis, occurred three times weekly.

However, because of her intrapsychic tension, her excessive need for approval and her exorbitant fear of humiliation, the patient found it next to impossible to interact effectively with her therapist. Severe psychophysiological tension left her powers of verbalization almost completely blocked. For the balance of her sessions her throat became dry, her tongue thick. She reported feeling "giddy" and "sick all over." Try as she might, the words would not come. The psychoanalyst, meanwhile, often stared at his notebook or at his patient's face. Hoping to open up some sort of communication, he finally urged the patient to make "guttural sounds." Still nothing came. For six months the patient appeared to have a partial aphonia during the therapeutic hour. She became only slightly more communicative as time went on. She got to a point at which she could volunteer occasional short phrases or reply to direct questioning with one- or two-sentence answers. These underproductive verbalizations continued for two and one-half years.

When it appeared that neither she nor her psychoanalyst could break through the communication barrier, the patient became increasingly tense and frustrated. She became intensely ambivalent toward the whole situation, with mounting resentment offset against her strong dependent needs. The patient wavered over the question of terminating therapy for over a year but continually postponed such action because of her dependency and her feelings of shame and humiliation. Finally, in a burst of resentment directed at her therapist, she suddenly broke off treatment. This action was followed by intense feelings of guilt.

Status of the patient during trial period of psychotherapy. The patient appeared frozen. She had the greatest difficulty in expressing herself on any level. Her face showed little emotion. When questioned she would answer in short, staccato sentences. She spoke in soft, hoarse or muffled tones. Her palms and forehead were visibly damp. She was pale. Her body trembled. The patient grew more tense with each interview. The usual psychotherapeutic methods seemed doomed to failure. Hence, the resort to pharmacologic psychotherapy.

History of treatment with pharmacologic psychotherapy. From the first interview forward, the patient was able to express herself in an increasingly free-flowing, spontaneous manner. Her mode of vocalization changed markedly. Instead of muttering, she began to speak in more or less clear, emphatic, and audible tones. She could discharge greater emotion during her interviews, especially when touching on the theme of her reaction to aggressors. Little by little she became a warmer sort of person. She looked forward to her interviews. By the thirtieth visit or thereabouts, one could detect various signs of growth. The patient could report a better adaptation in her social life and on the job. Her relationships with people had picked up to a noticeable degree. She could indulge in ordinary chit-chat without mental preoccupation. Her general outlook became more optimistic for the first time in her life. She managed to establish a warmer, two-way relationship with her psychotherapist. Treatment is still in progress with continuing productive results.

2. *Passive-Aggressive Personality Disorder (Passive-Dependent Type; Mixed Verbalization: Underproductive and Overproductive)*

The patient here is a 25-year-old married male of high intellectual capacity whose main complaints had to do with his inability to "finish anything." This young man seemed quite unable to carry any significant life task to a successful conclusion. His entire history—social, sexual, occupational—was a succession of abandoned goals and strivings. The patient's drive had often collapsed just when success was within his grasp. At such moments he would become blocked, incapable of working, and unable to pull himself together. The exhortations of his wife or parents during such crises meant nothing. The pattern of abortive and constantly redirected striving was accompanied by a rich fantasy life in which the patient played the role of a superman with limitless powers.

In addition, this young man was racked by conflict and indecision. The necessity of making any significant life choice touched off intensely ambivalent feelings. The desire to become a mathematician without doing any sustained work in that direction competed with a strong inclination to enter the family business which the patient had long held in contempt. The patient was similarly torn between seeming enjoyment of his role as husband and father and an unwillingness to relinquish the freedom of bachelorhood. There had been a series of sudden, short, extramarital affairs. Yet this patient remained at heart a thoroughly conventional middle-class husband and father. Here as elsewhere, he vacillated back and forth, finding no resting points of satisfaction.

The parents in this case were well-meaning but extremely anxious and overprotective individuals who had tried in every way to shield their son from the ordinary stresses of boyhood. They went to absurd lengths to guard the boy's health. Insofar as they were able, they bribed other children to make certain that their son would be gently handled and permitted to win in games or sports. In such a climate the youngster became impossibly demanding. When crossed, he simply withdrew from communication, becoming silent or sulky or distant with his parents or with other children. To bring the boy "back into communication" the parents usually bribed him with some unusual gift. The learning of this pattern of social control was reinforced over and over again during the patient's childhood. It became, finally, the key to his adult adaptation. Long before he reached the age of 25, the patient had found that fantasy was the easiest route to achievement. The prospect of realistic accomplishment on his own had also time and again plunged him into a state of near-panic. He was, it would seem, fearful lest he lose the advantages which inhered in his highly dependent relationship with others.

Meanwhile, danger signals continued to mount. The patient felt chronically tense and anxious. He would ruminate painfully or suddenly show no indications of normal aggressive behavior. During frequent periods of withdrawal, he would treat the members of his family in a sullen manner.

History of the treatment with psychoanalysis. The patient went for treatment to a leading Freudian psychoanalyst. This is the history of the ensuing experience, as we interpret the patient's report: He lay on the couch for dozens of hours, completely silent. In the face of such severe blocking, the therapist frequently looked out of the window or at the ceiling. At other times he played a more active role; he implored the patient to "say something" or suggested that he continue in school or "do something." When the patient did manage to speak, he engaged often fluently in pseudocommunication. He expatiated on the state of the world or on the value of some possession which he coveted, or he tried to enlist the support of the therapist in squeezing some new concession from his parents. In either case he sedulously avoided touching on any topics that were tinged or laden with anxiety. To the extent that he was successful in some of his manipulative operations during the therapeutic hour, the patient lost respect for his psychoanalyst. At no time was he aware of the existence of any warm feelings towards his therapist. Toward the end of the third year of this relationship, the patient broke off treatment, first in a fitful "off again, on again" manner, and then for good.

History of the trial period of psychotherapy. The patient again tried to manipulate the therapist for the purpose of extorting special privileges from his parents. He repeated the pattern of responding alternately with silence and with over-voluble reiteration. These rigid defenses persisted for several months. It seemed reasonable to suppose that ordinary psychotherapy would prove to be no more successful than the treatment that had preceded it.

Exposure to pharmacologic psychotherapy. The patient's first response to pharmacologic psychotherapy was one of great psychophysiologic relief. He expressed the feeling that he would have been spared a great deal of "unnecessary suffering" had this new approach been employed two or three years earlier. The silences and the evasive, over-voluble speech began to taper off. The patient seemed much readier to exchange really vital feelings and information with his therapist. He could gradually bring into the open thoughts that he had hidden from his psychoanalyst, such as fantasies in the realm of incest and homosexuality. He could interact more warmly with his therapist. He was able to bring within much more reasonable limits the old pattern of using illness or failure as a means of forcing ever-new concessions from his wife or parents. Little by little he became a somewhat more purposive and more productive person. These gains were achieved after two years of work. They were, to be sure, only moderate or relative in character. But they seem to be real and more or less enduring. This, one year after the termination of therapy, is the report we get from the patient's family, from the patient himself, and from the psychoanalyst who undertook treatment in the first place and has had a good subsequent opportunity to observe the patient independently.

Comment

We cast about for some explanatory framework which would tie together these observations on the psychopathology of communication. In search of such concepts we turned to three separate disciplines: (1) communication theory, (2) the social sciences, and (3) psychophysiology.

From the work of Shannon,[38] McCullough,[27] Wiener,[44] and others,[1,41] we could find few conceptual models that were clearly pertinent to our problem. No one would deny that such colorful terms as "information," "negative and positive feedback," "negative entropy," etc. have enriched our language. The use of such terms certainly has some value on the level of analogy. At this writing, however, we share Benedict's[2] feeling that the engineers, physicists, and mathematicians who are working with servo-mechanisms and communication theory differ considerably among themselves and that many of the concepts enunciated by Wiener, Shannon, and others rest upon mathematical definitions that are far from agreed upon. After reviewing the transcript of the Josiah Macy, Jr. conferences of 1951 and 1952,[6, 7] we carried away the impression that cybernetics, at least in its present state, bears a good deal of resemblance to the Tower of Babel.

Basic concepts drawn from the social sciences, on the other hand, seem to throw considerable light on the communicative behavior of our intractable patients. We found the concepts of the self introduced by the social psychologists Cooley,[5] Mead,[39] and Newcomb[29] closer to the kind of model that we could use. We begin with the premise that verbal communication is the principal medium of social interaction. Social interaction, operationally defined, is what happens when two or more persons come into contact with a resulting modification of behavior. We have some idea of the conditions that must be satisfied if fruitful two-way communication is to come into being. The maintenance of these conditions would seem to be one of the primary goals of psychotherapy.[45] For patient and therapist to understand one another, certainly the "sender" of "messages" in either direction must at some point be able to express his feelings in meaningful language. The "receiver," likewise, must be able to decode the incoming "messages," to react to them in a responsive manner, and to let the "sender" know—via appropriate verbalization, vocalization, and gestures—that his "messages" are understood. Unless this happens both participants in the therapeutic process remain mutually "excommunicated."[33]

Using analogies from communication theory, we might say that the type of patient we are describing has unusually sensitive "antennae." During previous psychoanalysis and psychotherapy, these "antennae" picked up a good deal of "noisy interference" in the form of mounting alarm reactions and heightened disturbances of an intrapsychic and interpersonal nature. Under such circumstances and so long as he remained in therapy, the patient did the best he could to protect himself. He made use of the defenses he had employed in all similar situations from childhood on. On the one hand he remained for the most part relatively silent and sometimes sullen. On the other hand he leaned towards compulsive, never-ending loquacity and reiteration. If sufficiently blocked he developed a partial or total aphonia. It would appear, in brief, that the refractory and highly insulated patient responds to the threat of self-exposure in the conventional psychotherapeutic setting by using defensively either the hyper-functioning or the hypo-functioning of all the means of communication at his disposal.*

With the patient who finds it very difficult or almost impossible to respond fruitfully to psychoanalysis or psychotherapy, it makes sense

* This polarity calls to mind the Pythagorean concept (based on an analogy to the Greek lyre) that "diseases of the soul" occur when "the strings" are "too loose" or "too tight."[3, 20]

to us, finally, that one must reckon with the possibility of a psychophysiologic barrier to communication. Our ignorance concerning this phenomenon makes it imperative that future research along conditioning principles be done with both humans and animals as subjects of the investigation. We are intrigued by Gerard's[14] recent speculation that an unresolved stressful situation leads to neural activation of primitive brain stem structures and then to the liberation of sympathin-type agents. According to this hypothesis, those agents with a positive feedback effect on the brain could, in turn, give rise to mounting tension, alertness, and anxiety (corresponding to what Howard Liddell[24] has termed "acute vigilance"). Some such neural mechanism may indeed block communication in the patient who is out-of-communication. Conversely, we might speculate on our own by saying that the chances of reducing "chronic, diffuse vigilance" or of restoring effective two-way communication with inaccessible patients is measurably increased by the use of any chemicals that adequately block neural over-activity of the primitive brain stem structures and at the same time stimulate the activity of higher centers. By their euphorizing effects, such chemical agents help to restore "broken lines" of communication through reinforcement of healthy social interaction. Changes of this character on a psychophysiologic level seem to follow from intravenous injections of sodium pentothal and Desoxyn. This integrating experience rewards or reinforces speech[10] so that the hidden anxiety attached to it is more readily extinguished, thus enhancing the patient's capacity for fuller communication. The pharmacologic psychotherapy of the future, we are sure, will have still more effective drugs and techniques at its disposal.

Summary and Conclusions

This paper is a report on 31 patients with refractory psychoneuroses and personality disorders, all of whom had undergone long-term psychoanalysis or psychotherapy without success. One of the chief causes of failure was the existence of more or less severe impairments of verbal communication. Judged in terms of their *prevailing* patterns of speech, these cases seemed to fall roughly into two classes: (1) the underproductive verbalizers and (2) the overproductive verbalizers. The former group comprised the "silent ones" whose verbal productions were sparse and often obscure or disorganized in content. The second group we categorized as over-voluble reiterators, given to long-winded pseudocommunication. Both of these somewhat contrasting types of patients used their characteristic mode of speech as a means of withdrawing the self from communication in the therapeutic situation. During previous psychoanalysis and psychotherapy these patients had developed heightened psychophysiologic tension and mounting intrapsychic preoccupation. They had also exhibited increasing hostility and resentment toward the therapists who, in their eyes, had not participated warmly in the communicative process. During a trial period of psychotherapy with these same patients we detected a recurrence of the difficulties that had doomed the previous efforts at psychoanalysis or psychotherapy. We sensed the imminence of a second psychotherapeutic failure. Therefore we instituted a program of pharmacologic psychotherapy, employing intravenous injections of sodium pentothal and Desoxyn in sequence. In the majority of cases this procedure induced a psychophysiologic state which had a relatively facilitating effect on the psychotherapy that followed. A warmer and more responsive two-way relationship came into being. The characteristic verbal defenses were more or less minimized. There was a greater or lesser reduction of the proneness of the patient to distort feelings and information about the self and others. In most, but by no means in all, cases, the patient's capacity to communicate was enhanced to the point where he could participate more or less actively in the rewarding and integrating experience of intensive psychotherapy. The majority of these intractable cases seemed to derive some benefit from this method of approach. Pharmacologic psychotherapy shows promise of becoming a method of choice for the treatment of refractory psychoneuroses and personality disorders that are accompanied by moderate-to-severe difficulties of communication.

REFERENCES

1. Ashby, W. R.: The cerebral mechanisms of intelligent action. In D. Richter, Ed., Perspectives in Neuropsychiatry. London, H. K. Lewis, 1950.
2. Benedict, Elliot: Personal communication.
3. Burnet, John: Greek Philosophy. I. Thales to Plato. London, Macmillan, 1928, p. 50.
4. Bleckwenn, W. J.: Sodium Amytal in certain nervous and mental conditions. Wisc. Med. J. *29*: 693-696, 1930.
5. Cooley, Charles H.: Social Organization. New York, Scribner's, 1909.
6. Cybernetics: Circular causal and feedback mechanisms in biological and social systems, *ed. by* Heinz von Foerster. New York, Josiar Macy, Jr. Foundation, 1952.
7. Cybernetics: Circular causal and feedback mechanisms in biological and

social systems, *ed. by* Heinz von Foerster. New York, Josiah Macy, Jr. Foundation, 1953.

8. Diagnostic and Statistical Manual: Mental Disorders. Washington, D.C., American Psychiatric Association, 1952.
9. DIXON, W. J., AND MASSEY, F. J.: Introduction to Statistical Analysis. New York, McGraw-Hill, 1951.
10. DOLLARD, J., AND MILLER, N.E.: Personality and Psychotherapy. New York, McGraw-Hill, 1950.
11. FISHER, R. A.: Statistical Methods for Research Workers. New York, Hafner, 1950.
12. FREUD, SIGMUND: New Introductory Lectures on Psycho-analysis. New York, Norton, 1933, p. 214.
13. ——: Analysis terminable and interminable. In Collected Papers, vol. 5. London, Hogarth Press, 1950, pp. 316-357.
14. GERARD, R. W.: Biologic roots of psychiatry. Science *122*: 225-230, 1955.
15. HOCH, PAUL H., AND POLATIN, PHILLIP: Narcodiagnosis and narcotherapy. In Specialized Techniques in Psychotherapy. New York, Basic Books, 1952, pp. 1-23.
16. ——: Evaluation of newer pharmacodynamic therapies. Including the narco-analytic use of drugs. In Psychiatric Treatment. Baltimore, Williams & Wilkins, 1953, pp. 239-244.
17. ——, CATTELL, JAMES P., AND PENNES, HARRY H.: Effect of drugs: theoretical considerations from a psychological viewpoint. Am. J. Psychiat. *108*: 585-589, 1952.
18. ——: Aims and limitations of psychotherapy. Am. J. Psychiat. *112*: 321-327, 1955.
19. HORSLEY, J. STEPHEN: Narco-analysis: A New Technique in Short-cut Psychotherapy: A Comparison with Other Methods and Notes on the Barbiturates. New York, Oxford University Press, 1946.
20. JOWETT, B.: The Dialogues of Plato, vol. 2, ed. 3. London, Oxford University Press, 1931, p. 230.
21. KEANE, KEITH M., AND KANT, FRITZ: Investigations on the use of cortical stimulants with Sodium Amytal for narcoanalysis. J. Nerv. Ment. Dis. *117*: 140-143, 1953.
22. LASAGNA, L., VON FELSINGER, J. M., AND BEECHER, H. K.: Drug-induced mood changes in man. I. Observations on healthy subjects, chronically ill patients, and "postaddicts," J.A.M.A. *157*: 1006-1020, 1955.
23. LEVINE, J., RINKEL, M., AND GREENBLATT, M.: Psychological and physiological effects of intravenous Pervitin. Am. J. Psychiat. *105*: 429-434, 1948.
24. LIDDELL, H. S.: The Role of vigilance in the development of animal neurosis. In P. H. Hoch, and J. Zubin, Eds., Anxiety. New York, Grune & Stratton, 1950.

    ——: Adaptation on the threshold of intelligence. In J. Romano, Ed., Adaptation. Ithaca, N.Y., Cornell University Press. 1949, pp. 53-76.
25. LINDEMANN, ERICH: Psychological changes in normal and abnormal individuals under the influence of Sodium Amytal. Am. J. Psychiat. *11*: 1083-1091, 1932.

26. Malinowski, B.: The problem of meaning in primitive languages. Suppl. in C. K. Ogden, and I. A. Richards, Eds., The Meaning of Meaning. New York, Harcourt Brace, 1945.
27. McCulloch, W. S.: Fed. Proc. *6*: 448, 1947.
28. Moses, P.: The Voice of Neurosis. New York, Grune & Stratton, 1954.
29. Newcomb, Theodore M.: Motivation in social behavior. In Current Theory and Research in Motivation: A Symposium. University of Nebraska Press, 1953, pp. 139-161.
30. Nowlis, Vincent: The Development and modification of motivational systems in personality. In Current Theory and Research in Motivation: A Symposium. Lincoln, University of Nebraska Press, 1953, pp. 114-138.
31. Rioch, David McK.: Circular causal and feedback mechanisms in biological and social systems. Eighth Conf. (1951) New York, Josiah Macy, Jr. Foundation, 1952, pp. 78-79.
32. ——: Op. cit., pp. 124-125, 128.
33. ——: Theories of psychotherapy. In Current Trends in Psychological Theory. Pittsburgh, University of Pittsburgh Press, 1951, pp. 140-164.
34. Rothman, Theodore, and Sward, Keith: Studies in pharmacological psychotherapy. I. Treatment of refractory psychoneuroses and personality disorders with thiopental (Pentothal) sodium and methamphetamine (Desoxyn). Arch. Neurol. & Psychiat. *75*: 95-105, 1956.
35. Ruesch, Jurgen, and Bateson, Gregory: Communication. The Social Matrix of Psychiatry. New York, Norton, 1951.
36. Sapir, E: Selected Writings in Language, Culture and Personality, *ed. by* D. Mandelbaum. Berkley, University of California Press, 1949.
37. Sapir, E.: Language. New York, Harcourt Brace, 1949.
38. Shannon, C. E., and Weaver, Warren: A Mathematical Theory of Communication. Urbana, University of Illinois Press, 1949.
39. Strauss, A., Ed: The Social Psychology of George Herbert Mead. Chicago, University of Chicago Press, 1956, pp. 212-260.
40. Trager, G. L.: Language. In Encyclopedia Britannica, Vol. 13. Chicago, Britannica, 1955, pp. 696-703.
41. Walter, W. G.: The Living Brain. New York, Norton, 1953.
42. Wendt, G. R., et al.: Chemical influences on behavior. II. Development of methods and preliminary results on the effects of some drugs on emotional and social behavior. Unpublished Report. Department of Psychology, University of Rochester, 1953.
43. Wendt, G. R., et al.: Chemical influences on behavior. III. The effects of Dramamine and scopolamine on emotional and social behavior with comparison data on the effects of other drugs. Unpublished report. Department of Psychology, University of Rochester, 1953.
44. Wiener, Norbert: Cybernetics. New York, Wiley, 1948.
45. Whitehorn, John C.: Understanding psychotherapy. Am. J. Psychiat. *112*: 328-333, 1955.
46. Von Felsinger, J. M., Lasagna, L., and Beecher, H. K.: Drug-induced mood changes in man: II. Personality and reactions to drugs. J.A.M.A. *157*: 1113-1119, 1955.

Discussion of Chapters 11-12

By PAUL H. HOCH, M.D.*

IN THEIR very interesting paper, Drs. Rothman and Sward described a group of patients who failed with conventional psychoanalysis or psychotherapy. However, the patients responded quite well to a therapy which consisted of administering drugs and psychotherapy. The authors' paper brings up several points, but mainly—is it necessary that patients with an obsessive, passive, or aggressive and markedly schizoid structure be treated year after year with techniques not suitable for them? I am sure that we could classify a number of patients described by the authors as pseudoneurotic schizophrenic. Most of these patients have a great dependency need and therefore will cling to a therapist for many years even though no actual change takes place in their condition. Some of these patients need support for a long period of time, but it is important to decide whether they should have treatment which is more supportive or more reconstructive.

I do not believe these patients benefit from reconstructive treatment which takes seven, eight, or even more years. In most instances the treatment of these patients becomes a supportive measure and if that is the case it is sufficient to see them at less frequent intervals and, of course, the treatment procedure is different from what it would be if reconstructive treatment is attempted. These patients are prone to be precipitated into a psychosis if seen very often and treated with classical analytic techniques. Yet it is sometimes difficult to decided immediately what treatment procedure should be used. In those patients in whom the structure of the disorder is not obvious standard treatment should be given for about three months. In the majority of patients it is possible at that time to assess different factors in the case and to select the proper treatment. It is not always easy to determine what treament procedures should be used in the type of patients the authors describe and there is even less agreement on whether and when drugs should be used in conjunction with psychotherapy. Today drugs are essentially used as adjuncts to psychotherapy and to remove suppression or repression of psychic material. As far as we know, the drugs which are used do not

* College of Physicians and Surgeons, Columbia University, New York.

have any specificity in the sense that patients under the influence of these different drugs do not necessarily reveal psychic material specific to any one drug. In the literature the same mechanisms are claimed with the use of such a drug as amphetamine which was described years before in conjunction with barbiturates and CO_2. It is, of course, conceivable that on the basis of physiological and psychological factors one patient will respond better to one drug than to another.

It was assumed originally that the drugs facilitate catharsis. We know that with the exception of some very special conditions catharsis alone is not sufficient to produce improvement and that, in addition, systemic psychotherapy is necessary. If the patient is very tense or anxious the use of drugs is of advantage in relieving these symptoms and eliminating the block which exists in communication. In most patients the elimination of tension also produces a feeling of well-being (not euphoria) which gives the patient hope that a change can be effected, which then can be constructively utilized in psychotherapy. The drugs may or may not increase the suggestibility of the patient, which also could be used effectively in a psychotherapeutic setting.

The authors' case material clearly indicates that elasticity in psychotherapy and especially flexibility in linking psychotherapy with pharmacotherapy is of importance and pays off in therapeutic successes in individuals who have not responded to therapy before. It is obvious that we have patient groups, of which the pseudoneurotic schizophrenic is one, which do not respond too well to any treatment which we are able to employ today. However, many patients can improve appreciably if techniques are used which are far more suitable than the approaches which were evolved with neurotic patients.

Dr. Lauretta Bender gives us a very interesting paper in a field which is still obscure in many of its aspects. Since strephosymbolia was described, we know that this affliction leads to behavior disorders, delinquency, impairment of action patterns and different emotional disturbances. Occasionally, if these individuals have emotional disturbances, they impress one as being schizophrenic. However, this is not the case in the majority of the cases. Schizophrenia is a far more extensive disorder than strephosymbolia. It also has to be emphasized that patients suffering from strephosymbolia are not feeble-minded. Many have above average intelligence even though they are not able to perform well in circumscribed areas. There is very little known about the origin of this disorder. It is explained by some as a poor development of hemispheric dominance. The explanations fall into three groupings: (1) the assumption that they are congenital anomalies, (2) those assuming that they are functional, and (3) those assuming they are due to maturational defects. This is a mixed concept, based partly on genetic and partly on functional considerations. Our knowledge of the maturation of the nervous system has great gaps. We do not know how certain areas mature and we are especially lacking in knowledge of how different perceptive functions are integrated into a Gestalt. Also we are not quite clear about whether the disorders under discussion are due to a circumscribed disability or to a diffused one. Aphasias, agnosias and alexias are considered impairment of focal function compared to normal intellectual development. In other words, they are considered focal impairments or partial disabilities. This was the older view, essentially neurologically oriented.

The question of whether this is correct arises particularly in those cases in which focal lesions are not present. We have the impression that in many cases we are dealing with an integrative disturbance which is not just focal but due to some ego impairment. It is interesting that in many of these disorders the most striking fact is the inability of the person to perceive sequences.

We do not know what mechanism in the psyche regulates sequences or how perceptive sequences are arranged, and how they form a Gestalt remains unclear. To explain all this with the hemispheric dominance theory is unsatisfactory. If an integration of impulses coming from different sensory fields is impaired, concept formation is distorted because the reality appears different in these individuals, or at least partially so. The relationship of cortex and subcortex is also unclear in these disorders. It is interesting that in certain emotional situations these difficulties can be overcome in the same way as aphasic disturbances. In some individuals, however, certain emotional situations aggravate the disturbances. How derangements relate to schizophrenia is not clear. The individuals afflicted with them are not schizophrenic. However, some of them may become so. The question arises—is difference only a matter of degree or is schizophrenia something "added," in these individuals, to the perceptual integrative disorganization? Does schizophrenia develop in some individuals as a reaction to the handicap of not being able to integrate perceptions? In this case we have to assume that two pathological processes are present in the same individual. Some, of course, feel that the integrative impairment in some of these individuals is itself a form of schizophrenia.

Many of the symptoms Dr. Bender describes in these individuals we also see in schizophrenics, but it has to be emphasized that the vast majority of schizophrenics do not show strephosymbolia and vice versa. Dr. Bender recognizes the combination of these disorders in some individuals. Of course the final decision will be made only when we know what the primary symptoms of schizophrenia are and not while we confine our discussion to the secondary symptomatology in this disorder. When we know the primary disturbances we shall of course be able to delineate the relationship of schizophrenia to disorders like strephosymbolia more sharply and effectively than today.

13

Samuel W. Hamilton Award

PSYCHOTHERAPY: A PROBLEM OF CONTROLLED INTERCOMMUNICATION

By SANDOR RADO, M.D.*

At the present stage of its scientific development, psychotherapy has become applied psychodynamics. Its effective principle may be described as the methodic use of human influence. Its goal is to make the patient's behavior less disordered and more adaptive. On the basis of the goal pursued, the methods of psychotherapy may be divided into two classes: reconstructive and reparative. Strictly speaking, we possess at present only one reconstructive method—the adaptational technique of psychoanalytic therapy. The class of reparative methods includes all other techniques of psychoanalytic therapy, hypnotherapy, and certain trouble-shooting and easing methods still in the experimental phase.

In line with the topic of this annual meeting, I should like to examine the psychotherapy of over-reactive disorders (psychoneuroses) as a problem in controlled intercommunication. Let me introduce this new point of view with old quotations. In the opening chapter of his *General Introduction to Psychoanalysis*, Freud writes:

"In psychoanalysis [in contrast to the rest of medicine] all this is different. In psychoanalytic treatment nothing happens but an exchange of words between the patient and the physician. The patient talks, tells of his past experiences and present impressions, complains, and expresses his wishes and his emotions. The physician listens, attempts to direct the patient's thought processes, reminds him, forces his attention in certain directions, gives him explanations and observes the reactions of understanding or denial thus evoked."[5]

The patient's unenlightened relatives, Freud continues, "never omit to express their doubts of how 'mere talk can possibly cure anybody.' "

* Professor of Psychiatry and Director of the Graduate School of Psychiatry, Downstate Medical Center, State University of New York.

Freud then proceeds to dissipate this doubt: "Words and magic were in the beginning one and the same thing, and even today words retain much of their magical power. By words one of us can give to another the greatest happiness or bring about utter despair; by words the teacher imparts his knowledge to the student; by words the orator sweeps his audience with him and determines its judgments and decisions. Words call forth emotions and are universally the means by which we influence our fellow-creatures. Therefore let us not despise the use of words in psychotherapy."[5]

In this thumbnail sketch of the psychoanalytic procedure, Freud establishes the fact that psychotherapy, like all other human relationships, is built on verbal intercommunication. It is through the use of words that the patient opens up himself to the physician who in turn exerts his therapeutic influence upon the patient. By a series of illustrations, Freud then convinces his readers of the *power* of words, or rather of language, thought and feeling.

Freud saw the problem of verbal influence but left it unexplored. Taking this observation as a point of departure, let me first shift the emphasis from the speaker's intentions to the listener's responses. One may react to a verbal utterance at the level of *unemotional* thought, at the lower level of *emotional* thought, or at the still lower level of preverbal brute emotion. In recent years, in outlining adaptational psychodynamics, I have suggested that these levels of our mental organization reflect stages of evolutionary history.[8,9,11,14-16] We have thus come to assume that the psychodynamic cerebral system includes an integrative apparatus which is hierarchically organized and composed of five units. Of these, the oldest, most primitive, and most fundamental is the unit of hedonic self-regulation, which integrates behavior according to the indications of pleasure and pain. By way of evolutionary extrapolation, one may surmise that some forerunner of this unit may already have appeared in the protozoan. We further distinguish, in ascending order, the units of preverbal brute emotion, emotional thought, and unemotional thought. The designation of each of these four units refers to the means by which it fulfills its integrative task. The fifth unit, located axially to the four units just described, is designated as the action-self. Of proprioceptive origin, it arises from the circular pattern of self-awareness and willed action. Shaped under the influence of the (social) environment, it provides the basis for the selfhood of the conscious organism and is viewed as the supreme unit of central integration.[15,16] A drawing of this hypothetical apparatus* is shown in figure 1.

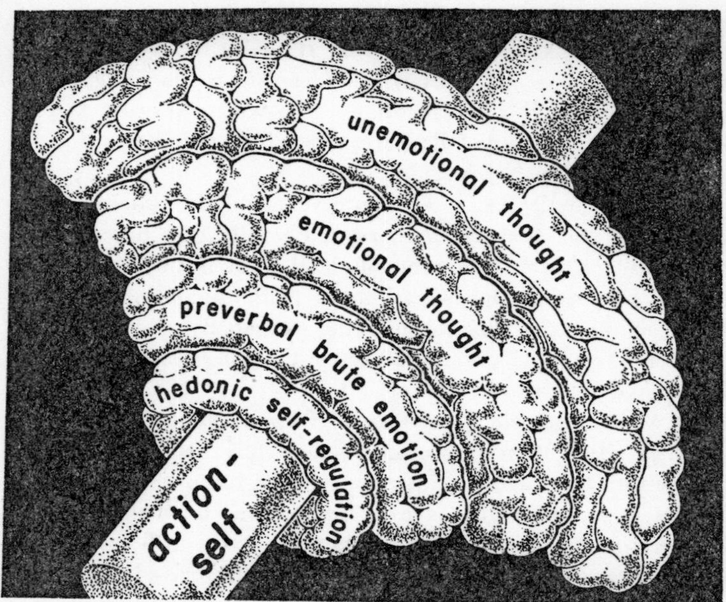

FIG. 1. Integrative apparatus of the psychodynamic cerebral system.

This apparatus originates and organizes both the verbal messages sent and the verbal responses given to the messages received in human intercommunication, including of course the therapeutic intercommunication of patient and physician. I hope that in the context of this apparatus we shall see more clearly the significance of the differences between the levels of unemotional and emotional thought.[10] Unemotional thought has created the tools of common sense and science—its most advanced form is mathematical thought. It enables us to explore objectively the phenomena to which our senses are exposed and thus

* The idea of this apparatus derives from an evolutionary interpretation of the material of psychodynamic observation. Its physiological correlate should be visualized as a *functional* arrangement somewhere in the brain. Brain anatomy is a poor guide to the study of brain function. On the other hand, a significant part of brain function may be conveniently explored as psychodynamic function. If the above hypothesis proves its value in psychodynamics it may also offer a clue for the brain physiologist.

to accumulate dependable knowledge. The supreme test of dependability is the successful prediction of what will happen in consequence of changes we can make or observe. Since it is ultimately motivated by *desire,* even unemotional thought operates within the framework of hedonic self-regulation, modified however by the delaying action of intelligence and foresight.

By comparison, emotional thought is an inferior instrument for exploring and interpreting the things and events to which we are actually exposed; it is not objective, but selective, and tends to justify and thus to feed the emotion from which it springs and by which it is controlled. For instance, loving thought is dominated by the power of the wish and hating thought by the combined powers of anger and fear. The primary function of emotional thinking is not comprehension but the accumulation and discharge of emotional tensions.

We can readily understand this characteristic because in the course of phylogenetic history integration by emotional thought appeared as an intermediary stage. It evolved from integration by preverbal brute emotion and in turn prepared the ground for the evolutionary rise of integration by unemotional thought. Emotional thought, too, is a modified means of hedonic self-regulation but one modified by less intelligence and foresight.

The part played by emotional thought in the shaping of behavior cannot be overestimated. Much of our motivation stems from the unconscious strata of the mind or, as we prefer to say, the nonreporting range of the psychodynamic cerebral system, and that range is almost completely dominated by emotional thought. If the human organism is a computing machine it is one whose performance is regulated by a sort of emotional calculus.

Let me now apply these elementary insights to the therapeutic situation. Can the therapist by his mode of speaking control the patient's responses? Can he engender in an aloof, withdrawn patient an emotional reaction of the intended kind or, on the other hand, cause an excited patient to calm down and induce him to respond in terms of clear and rational thought? Clinical experience shows that such effects can be achieved by means which include choice of the "right" meaning, diction, stress, pitch, and facial expression. But such regulative use of spoken language is still an art. At present, we do not possess even the beginnings of a technology of therapeutic talk. It depends solely upon the therapist's intuition and skill when, where, and how he uses informative (referential) or emotive language.

Naturally, in reconstructive therapy the task is vastly more complicated than calming an agitated or panicky patient or rousing an inert one to active interest in his affairs.[13,17] Schematically speaking, work on the patient's emotions falls into five phases. In the first phase, we must see to it that he should enter upon his self-exploration in a mood of self-confidence and hopeful expectation. Whenever, in the course of work, this mood vanishes, it must be promptly restored. In the second phase, the patient must face his inappropriate and excessive emergency emotions. Above all, he must release his defiant rages which are repressed (or retroflexed) by the automatic action of his submerged guilty fears. This underground emotional dynamics, designated as *guilty fears over defiant rages,* is chiefly responsible for the patient's self-damaging inhibitions; its removal is a reconstructive task of paramount importance. Without the cushioning effect of a sustained mood of self-confidence and hopeful expectation, he would be victimized by these reactivated emotions rather than freed from them. When the swell subsides and the patient's corresponding inhibitions lose their strangulating strength, the patient enters upon the third phase of work. He is now for the first time capable of arriving at a better *intellectual* understanding of himself and can begin to formulate more realistic plans. In the fourth phase we help him array his welfare emotions, that is, his love, affection, joy, self-respect, and pride, for the support of his new activities. In the fifth phase we guide him in evolving or recapturing the realistic techniques of a healthy life performance.

Let me repeat that this description is of necessity a schematization but it serves to convey the idea that work on the patient's *emotions* is the decisive task. The scientific exploration of this area is an urgent need which has been neglected.

Let me now turn from the verbal exchanges of treatment to its underlying motivational dynamics. In other words, we shall leave the stage itself and inspect the complex machinery behind the scenes. The working of this machinery determines the events that will take place down to the most minute detail on the stage. We shall first take a look at the patient and then at the physician.

The patient is ready to cooperate with the physician who offers him the help he needs. However, observation of the patient's treatment behavior shows that he shifts from one design for cooperation to another, usually without being aware of either of them.[13,17] These designs fall into an hierarchical order of levels corresponding closely to the developmental stages of his maturation. Even from the most advanced level of cooperation he may at any time regress to the most childish one and then shift back again. These levels of treatment behavior are shown in table 1.

A bold line divides this diagram into an upper and a lower half.

TABLE 1.—*Levels of Treatment Behavior*

Level	Patient's attitude
ASPIRING Level: Available only in the adult who is capable and desirous of self-advancement by extensive learning and maturation.	"I am delighted to cooperate with the doctor. This is my opportunity to learn how to make full use of all my potential resources for adaptive growth."
↑ ↓	
SELF-RELIANT Level: Available in the average adult who is capable of learning the simple know-how of daily life.	"I am ready to cooperate with the doctor. I must learn how to help myself and do things for myself."
↓	
Adult	
Child-like	
↑	
PARENTIFYING Level: When the adult feels like a helpless child, he seeks parental help and therefore parentifies the therapist.	"I don't know what the doctor expects of me. I couldn't do it anyway. He should cure me by *his* effort."
↑ ↓	
MAGIC-CRAVING Level: The completely discouraged adult retreats to the hope that the parentified therapist will do miracles for him.	"The doctor must not only cure me, he must do everything for me—by magic."

↑ = advance. ↓ = regression.

Above this line, the patient behaves like an intelligent adult: at the *self-reliant* level, he knows he must learn how to help himself; at the *aspiring* level he has in addition the desire to take full advantage of the treatment as a unique opportunity for growth and development.

Below the dividing line, at the *parentifying* level, the patient behaves as a helpless child who reaches out for parental help. He sees in the therapist, often unknown to himself, an idealized reincarnation of his own parent brought back to the scene by the power of his desire. He cares little for learning and maturation. He seeks to obtain the privileges of a favorite child. His treatment behavior has thus regressed to the pattern of infantile dependence. When he regresses still deeper to the *magic-craving* level, the physician becomes in his eyes an omnipotent being who will do miracles for him.

To sum this up in one sentence, the crucial difference between adult and childlike treatment behavior is that at the adult level the patient realizes that *he* must learn to do things *for himself,* whereas at the infantile level he is wedded to the idea that *the physician* will do things *for him,* if need be, by magic.

Patients can be successfully treated at each of the four levels of cooperation. However, the goals and techniques of treatment are different from level to level. Since the patient inclines to shift from one level to another, it is an important technical task to stabilize him at the level selected for his treatment. We term the measures devised for this purpose *priming measures;* in contradistinction, we call the measures devised to modify his life performance *modifying measures.* Thus, in psychotherapy, each particular method must evolve two plans of its own: one for priming and another for modifying. These combined plans form the proper psychodynamic basis for a comparative examination of all psychotherapeutic methods.

The magic-craving level is used in hypnotherapy. As a child, the patient learned that he must purchase the "magical" ministrations of his parents by his obedience. Now, in order to materialize his dream of magical cure, he enters by the action of his own desire upon an hypnotic state—a state of almost automatic obedience. The physician then tells him how he should think, feel, and act, persuading him that he is capable of doing so. Imposing hypnotic discipline upon a patient who craves it is probably the oldest and certainly the easiest method of psychotherapy.

Historically, Breuer's introduction of hypnocatharsis was a revolutionary move. This procedure rewards the patient for his automatic obedience by inviting him to release his pent-up resentments with the full approval of the physician.

The parentifying level is used in the classical and certain other techniques of psychoanalytic therapy and in the various reparative methods. I must limit myself to a few words about the classical technique. It is based on Freud's discovery of the combined investigative tools of free association and interpretation by contextual inference. With these tools Freud pried open the locks of repression in the patient's mind, thus achieving a therapeutic release of his pathogenic thoughts, feelings and impulses. However, this procedure of "making the unconscious conscious" was complicated by the apparent vagaries of the patient's treatment behavior. The patient was supposed to explore his past; instead, he plied the physician with smiles, tears and lashings as shown schematically in table 2.

TABLE 2.—*Plying the Parentified Physician with Smiles, Tears and Lashings*

Ingratiating:	"I am courting your favor, doing everything you wish, be nice to me."
Impatient:	"It's time for you to cure me (by magic)."
Seductive:	"Meanwhile, make love to me (the magic of your love will cure me)."
Upon feeling rejected by the physician:	
Expiatory:	"Your aloofness fills me with guilty fear. I should like to expiate for my disobedience and promise to be obedient—please forgive me."
Resentful:	"When I was a child my parents never let me have my way. You said yourself that's how they started my intimidation and illness. It's *your* job to undo the wrong they did me. True, you urge me 'to get it off my chest,' but you hold me in your clutches just the same. You can't fool me."
Coercive:	"Now I am really furious. Stop this double talk and cure me."
Vindictive:	"I shall get even with you . . . I never wish to see you again."

Freud realized that the patient automatically reactivated in his treatment behavior his emotional pattern of infantile dependence,[1,3] but alas, the German language has no term equivalent to "pattern," and of course no term equivalent to "behavior pattern." Hence, for the description of his discovery, Freud invented the less fortunate concepts of "transference" (Uebertragung) and "compulsion to repeat" (Wiederholungszwang).[4,6] Seeing the patient's childlike behavior he made a momentous decision. The patient's affectionate attachment to the physician, he advised, must be preserved and used for the purpose of therapeutic influence. To achieve this, his hostile and sensual impulses must be dissolved by being interpreted as repetitions of his infantile past. This theory viewed parentifying treatment behavior as but another form in which the patient reproduced his past; his recollections and re-enactments complemented one another.

By shifting the emphasis to the investigative aspect of the therapeutic procedure, this theory benefited enormously the developing young science of psychodynamics. Only decades later were its serious therapeutic drawbacks disclosed. Living in imperial Vienna, Freud did not and perhaps could not realize that one cannot lift the patient to a higher level of maturity, as he intended, by keeping him in a state of more or less uncritical emotional dependence on the physician throughout the course of treatment. Freud did advise that at the completion of treatment this emotional dependence should be dissolved but he did not say how this should be done.

In fact, the classical technique perpetuated the old idea of hypnotherapy, that the patient should be held at an infantile stage of maturity. But it replaced the rigid measures of hypnotic discipline with the flexible measures of an enlightened discipline. Accordingly, in facing the resentful, coercive and vindictive phases of the patient's parentifying treatment behavior, the physician took not a prohibitive but a quasi-permissive attitude. The patient was allowed to unload his repressed infantile rages upon the physician who transiently played the part of a scapegoat in this procedure. At the end of such phases the patient was shown by the usual technique of historical interpretation that the true object of his rage was his father rather than the physician. This cumbersome procedure did less for the patient than did Breuer's hypnocatharsis in which the released rage retained its original object. Only Freud's preoccupation with the (erroneous) idea that this scapegoat technique would allow him to explore otherwise inaccessible phases of the patient's past could have persuaded him to consider it an effective therapeutic measure.

A further flaw in the classical technique was its excessive concentration on the patient's past. The constant search for the presumed developmental origins of his behavior tended to divert attention from the determinants residing in the here and now, that is, from the problems of the patient's present and future.

The self-reliant and aspiring levels of treatment behavior are used in the adaptational technique of psychoanalytic therapy. We call this method, briefly, reconstructive therapy, because it aims at fulfilling the Freudian goal of lifting the patient to a higher level of inner independence and social maturity. It must suffice here to enumerate but a few of the innovations upon which this method rests.

In the adaptational technique, we seek to stabilize the patient at the adult levels of cooperation. As soon as he shows signs of childlike emotional dependence on the physician we bolster up his self-confidence on realistic grounds and, upon such preparation, bring him back to the adult level by interceptive interpretation. We know the repertory of his infantile emotional responses from his case history, from his past behavior towards his parents, and from the series of ersatz parents he had leaned on before he entered treatment. We attach utmost therapeutic importance to the continuous release of the patient's repressed rages and resentments whether they are of recent origin or reactivated from the past. But we do not allow him to substitute a scapegoat. We teach him to reproduce in his memory the actual rage-provoking scene with the original cast. We interpret the patient's life performance in an adaptational framework. He must learn to view himself and others in terms of opportunities and responsibilities, successes and failures. He must learn to understand his doings in terms of motivation and control, to evaluate his doings in terms of the cultural context, and to understand his development in terms of his background and life history. In our view, the excavation of biographical material is not in itself therapeutic—it may even be harmful. It is of therapeutic value *only* if it significantly aids the patient in his present adaptive task. We seek to change the emotional matrix of the patient's life performance in a manner that will enable him to look out for his welfare rather than cope with emergencies that do not exist. Earlier in this paper I outlined our five-stage scheme for his emotional re-education. We have introduced measures for the therapeutic re-interpretation of the patient's guilty fears, the emotional redefinition of his memories, the therapeutic analysis of his dreams, etc. Viewed in its entirety, treatment with the adaptational technique takes place in an intellectual and emotional climate profoundly different from that of the classical technique.

The therapeutic dialogue between patient and physician is improvised on the spot. It is the physician's task to keep it moving in the right direction. From the many difficulties encountered in this pursuit I shall first single out the one most readily solved. It may occur that the patient remains silent for a period of time. Silence is a form of "resistance." It indicates that the treatment has become painful or uninteresting and unrewarding to the patient. He may be afraid or ashamed of facing some of his past or recent experiences, actions, intentions, feelings, or thoughts. In this case, he uses silence as a defensive mechanism of avoidance. He may feel frustrated and rejected by the physician and use silence as a vindictive attention-getting device. A patient may be sincerely bored and disillusioned, so that his silence foreshadows his impending departure. Let me stress the fact that in most instances the patient himself is totally unaware of the reason for his silence and would hardly be able to detect it without our help.

May I now turn to the most delicate and often most difficult single operation in our therapeutic technique: The physician must be able to detect the patient's emotional state.[12] The presence of a strong emotion is usually revealed by changes in the patient's expression, tone of voice, etc., even if he does not describe explicitly how he feels. The physician may be able to pick up almost imperceptible changes of expression by means of his own *emotional resonance.* He then ascertains the presence of the emotion concerned chiefly by intellectual means. Listening to the patient's running account, he traces the patterns of his thoughts and actions. We are familiar with the characteristic patterns of emotionally inspired thought and action and can readily infer from the emerging patterns the emotions that shaped them. Clinical experience conclusively proves that the subjective feeling aspect of a certain emotion, say of fear, rage, or love, may be completely removed from the patient's awareness by repression, and yet this emotion may nonetheless be present in the organism and exert its motivating influence on the patient's thoughts and actions. In these instances we speak of nonreporting fear, rage, love, etc. Sometimes the presence of a nonreporting emotion is indicated by a feeling of qualitatively undifferentiated tension. In general, in the exploration of the emotions, their feeling aspect and motivating action complement one another.

The motivational factor still to be considered briefly is the influence of the physician's personal psychodynamics on his therapeutic work with patients. The physician is guided by the psychodynamics of the various treatment methods. Upon examining the patient, he decides upon the procedure to be followed on well-known diagnostic and practical grounds. His work with the patient may thus be viewed as an organized sequence of planned therapeutic measures. Ordinarily this intellectual work is rich in emotional gratifications, which are augmented by satisfactions from a variety of motivations. To begin with, the physician may wish to make a living; have a strong urge to help; a keen scientific investigative interest; an ambition to make a name for himself; a desire to feel important; a need to find a vicarious outlet for his frustrated paternal or maternal feelings, etc. The predominance of one or the other of these motives may strongly influence his choice of method and style of work. However, as long as these personal motives do not interfere with the scientific soundness and practical utility of his treatment procedure, they are of interest only as problems of the physician's personal welfare and happiness.

His personal motivation becomes a problem for us when it *does* interfere with his therapeutic work. We may refer to this occurrence as an *intrusive personal involvement.* The physician may become involved with the patient as a "case," as a person, or both. His involvement may be acute, subacute or chronic. It may be prompted by inappropriate emergency emotions such as fear, anger, resentment, guilty fear, and even guilty rage, or by inappropriate welfare emotions such as love, affection, sensual desire, desire for admiration, etc. In consequence, the physician's planned therapeutic procedure may be distorted through direct influence of these emotions, or if he becomes aware of the disturbance, by some inappropriate moves he may make to extricate himself from the involvement. For example, the physician may in his imagination project himself into the place of the patient, take pride in the patient's cultural achievements, or suffer vicariously from the patient's reverses; he may have to protect himself from being carried away by the patient's misery. The male-female situation may give rise to highly disturbing temptations. It may also happen, of course, that the physician becomes distracted by outside concerns. His therapeutic work may suffer from his diminished interest, or again from the faulty remedial measures he may take to force his attention back to his work. A triangular situation develops when the psychotherapist himself maintains a strong infantile dependency relationship to the originator of the method he uses. He is inordinately proud of being one of the *master's* disciples. Inevitably, he instills his dependent feelings into the patient. The intended therapeutic procedure is thus tacitly transformed into the shared emotional experience of a ritual and works (if it works) as a faith-cure. As in planned hypnotherapy, here too the therapist and patient, though unwittingly, reinforce each other's craving for magic.

The psychotherapist's own analysis is supposed to obviate the above eventualities. However, experience does not bear out this expectation. The best remedy is for the psychotherapist to be aware of this fact and constantly re-examine himself.

As this sampling survey indicates, in the last analysis our entire psychotherapeutic armamentarium derives from principles and procedures used by parents in the rearing of children since time immemorial. What have transformed this heritage into a psychodynamics of treatment are the analytic and synthetic powers of the scientific method. Thanks to this advance, we have during the last sixty years or so accumulated an impressive amount of knowledge in psychotherapy. In the present paper I have attempted to organize the highlights of this knowledge from the point of view of controlled intercommunication.

In conclusion I should like to say that this point of view sharpens our perception of our problems and therefore may in the future aid us in their solution. Let me close on this optimistic note.

REFERENCES

1. FREUD, SIGMUND: Psychotherapy of hysteria. In J. Breuer and S. Freud, Studies in Hysteria. New York, Nervous and Mental Disease Pub. Co., 1936, pp. 198-199.
2. ——: Freud's psychoanalytic method. Collected Papers, Vol. I. London, Hogarth Press, 1924.
3. ——: Fragment of an analysis of a case of hysteria. Collected Papers, Vol. III. London, Hogarth Press, 1925, pp. 183-144.
4. ——: Recollection, repetition and working through. Collected Papers, Vol. II. London, Hogarth Press, 1924.
5. ——: A General Introduction to Psychoanalysis. New York, Liveright, 1935, p. xix.
6. ——: Transference. Psychoanalytic therapy. Ibid.
7. RADO, SANDOR: The relationship of patient to therapist. Psychoanalysis of Behavior. Collected Papers. New York, Grune & Stratton, 1956.
8. ——: Pathodynamics and treatment of traumatic war neuroses (traumatophobia). Ibid.
9. ——: Psychodynamics as a basic science. Ibid.
10. ——: Mind, unconscious mind, and brain. Ibid.
11. ——: Emergency behavior, with an introduction to the dynamics of conscience. Ibid.
12. ——: On the psychoanalytic exploration of fear and other emotions. Ibid.
13. ——: Recent advances in psychoanalytic therapy. Ibid.
14. ——: Dynamics and classification of disordered behavior. Ibid.
15. ——: Hedonic control, action-self and the depressive spell. Ibid.
16. ——: Adaptational psychodynamics; a basic science. Ibid.
17. ——: Adaptational development of psychoanalytic therapy. Ibid.

14

WAITING ROOM OBSERVATION AS A TECHNIQUE FOR ANALYSIS OF COMMUNICATION BEHAVIOR IN CHILDREN AND THEIR PARENTS

By EMMA M. LAYMAN, PH.D., AND REGINALD S. LOURIE, M.D.*

AS COMMUNICATION THEORY has evolved in the last few years and has found application in various behavioral sciences, the value of observation made under as many conditions as possible has become apparent. One type of readily available direct observation has long been known to offer material pertinent to the understanding of the communication of feelings. Classic, alluded-to examples have been the behavior of the expectant father in the obstetrics ward, the nervous job applicant, and the student about to take an examination. The present study consists of an exploration of one approach to the use of similar direct observation as a technique for analysis of communication behavior in children and their parents. It is proposed to consider the contributions which can be made by waiting room observations in a psychiatric clinic for children.

OBSERVATION AS A CLINICAL METHOD

It has been stated repeatedly that observation is the basic unit of science. As with scientific method, the clinical method is based on observation. In the psychiatric setting, the observation consists of "the noting of behavior as it occurs,"[5] with the examiner or therapist functioning as a participant-observer. Without such observation there would be no diagnostic interviews, no psychological testing and no therapeutic sessions.

In the arrangement of the modern child guidance clinic, social workers seldom make home visits. Hence, in the usual clinic, direct observation of the parents takes place in the office of the social worker and/or that of the psychiatrist; direct observation of the child takes place

* Department of Psychiatry, Children's Hospital of the District of Columbia, Washington, D. C.

in the playroom and in the office of the psychologist. Ordinarily there is little or no systematic direct observation of parent and child together, so that conclusions concerning the nature of parent-child relationship or communication must be inferred from the evaluative comments of parents, teachers and agency workers, and from the indirect approach to the study of such relationships and communication patterns through the play interview and other projective techniques. As members of the clinic staff walk through the waiting room, they note the behavior of children and their parents; but reports of these observations may or may not find their way into the permanent records of the patients involved. The various examiners also tend to note and record routinely observations of communication behavior involving parent and child when the child is asked to leave his mother or father to accompany the examiner. Not infrequently the clinic secretary or receptionist relates to a member of the professional staff incidents which she has noted in the waiting room. Behavior which she observes is often described and discussed in staff conferences but these descriptions or reports seldom become a part of the clinic files.

The need for more extensive direct observation of parent and child together and for more observation of spontaneous behavior of the child has been recognized by child guidance workers, and various clinics are experimenting with different approaches to meeting this need. One such approach being tried in several clinics consists of "group" interviews with the child and his parents together. A variation of this procedure, suggested by Frankl,[1] consists of having a short play observation preceding the interview with the mother and taking place in the presence of the mother. Such approaches represent rather radical departures from usual child guidance clinic practices.

Regardless of the basic framework within which a psychiatric clinic for children operates, it would appear that the behavior manifested by children and their parents in the waiting room may provide a wealth of material which can contribute significantly to the understanding of the child and his family, particularly from the standpoint of communication patterns. However, the full realization of the clinical insight which could be gained from such observations is not possible unless these observations are made more systematically and under conditions designed to render them considerably more scientific than they tend to be in most clinics.

Direct observation of spontaneous behavior has long been considered a respectable method of gathering research data and of acquiring solutions to a variety of problems in nonpsychiatric settings such as well baby clinics, nursery schools, child development laboratories, and industrial organizations. In these settings much has been learned about the usefulness of such observation for gaining information about people and most of the knowledge acquired is applicable in the clinical setting. It has been generally recognized that sporadic and undirected observations take into account only the more startling and conspicuous events or those to which the observer has some emotional reaction, so that equally significant behavior of a less obtrusive nature may be overlooked. In all settings where direct observation has been used for the gathering of scientific data, the importance of using trained observers has been stressed. On this basis, it might be postulated that the observations of a psychiatrist, psychologist or social worker would possibly have more to contribute than would those of the clinic secretary. However, it would seem that there are many secretaries and receptionists who could be trained to be quite competent observers; too, these persons are able to observe shifts in the parents' handling of the child whether a professional staff member is present or absent, whereas the professional staff member makes observations under conditions such that the parent may feel that he is perhaps "under observation."

Preliminary Study

The present study grew out of an earlier study in which the practicality of using waiting room observation as a diagnostic tool was explored. In the preliminary study, an attempt was made to identify and define certain significant behavior patterns which might be conveniently observed in the waiting room of a child guidance clinic, and to construct a guiding outline indicating specific behavioral incidents to be observed and recorded. This was accomplished in four steps: (1) A collection was made of incidental waiting room observations reported by members of the professional staff of the Department of Psychiatry at Children's Hospital and recorded in the clinic charts of one hundred children. To this collection were added the observations made by secretaries for ten cases seen in the clinic, and observations on fifteen children and their mothers made by nursery school teachers in the waiting room of the hospital well baby clinic. (2) The observations were broken down into specific behavioral items and these were classified in terms of general areas of behavior or development. (3)

The lists of items and areas were presented to the members of the staff of the Department of Psychiatry for discussion. This discussion resulted in the deletion or addition of some items and reclassification of others. (4) An observation outline was prepared, based on the staff discussion. This outline served as the basis for a form to be used in recording observations. The form (included at the end of this chapter) consists of three parts. Part I is used for recording information concerning the circumstances under which the observations were made. Part II is an observation check list on which the observer checks items descriptive of the characteristics or behavior patterns which he observes and writes in explanatory phrases as needed. Part III is a blank space on which the observer writes a narrative, chronological summary of his observations.

The observation outline has been tried out in the Department of Psychiatry at Children's Hospital with secretaries serving as observers. In many instances the results of these observations have been found to be very helpful in rounding out the diagnostic picture.

Procedure in Present Study

Initial experiences with the observation outline indicated that a different kind of communication behavior was observed in the waiting room setting from that manifested in the formal examination situation, so that this might be especially valuable as an additional approach to the problem of understanding impairment of communication in children and their parents. As a means of testing out this impression, the following procedure was carried out: (1) The two clinic secretaries were given instructions concerning observational procedures and the use of the observation outline. In these instructions, stress was placed on the importance of recording everything observed and on avoiding participation in a relationship with the child or his parents except as such participation was called for by the role involved in the other clinic duties of the observer. (2) Thirty children (each with one or both of the parents present) were observed in the waiting room during diagnostic study and five children undergoing treatment were observed two or more times, with intervals of two to six months occurring between observations. In all, 43 sets of observations were made. Thirty of these were made by secretaries and the remainder by other staff members—psychiatrist, psychologist or social worker. The observation reports on each child were filed in his case folder for the use of staff members and were included in data discussed at diagnostic and treatment conferences. (3) Each set of observations was analyzed in terms of its significance from the standpoint of communication patterns. In making this analysis, the observations were scrutinized in terms of what they had to offer in answering each of the seven questions about communication suggested by Ruesch[3] as being basic for the analysis of disturbances in any communication system. (4) The observations were evaluated on the basis of their clinical usefulness in facilitating diagnosis and treatment.

Observation Setting

All observations were made in the waiting room of the Department of Psychiatry, Children's Hospital. This is a very small room which also serves as the office for the two clinic secretaries. It contains desks and other equipment for the secretaries, open book shelves filled with books and magazines, and three or four chairs for patients. A door to the outside opens off this room, as do doors to the rest room and to three offices.

Results of Study

Analysis of the 43 sets of observations and assessment of the uses to which they were put in the clinical setting yielded the following findings: (1) In all cases the waiting room observations were found to lend themselves readily to analysis in terms of disturbance in the various aspects of communication. (2) When used clinically to supplement other diagnostic approaches, such observations made significant contributions to the understanding and evaluation of problems involving impairment of communication in children and their parents. (3) In the therapeutic situation, the waiting room observations were found helpful as guides in planning treatment sessions. The samples of parent-child interaction observed provided material which, in the interview or in play therapy, could be analyzed and discussed with the individuals involved. (4) When used with children and parents who were undergoing therapy, the waiting room observations reflected improvement in parent-child communication resulting from treatment. Such improvement was usually noted in the waiting room behavior before it became characteristic of the parent-child communication patterns outside the clinic, so that waiting room behavior in a sense served as a prognosticator of what was to come. These findings can best be illustrated by excerpts from the narrative summaries of observations on a few typical cases. (These excerpts are of necessity condensed, and represent only a small fractional part of the observations actually recorded.)

Case 1. *Jane*

Jane is an eight-year-old girl with a six-year history of asthma, which resulted in the mother's sleeping with the child almost every night and the mother's life in general being controlled by the child's symptoms. For a period of two weeks preceding the diagnostic study the patient had been free of asthma but refused to go to school, complaining of other physical ailments which were found to have no organic basis. The mother had been married three times and divorced twice. Jane was the child of the second husband, and the mother apparently had many men in the home between her second and third marriages. The waiting room observations show clearly the type of disturbance in communication involved in this mother-child relationship.

Jane and her mother entered the clinic hand in hand. The child did not respond to the secretary's greeting and the mother just looked at the clock and noted that they were early. The mother unbuttoned and removed Jane's coat while the child stood passively. Then, after removing her own coat, the mother took Jane on her lap and the youngster leaned against her mother's shoulder. Jane looked rather pale and listless and the mother stated that the child had been nauseated that morning. As they were waiting, Jane occasionally whimpered, and the mother responded to this by holding her more tightly and saying, "Poor baby." The child would then cling more tightly to her mother. Toward the end of the waiting period the mother's voice took on overtones suggestive of annoyance, and when the examiner led the child away, the mother heaved a sigh of relief. After Jane had left, the mother said she hoped the child would not be sick in the playroom, and commented about what an inconvenient time it was for her to have become ill.

Case 2. *Sandra*

Sandra is a ten-year-old girl referred for psychiatric study because of obesity. The sixth of seven children, she is her father's favorite. When she is frightened by storms at night she goes to her parents' bed, making it necessary for her father to move out. The mother complains that the child will not stay on her diet and that the father, who is diabetic, will not stay on his diet either. The very distorted communication patterns in this family are brought out in the waiting room behavior observed.

Sandra is a large, very obese child who came to the clinic accompanied by both parents. The mother's response to the secretary's greeting was, "Can you buy food here?" After learning that she could she removed Sandra's coat, smoothed the child's dress, and asked her if she were hungry. Sandra smiled inappropriately and said, "No." The mother then told her firmly that she *was* hungry, that mother would get her food, and that she would eat it. Sandra said, "Yes," as easily as she had said, "No," and with the same mechanical, fixed smile. Her "yes" and "no" were spoken with inflections like those of a child of three or four. The father in the meantime had quietly removed his hat and sat down. The mother, seating herself and Sandra, turned to the father and instructed him to "go sit in the car and smoke." He put his hat back on and left without a word. After the father had departed the mother went to the snack bar for food, announcing that Sandra must be starved as she had not eaten since seven o'clock and it was then ten. During her mother's absence Sandra sat silently, remaining motionless. The mother returned with bags of food—all sweets. She sat down next to Sandra and said, "Eat it—you're hungry." Sandra accepted the food and drank two cups of cocoa. When the examiner entered the room and greeted the child, Sandra had not quite finished eating, but put down her roll and prepared to leave. However, the mother insisted that she finish her snack and said that the examiner could wait. After finishing, Sandra got up and went docilely with the examiner. During the waiting time the mother kept moving her chair closer to Sandra's. She also looked at the child constantly and kept fussing over her, fixing her dress and wiping her face. Most of the mother's verbal communications directed at Sandra had to do with food, although before the child left the mother also said, "I hope they don't find nothing wrong with you because they ain't nothing wrong anyhow." She commented to the world at large, "Hope we don't have to come back here no more. It's a long trip and I don't see what for anyhow."

Case 3. *Wendell*

Wendell is a four-year-old referred for psychiatric evaluation because of retarded development and hyperactive, distractible, and aggressive behavior. The diagnostic study indicated that the presenting symptoms were probably secondary to organic brain damage, but that out of the basic disturbance had grown a distorted mother-child relationship, with the mother needing to exert control all the time and neither mother nor child being able to trust the other. The communication of these feelings was noted in the waiting room behavior.

When the secretary entered the waiting room, Wendell and his mother were seated together, each looking at a comic book. The mother responded briefly to secretary's greeting. Soon Wendell got up from his chair and began moving about, picking up and examining objects on the secretary's desk, and investigating the bookcase, although he did not move more than a few feet from his mother. He made throaty noises, moved his hands in a jerky fashion, grimaced, and hit himself on the head from time to time, but did not speak. The mother remained seated while Wendell was moving about, but appeared stiff and tense.

She followed the child with her eyes and scolded him continually, anticipating that he would do something he shouldn't and objecting to everything he did do. The child responded in such ways as to cause the secretary to comment that he "seemed like a puppet with strings, manipulated by a passive but domineering mother." When the examiner invited Wendell to the playroom he hung back, and the mother pushed him toward the examiner, saying, "Go see what it is." After five minutes in the playroom Wendell came out crying, looking for his mother. She said, "I'm not going anywhere, boy," and he reluctantly returned to the playroom. This procedure repeated itself a few minutes later, at which time the examiner requested that the mother go to the playroom with the child.

Case 4. Billy

Billy is a nine-year-old who at the age of seven was referred to the Department of Psychiatry because of enuresis, encopresis, and destructive behavior. The second child and only boy in a family of four children, Billy is the son of very immature parents; a disinterested father who expresses himself by means of temper tantrums and psychosomatic symptoms and an unconsciously seductive mother who sets no limits. Both parents make extensive use of withdrawal as a means of expressing aggression and as a defense against anxiety. Mother and child have been in treatment for approximately a year. The first set of observations reported showed the patterns which were characteristic of the communication disturbances still in existence after six months of treatment. The second set of observations, six months later, gave a glimpse of a healthier type of communication which was beginning to develop, but with more than a trace of the old pattern still present.

First Observation Session. Billy and his mother frowned their way into the clinic, with mother grunting in response to secretary's greeting and Billy saying nothing. After removing their wraps, both selected reading material and sat down with a vacant chair between them, the chair serving as a repository for the mother's purse and shopping bag. Both became engrossed in their reading and neither spoke during the ten-minute waiting period. When Billy and his mother were greeted by their therapists, the mother scrambled to her feet, gathered up her possessions, returned her magazine to the bookcase, and entered her therapist's office, all without a word. Billy mumbled an almost inaudible acknowledgement of his therapist's greeting but did not look up from his comic book. The therapist suggested that he come to the playroom when he was ready and left the waiting room. Billy remained there for perhaps another five minutes, then moved off to the playroom, nose still buried in the book.

At the end of the playroom session, Billy returned to the waiting room and again sat down with a book. The mother joined him shortly, put on her coat, then held out Billy's coat to him, saying in a monotone, "Come on, let's go." Billy made no move to comply. For several minutes the mother stood over him silently, holding the coat, frowning, and grinding her teeth. Then she moved to the door and opened it. Finally she spoke impatiently, saying, "Come *on!*" Billy moved slowly out the open door, still reading, while the mother followed, carrying his wraps.

Second Observation Session. Six months later Billy and his mother came in talking and smiling. They both spoke pleasantly to the secretaries as they removed their coats. The mother sat down while Billy went to the bookcase, and she exchanged comments with a staff member about vacation trips which both had taken. When Billy sat beside his mother, she turned her attention to him as he read aloud to her from the book of riddles which he had selected. When his therapist approached. Billy looked up and said, "Hi." He and his mother continued to read for a few seconds, laughed about one of the riddles, and got up together to go for their appointments.

After his therapy session Billy resumed his reading, draping himself over two chairs. He accepted candy from the secretary, smiling and saying, "Yes, please." When the mother returned to the waiting room she told Billy that they would have to hurry, because she had an errand to do. He slumped back in his chair playfully, with a grin on his face, but got up as the mother handed him his coat. Both responded appropriately to the secretary's goodbyes and left the clinic with a relaxed and companionable air, talking about what they were going to do on the way home.

Case 5. Carl

Carl is a six-year-old who has been in treatment for three years, originally having been referred for psychiatric study because of convulsions due to lead encephalitis, excessively aggressive behavior toward his infant brother, and depression following his father's desertion. The mother is a passive individual whose effectiveness in functioning has been further hampered by a progressive loss of vision of unknown etiology. Improvement in communication functions in mother and child is illustrated by two sets of observations made about a year apart. These represented the first and last of a series of observations made during the third year of treatment, with the last set of observations made when treatment was being tapered off preparatory to termination.

First Observation Session. Carl ran out of the playroom following his therapy session but ignored his mother who was sitting in the waiting room waiting for the social worker. Carl ran around the room, grabbed at papers, and attempted to bang on the typewriter. When the secretary asked him to stop, he hit her, tried to kick her, and called her a vulgar name. The mother's reaction to this was to say rather blandly, "You mustn't do that, Carl—it's not nice." Carl then said something "silly" which the secretary did not quite get and swaggered off to the playroom. He returned almost immediately with a toy locomotive, which he played with on the floor by the secretary's desk. He looked up and said, "Will you help me with this?" The mother said, with irritation in her voice, "You know how to do that yourself." The secretary wound the engine for Carl, giving him a smile that was intended to be reassuring. At this point the social worker returned and spoke to the mother. The mother got up and said, "Come on, Carl, we're going." Carl ran to the playroom and then tore out into the courtyard, yelling at the top of his lungs.

Last Observation Session. A year later, Carl dashed in, ignored secretary's greeting, and sat down next to another child who was reading, looking over the boy's shoulder until the other boy relinquished the book to him. The mother followed him in. She remained seated and almost immobile. When she spoke her voice was soft and without much inflection and her face was without expression. Carl's voice was loud and he made strange sounds. After a few minutes with a comic, he got up, looked at the pictures on secretary's calendar and asked, "What's this?" The secretary explained, "England—a country across the water." Carl said, "So people can drop in." His comment about the English houses pictured was, "They're blown up—BOMBS!" He ran to the typewriter and said, "Please?" The mother urged him to type his name and spelled it for him. The secretary indicated that he might type for just a minute, if he were very careful. During the waiting period the mother, although passive, watched Carl continually and was constantly criticizing and giving directions, saying, "Answer her, Carl," "Be careful, you'll break it," "That's not polite," but she made no attempt to keep him from bothering the secretary. When the secretary turned away from Carl to answer the phone, his eyes darted to her desk and he grabbed for her stapler. The mother's verbal admonishing at this point worked. After he had been typing for several minutes the mother said, "Don't you think it's enough? Come look at a comic book—come on now, *Carl!*" He obeyed quietly. For the remainder of the waiting time he sat and read, offering the mother a comic book, but did not talk to the mother except to make one comment about the book.

Discussion

Insight into disturbances in parent-child communication patterns is basic to an understanding of the psychopathology of childhood. An analysis of these disturbances is essential to adequate diagnostic formulation in cases referred to child guidance clinics, and improvement in communication is one of the major goals of psychotherapy. In waiting room behavior we see the elements of parent-child communication which characterize their relationship at home and which therefore provide valuable information for use in diagnosis and therapy.

A review of the cases cited indicates that each one involves disturbance in various aspects of parent-child communication. In the case of Jane we find a relationship based on a type of physical contact inappropriate to the child's age, with the child and mother both communicating in terms of the infantile role assumed by the child. This is exemplified in the lap-sitting and in the mother's verbalizations. We find somatic symptoms and physical contact used by the child to express anxiety and hostility and to control the mother. The mother responds with anxiety and hostility expressed in voice inflection, words, sighs, and clutching of the child. She also responds with compliance in the sense of letting the child control her. The feedback mechanisms involved are illustrated in the child's increased clinging. Thus we see in the waiting room behavior evidences of disturbance in communication which, against a background of information about life experiences, help to explain the symptoms which brought the child to a psychiatric clinic.

Sandra also plays an infantile role in the mother-child relationship. Communication between mother and child centers about food and dependency, with mother apparently expressing aggression as she plies the child with food and fusses over her, and Sandra being the infant to the point of using speech minimally, with babyish inflections, and submitting to the mother's manipulations. We find the father reacting much as Sandra does, compliantly and silently carrying out his wife's demands. The mother's distortion of reality for the sake of perpetuating the eating patterns of which she complains was brought out quite clearly in the waiting room. This distortion of reality and the mother's infantilizing overprotectiveness would seem to constitute expressions of her need to relieve her feelings of guilt about her hostility toward this child. The child's difficulty in communicating adequately with anyone was shown by her inappropriate smile and by her very limited verbalization. The mother's anxiety was revealed in her comments about hoping that there was nothing wrong with Sandra, and the fact that this was communicated to the child was evidenced in her subsequent behavior in a session with the psychologist.

In the case of Wendell, especially outstanding was the mother's assumption of the role of control system for the child so that his dependency was expressed in terms of his need for control, and child-parent communication centered about this need. In this area, the mother's verbal communication apparently was successful in attaining the desired result of restraining the child's actions. It was chiefly through the waiting room observations, however, that it became clear that the child's nonverbal attempts at communication got through to the mother to only a limited degree, although she did recognize the manifestations of his separation anxiety.

Clinical use of the data obtained for this study has indicated that having access to information obtained through direct observation of mother and child in an extraclinical setting saves time in the diagnostic study and makes the diagnostic picture more complete, since it is then possible for material not included in the history or complaint to become a part of the diagnostic formulation. It opens up areas about which the mother has been sufficiently anxious or unaware to make it possible for her to keep them out of the information given in the initial history. Where mother-child interaction involves a passive mother this is especially valuable. This material also helps the examiner to know how a particular child should be approached in terms of the type of anxiety he is exhibiting. If the anxiety is primarily around separation, then separation can be made less traumatic by including the mother at the beginning in a session with the child. If the mother's feelings about the nature of the child's relationship with the examiner involve anticipations and distortions of such a nature as to create apprehension in the child, knowledge of this situation can guide the examiner in selecting an appropriate kind of reassurance. When the child in the waiting room has been allowed to build up excitement to such a pitch that he is difficult to control, handling by the examiner can be geared toward supplying controls from the beginning. Helpful to the examiner, also, are information about the manner in which the child becomes involved in the parent's anxiety and vice versa, and information about the ways in which the parent reacts to the child's fears.

In interpreting diagnostic findings to parents and giving them suggestions, it has been found that the examiner can make his suggestions much more specific and practical if a member of the staff has actually seen and heard the interaction between parent and child so that the examiner has concrete information about the ways in which the parent and child function together.

When a child and his parents are in therapy, any observable pattern of interaction between parent and child in the waiting room is as much a part of the treatment session as what goes on in the office or playroom. In fact, some forms of acting out of feelings about the therapy situation are possible only in the anteroom. The purpose, meaning, genesis, and modification of behavior observed can all be properly of concern to the patient and therapist, with discussion of the patterns being a part of the treatment procedure. Such discussion may serve as a means of opening up other areas of information which otherwise might not be available. In the case of Billy, the material reported in the first set of observations was used in treatment sessions with both mother and child. In working with Billy the pattern of withdrawal was brought into focus and it became clear to him that this was a pattern by which the parents communicated and dealt with each other as well as with him and that it had elements of aggression, avoidance, and substitution. The material was used with the mother in helping her to see it as a symbol of how isolated Billy felt and as a basis for discussing his need to have her reach out to him and assert herself with firmness, instead of fuming and remaining paralyzed. In the case of Carl, the behavior of the mother in the waiting room was used in therapy to give him a picture of how helpless the mother felt and how anxious it made him. Since he could not supply his own controls, his ineffectual mother increased his own feeling of helplessness, with an increase in frustration and aggression. In therapy he was able to see this and to build up a tolerance for his mother, who was having additional problems stemming from organic difficulties. His own waiting room behavior was used to help him understand the relation between his loss of control, aggression, and fear of not being liked. This material was used by the mother's therapist to help her to gain similar insights.

The case of Carl shows how waiting room behavior of parents and children in treatment may reflect improvement in parent-child communication. The last set of observations shows the mother still passively aggressive while at the same time permitting the child to interfere with the work of the secretaries. Carl is still having some trouble with impulse control, is still concerned about aggression as a source of bodily hurt, and still resorts to silliness as a defense against anxiety. However, improved intrapersonal communication is shown in his increased ability to supply his own internalized controls, and improved mother-child communication is shown in his response to his mother's directions. The improvement observed in the waiting room is characteristic of Carl's adjustment at home and in the community. Despite the mother's poor physical condition and a home situation characterized by much social pathology, Carl is understanding of his mother's difficulties, is participating in a rather mature fashion in family planning, and has been getting along well in kindergarten.

In the case of Billy, the picture presented in the waiting room at the time of the second set of observations was not characteristic of the typical mother-child communication pattern outside the clinic. However, this incident served as a preview of what was to come, for a few weeks later Billy began to abandon withdrawal in favor of more active involvement with people and the mother turned from a preoccupation with her own marital difficulties to a pattern of taking more positive steps to reach out to Billy and of dealing with the problem of limits with more firmness.

Not illustrated in these cases, but frequently observed, were differences in communication behavior before and after a diagnostic or treatment session. Such observations were extremely helpful in evaluating the effect of the experience on the patient and in assessing the significance of the material revealed by the parent or the child in the diagnostic or treatment interview.

The observational excerpts presented here were selected as being illustrative of communication disturbances involved in parent-child relationships. A more complete presentation of the observational reports would show more clearly the nature of the child's communication with other persons, which might or might not resemble his communication with the parents. In cases in which the child was observed once with the mother and once with the father, sometimes rather striking differences were observed in the two relationships.

In the present exploratory study, no attempt at quantification of data was made. However, the use of the observation check list provides information in a form which lends itself to easy coding, and so provides material which could be used in research requiring statistical treatment. Several studies of this sort are being planned, with observations and observers being more thoroughly trained.

When waiting room observation is used as a clinical tool, the use of both a check list and a narrative report has been found to provide a more complete record than can be obtained by the use of either the check list or running observations alone. In addition, when observations are made by observers who are not professionally trained, the use of the check list helps to minimize the distortions based on personal biases and interests, although even with the check list the examiner or therapist must evaluate the information in terms of what he knows about the observer.

Experiences with waiting room observations suggest that other peripheral or extraclinical observations would be of value in rounding out the picture of any patient being studied or in treatment. It is hoped that this type of experience would encourage the use of direct observation of the patient wherever he might be—whether in the clinic or outside its doors. In the hospital setting, ward observations and observations in various nonpsychiatric out-patient clinics have provided very useful material. It is suggested that specific training to develop observational skills might well be included in courses offered medical secretaries as well as in the training of those whose professions demand the use of observation as a clinical technique or for research.

CHILDREN'S HOSPITAL OF THE DISTRICT OF COLUMBIA
Department of Psychiatry

*Schedule C**

Waiting Room Observations

Name of Patient: ______________________ Date: __________
Observed by: ______________________

Part 1. Reference Data

Purpose of Visit—Diagnostic or Treatment

If Diagnostic,

- 1st, 2nd, or 3rd visit for child
- 1st, 2nd, 3rd, or 4th visit for parent
- Observations before, during, or after child's session with examiner
- Observations before, during, or after parents' session with examiner

If Treatment,

- Observations before or after treatment session

Observation of

- Parent alone (which parent?)
- Child alone (if alone, why?)
- Child and parent (which parent?)
- Others

Observations made for how many minutes?

Was patient early, on time, or late for appointment? Reason?

What others were in the waiting room when observations were made?

Part 2. Observation Check-list

I. Entering clinic

A. General

1. Child and parent together
2. Child first, followed by parent
3. Parent first, followed by child
4. Child and parent hand in hand
5. Parent pushing child
6. Parent pulling child

* A more recently revised check list, Schedule D, is now available.

7. Parent alone
8. Child alone

B. Child
1. No verbal response when greeted by secretary
2. Minimal response when greeted
3. Friendly response when greeted
4. Clings to parent when greeted
5. Turns away or hangs head when greeted
6. Removes coat
7. Keeps coat on
8. Accepts help with coat, if offered
9. Refuses help with coat, if offered

C. Parent
1. No verbal response when greeted by secretary
2. Minimal response when greeted
3. Friendly response when greeted
4. Removes coat
5. Keeps coat on
6. Removes child's coat

II. Child's characteristics and activities

A. General appearance
1. Neat, clean
2. Messy, dirty

B. Speech
1. No vocalizations observed
2. Babbling and jargon only
3. Speaks in single words, short sentences, or longer sentences
4. Baby talk
5. Foreign accent
6. Southern accent
7. Poor articulation
8. Unintelligible
9. Stuttering
10. Loud voice
11. Voice almost inaudible
12. Explosive speech
13. Excessively precise speech
14. Normal speech

C. Facial expression and posture
1. Facial expression
   a. Smiles (appropriately)
   b. Smiles (inappropriately)
   c. Frowns or glowers
   d. Cries
   e. Appearance of fright
   f. Unhappy appearance
   g. Expressionless

2. Posture
   a. Head down
   b. Erect
   c. Relaxed
   d. Suggestive of "cockiness"
   e. Belligerent stance
   f. Slumped
   g. Stiff

D. Motility and coordination
   1. Which hand preferred
   2. Sits motionless
   3. Runs around room—gets into things—hyperactive
   4. Awkward movements with hands
   5. Broad-based gait
   6. Poor balance
   7. Bumps into things
   8. Jerky movements
   9. Limps

E. Tics and habits
   1. Twitches
   2. Bites nails
   3. Sucks thumb or finger
   4. Tears cuticle
   5. Picks nose
   6. Drools
   7. Wets pants
   8. Soils pants
   9. Goes to restroom more than once

F. Requests made of adults
   1. Drink
   2. Food
   3. Toilet
   4. Toys
   5. Attention—"look at me"
   6. Help
   7. Reading material

G. Activities
   1. General characteristics
      a. Aggression
      b. Destructiveness
      c. Messiness
      d. Neatness
      e. Show-off
      f. Initiative in choosing activity
      g. Passivity
   2. Specific characteristics
      a. What toys did child bring with him? Does he play with them?

b. Preferred toys and activities
c. How toys are used
d. Theme of imaginative play
e. Drawings
(1) What child draws
(a) Appearance
(b) Child's statement
(2) Verbalizations about drawings
(3) Paper or blackboard
(4) Color or black and white
(5) Colors used
f. Exploration
g. Eating
h. Coloring
i. Activities with books
(1) Books chosen
(2) Looks at pictures
(3) Reads
(4) Talks about books
j. Other verbalizations—to whom, what subjects
k. Reactions to broken things

III. Parent's characteristics and activities
A. General appearance and behavior
1. Neat
2. Messy
3. Calm
4. Harassed
5. Agitated
6. Poised
B. Speech
1. Foreign accent
2. Southern accent
3. Articulatory speech defect
4. Stuttering
5. Speaks foreign language to child
6. Uses baby talk with child
7. Loud voice
8. Voice almost inaudible
9. Explosive speech
10. Excessively precise speech
11. Normal speech
C. Facial expression and posture
1. Facial expression
a. Smiles (appropriately)
b. Smiles (inappropriately)
c. Frowns
d. Appears frightened

e. Appears unhappy
f. Expressionless
2. Posture
a. Head down
b. Erect but relaxed
c. Erect and stiff
d. Slumped
e. Threatening posture
D. Motility and use of waiting room space
1. Sits still
2. Shifts about in chair
3. Gets up, walks around
4. Uses more than one chair for self or possessions
5. Moves chair away from others
E. Tics and habits
1. Twitches
2. Bites nails
3. Tears cuticle
4. Tears paper
5. "Doodles"
6. Twists handkerchief
7. Picks nose
8. Goes to restroom more than once
9. Chain-smoker
10. Giggles
F. Activities
1. Attention to child while child is present
2. Engages in activities or conversation not involving attention to child, while waiting with child
3. While waiting for child or waiting for own appointment alone
a. Looks at magazines
(1) Gets own material or has to be offered reading material
(2) Choice of reading matter
(3) Reads or leafs through magazines
b. Leaves clinic, if waiting for child
(1) Returns in time to meet child
(2) Returns late, making child wait
c. Sits silently and passively
d. Removes coat
e. Knits, sews, makes grocery list, or engages in other activities
f. Talks to secretary or other parents
(1) Complains
(2) Asks questions
(3) Compliments
(4) Talks about child
(5) Talks about self
(6) Other subjects

IV. Child-parent relationships—general

A. Closeness of parent and child in waiting room

1. Sit together and communicate
2. Sit together but do not communicate
3. Sit apart
4. Child on parent's lap
5. Child leaning against parent
6. Child clinging to parent
7. Other excessive bodily contact between parent and child (specify)
8. Parent encouraging clinging or contact
9. Parent passively submits to clinging or excessive contact
10. Parent trying to push child away
11. Child moving about but returning to parent who is seated
12. Child moving about and not returning to parent
13. Parent following child who moves about

B. Parent's behavior toward child

1. Ignores child
2. Criticizes or corrects child
3. Overly permissive (lets child annoy secretaries, play with typewriters, leave waiting room, hit other children)
4. Controls child to point of interfering with spontaneity
5. Anticipates destructiveness—"be careful—you'll break something"—expresses fear of child's destructive impulses
6. Instructs child about proper behavior—politeness, not breaking things, avoiding messiness
7. Is brusque with child
8. Threatens hurt or punishment
9. Praises child
10. Reassures child
11. Belittles achievements
12. Encourages to achieve
13. Expresses affection—how?
14. Discusses activities and events with child
15. Helps child
16. Change in behavior when professional staff member is present (specify)

C. Child's behavior toward parent

1. Ignores parent
2. Demands parent's attention
3. Runs away from parent
4. Hides from parent
5. Disobedient
6. Defiant (verbally)
7. Hits, kicks, or pinches parent
8. Obedient
9. Positive response to correction
10. Seeks praise or reassurance

11. Discusses activities and events with parent
12. Asks parent for help
13. Expresses affection—how?

V. Child's relationships with sibling, if sibling present
1. Ignores
2. Plays with sibling
3. Quarrels with sibling
4. Hits, kicks, pushes, or pinches sibling
5. Shares with sibling
6. Takes toys away from sibling or refuses to share
7. Defends self against sibling's aggression
8. Lets sibling impose on him, without trying to protect own interests
9. Competes with sibling for attention from adults

VI. Child's relationships with other children (not siblings)
1. Ignores
2. Plays with other child
3. Plays with older, younger, or child of same age
4. Quarrels with other child
5. Hits, kicks, pushes, or pinches other child
6. Shares with other child
7. Takes toys away from other child or refuses to share
8. Defends self against other child's aggressions
9. Lets other child impose on him, without trying to protect own interests
10. Competes with other child for attention from adults

VII. Child's and parent's reactions to secretaries and other adults in the waiting room

A. Child
1. Ignores
2. Approaches, wants attention from
3. Bothers secretaries and other adults (including excessive liberties—specify)
4. Hits or attacks adults
5. Spontaneous conversation

B. Parent
1. Ignores others while waiting
2. Talks with secretaries or other parents
3. Asks permission to smoke

VIII. Separation patterns—reactions to examiner's approach or parent's leaving

A. Child
1. Refuses to be separated from parent—clings
2. Wants parent to come with him but can be persuaded to leave without parent
3. Wants to go with parent
4. Accompanies examiner with reluctance
5. Pulls away from examiner—cries, whimpers
6. Accompanies examiner but looks back

7. Accompanies examiner after reassurance by parent
8. Accompanies examiner willingly but without eagerness
9. Goes eagerly with examiner, when invited
10. Goes eagerly and enthusiastically, anticipating invitation
11. Changes in behavior when parent leaves (specify)

B. Parent
1. Insists on accompanying child
2. Reassures child
3. Scolds child
4. Threatens child
5. Cajoles child
6. Passive acceptance of separation

IX. Reactions to reunion after separation

A. Child
1. Runs to parent
2. Clings to parent
3. Casual approach
4. Eager to talk about session

B. Parent
1. Reaches out for child
2. Clings to child
3. Casual greeting
4. Question about session

X. Leaving clinic

A. General
1. Parent and child go out together—no communication
2. Parent and child go out together—talking
3. Parent and child hand in hand
4. Parent strides ahead—child follows
5. Child runs ahead—parent follows

B. Reactions to leaving clinic
1. Child
   a. Expresses reluctance to go
   b. Seems neither reluctant nor eager
   c. Expresses wish to hurry away
2. Parent
   a. Lingers to talk
   b. Rushes self and child out of door
   c. Leaves with no suggestion of disturbance or relief

Part 3. Narrative Summary:

Write running observations and narrative summary on other side of paper.

REFERENCES

1. Frankl, Anni W.: Diagnostic methods in child guidance and psychological counseling. Ment. Hyg. *21*: 579-598, 1937.

2. Ruesch, Jurgen: Psychiatry and the challenges of communication. Psychiatry *17*: 1-18, 1954.
3. ——: The therapeutic process from the point of view of communication theory. Am. J. Orthopsychiat. *22*: 690-701, 1952.
4. Symonds, Percival M.: Diagnosing Personality and Conduct. New York, Century, 1931, p. 24.
5. Watson, R. I.: The Clinical Method in Psychology. New York, Harper, 1951, p. 64.
6. Wilson, E. B.: An Introduction to Scientific Research. New York, McGraw-Hill, 1952, p. 21.

15

DEFENSIVE VERBAL COMMUNICATION PROCESSES IN PSYCHOTHERAPY

By HARRY A. TEITELBAUM, M.D., PH.D.*

PSYCHOLOGICAL ADAPTIVE PROCESSES are essentially trifaceted, having *feeling, expressive* and *symbolic* aspects. Defensive psychological adaptions, which are ego-constricting and thus limit reality goal attainment, are analogous on a higher level to Selye's[4] "diseases of adaptation." Defensive adaptations can be experienced subjectively as feelings of guilt, hostility, jealousy, independence, kindness, truthfulness, devotion, loyalty, etc. Reich[3] and Anna Freud[2] have discussed the nonverbal expression of defensive adaptations evidenced by a patient's attitude, facial expression, motor activity, manner of speech, etc. Defensive adaptations are also communicated verbally, as revealed below.

In psychotherapy all defensive communications, verbal and nonverbal, are utilized to gain insight into the patient's inhibiting, defensive adaptations which serve as resistances to the understanding of the underlying conflicts. Often the nonverbal defenses are more significant than those that are verbalized. However, we shall center our attention on defensive verbal communications utilized by a number of patients.

Defensive verbal communications often reveal the areas in which a patient's behavior is confined to the exclusion of other phases of life. Such defenses occur in at least two forms:

1. The patient refers to his or her behavior or preoccupations in terms that symbolize aggression or hostility. Since the latter are intolerable to the patient, the behavior or preoccupations are likewise intolerable, with the effect that the preoccupations stir up guilt and behavior is inhibited. The preoccupations or behavior symbolized by this type of defensive verbal expression are not constituents of the patient's overt character but are rather manifestations of the repressed feelings

*Phipps Psychiatric Clinic, The Johns Hopkins Medical School, Baltimore, Maryland.

and indicate how the patient could behave and does if released from inhibiting defenses.

2. The second type of verbalized defense symbolizes socially, culturally and morally sanctioned attitudes such as kindness, truthfulness, etc., which keep in repression antithetical feelings and behavior, as of aggression and hostility. The preoccupations and behavior represented by these verbalized defenses are often essential constituents of the patient's rigidly organized character structure.

Case 1. This patient illustrates several instances of the first type of defensive verbal communication referred to above.

A slender, fair, 36-year-old married woman, with a rather shy, passive-dependent personality, was motivated to seek psychiatric help when she became overwhelmed by anxiety rather abruptly. She was also obsessed with a phobia of dying, and suffered flushes, fear of fainting, and episodes of terror while driving a car or attending social or other activities. She sometimes felt as though everything were closing in on her. To counteract this she resorted to protective rituals, such as playing the radio, singing or chewing gum. When alone and depressed she harbored thoughts of harming herself. She became preoccupied with cancer when she learned that a friend suffered from this illness.

The patient was extremely solicitous about the happiness of her seemingly well-adjusted parents. She had no insight into the underlying hostility related to the fantasy that her parents were unhappy or into the associated guilt she was attempting to relieve by trying so hard to make them happy in her own terms. She was married to a man whose personality was quite like her own. His business required that he be out of town for a week or two at regular intervals. The patient had never adjusted to these periods of absence even though she knew that their livelihood depended on them to a significant degree. Some instances of this patient's defensive verbal communications are cited below.

In discussing her reluctance to ask her husband to refurnish their home, the patient deplored her tendency to *nag* him, as nagging was such an undesirable trait. It was pointed out that if nagging was so intolerable to her, and that if she referred to her requests as such, that she would then have to curtail these demands on her husband and resume her submissive attitude not only in behavior but also in thought. The patient admitted that she really never had nagged her husband, for she had always complied with his wishes. However, when her very limited ability to be aggressive, as indicated by her defensive expression that she was nagging, became evidenced to her, she did become very critical of her husband. She cried uncontrollably and talked about his reluctance to please her when she was well. Now he had to spend so much money on therapy. Though she did not grasp the significance of her own passive defensiveness or of the aggressive role her illness was playing, she was nevertheless able to feel and express open resentment toward her husband. It might be added that he did go to the expense of renovating their home later, with the hopes that this would facilitate her return to good health. Thus, the patient's illness did accomplish that which she had failed to achieve while well.

In this instance the verbal communication, *to nag,* was the defensive production that permitted the patient to continue the repression of her latent hostility. The awareness that her passive-dependent personality would hardly permit her to nag anyone served as the basis for the interpretation that this verbal expression, which symbolized something so distasteful to her, was being used as a defense against gaining insight into and giving vent to her latent aggressiveness.

At a later date the patient talked about her reaction to a phone call from her husband while he was on one of his business trips. She felt angry during the conversation and wanted to hurt him. This hostility was promptly counteracted by the remark, "Not that I resent his doing things without me. I let him play cards and golf." With her guilt assuaged in her ambivalence, her attitude could then swing back to hostility, with the expression of hope that something would happen to keep him at home. "His tonsils hurt; not that I want him sick, but I hoped it would keep him from going. When he calls, I usually say all is fine. I'm sick and tired of covering up, so sometimes I tell him the children are bad." She was particularly resentful during the summer, she added, "when all the fathers are home sitting out in back."

When her attention was called to her reference to the fathers, she responded, "I don't know why I said that. I was all tied up with the children. It was lonely." She began to cry.

"Are you one of the children?" she was asked.

"I feel like that. It's wrong and immature. I feel frightened. Each time he goes away it's taken out of me. It goes on and on—."

"You feel like one of the children," it was suggested.

"He is home to take care of us." She cried, complaining that she was not up to emergencies, and continued, "It's an alone feeling. His trips are to places he doesn't know where he is going to be." That was when she was most fearful. At such times when the children fought during dinner she felt like vomiting, and sometimes she did. "He babies me and I enjoy it so much, being like a child."

Before she was married, the patient had felt more competent. She had talents as a painter and had held an advertising job that made her feel more important then. If she did part-time work after her marriage, she felt like a different person. She felt that if she could continue to work it would help her to grow up and she wouldn't mind her husband's trips. When he was away she had her older son stay up later with her sometimes. She was proud of his progress in school, "like he's a little man." They had cocoa together at night occasionally and she didn't have that lost feeling when she retired.

The regressive defensive adaptation is quite apparent in this patient. There is evidence of intense motivation to gratify earlier emotional needs that were left unsatisfied. With this unattainable goal ever before her, most of her energies were confined to its partial fulfillment and to the maintenance of defensive adaptation that restricted her interests to activities that included little in the way of independent adaptation involving the attainment of current reality goals. Her shyness and her dependent relationship to her parents, husband, and a few friends fit well into this scheme. She painted and if some one complimented her work she brushed it aside. She could not accept it graciously despite her avid need for attention. She had to deny this need, another defensive adaptation. When this denial was called to her attention, she admitted that she always wanted to be more than she ever was, even to this day. She would have preferred being like a number of other people rather than herself. She referred to any tendency on her own part to please herself as *selfish.* It was suggested that this inability to please herself implied a lack of self-respect and that by referring to it by such an intolerable term as *selfish* she was able to perpetuate this self-devaluating attitude as morally and socially acceptable. She was later able to admit that she did get a big lift out of buying things for herself and her children. However, she still did not realize how this merely placated her dependent needs momentarily.

The patient had kept her illness a secret from her parents. It would make them too unhappy. She was later able to expose them to this stress, which they were able to withstand quite well. Her mother sometimes kept the patient company while her husband was away. This gave rise to much dependent gratification and some guilt, particularly about the housework her mother did. Formerly, the patient would not permit her mother to help in such matters at all. In addition, the patient was able to allow her children greater freedom in her mother's presence. She also dared to retire early if fatigued. Formerly, she would remain up for fear she would worry her mother if she went to bed early.

Case 2. This patient represents the second type of defensive verbal communication in which the latter symbolizes an essential aspect of her rigidly organized, overt character structure.

A moderately obese, 44-year-old married woman with a history of asthma, hay fever, and eczema since childhood was motivated to seek help through psychotherapy because she had achieved little relief medically. She received some encouragement from a cousin who, under psychotherapy, had been able to free herself of headaches and obsessive preoccupation with a brain tumor.

This very productive patient, who in transference acted out her defensive character by being compliant and agreeable for a long time, soon revealed enough of her underlying conflicts to permit the formulation that she was an intensely hostile person with a reaction-formation of genial submissiveness to the wishes of others. She had many neurotic symptoms which were exploited defensively, such as fatigue, depression, and provocation with her husband because he was so good it was exasperating. If she argued with anyone she felt guilty or sorry afterward. Bugs terrified her but she could not kill them. She would awaken her husband at night to do this. A very significant defensive disability consisted of her tendency to remain in her apartment in bed much of the time. She would avoid answering the door bell or telephone. She had no desire to see anyone socially, claiming that she lacked the proper clothes to go out.

Her earlier history was quite fertile for the personality she developed. Her aggressive, self-centered mother and passive-submissive father were extremely incompatible. They were divorced when the patient was 23 years old. Her mother continued as a cold, punitive person who gratified none of the dependent needs of the patient or her two sisters, 39 and 43 respectively. The patient and her next younger sister had not talked to each other since the former was 18 because of an argument about a pair of stockings. The patient was married to a man who was the antithesis of her mother. He was like a "good mother" to her. Later in therapy the patient's hostility to her mother expressed itself explosively and with much guilt. She was able to break out of the confinement of her strangling defensive adaptations to a significant degree and become quite active socially; but not without much ambivalence in her relations with others.

As in case 1, this patient harbored a minimum of self-respect. Following a mastectomy for a malignancy, she had much discomfort. She had to put on a bold front. "If I stop laughing, I will break down and cry," she confessed. "I feel it is *selfish* to be concerned with my own comfort." Even at a time in therapy when her life had become considerably broadened she had to consider any self-interest in terms of selfishness, which was inexcusable. This made it morally untenable for her to seek gratification of her deep-seated personal needs. She continued to see herself as an unworthy person, just as her mother saw her. She did not want to worry her mother with her illness, as in case 1. She was really protecting herself from guilt rather than her mother from stress. The latter had never been sympathetic when the patient was ill as a child and even ridiculed her when injured. If one of the children became sick, the mother's reaction would be, "How can I stand this?" Her concern was for herself, not for the sick child.

On another occasion, the patient expressed doubts that certain people liked her. She had the desire to call them but set up a formidable barrier to such action with the thought, "Why should I go *crawling* after them?" It was called to her attention that by referring to initiative on her part by means of such a despicable expression as *crawling* she could more easily remain inactive. (Of course, the crawling also indicates her own self-evaluation.) The patient then admitted that these people had been lovely to her, yet she harbored doubts about them. She felt that they were drifting away. Finally, she thought, "I'm going to hold on for dear life." This kept going through her mind repeatedly. She experienced an awful feeling of shame. She wondered, "Why should I be so friendless that I have to hold on when not wanted?"

The continuing struggle with conflicts that were pertinent to actual experiences of her earlier years is quite evident here. With such strong motivation to achieve goals that were realistic at a much earlier period in life, when dependent-adaptation was appropriate, how could there be much motivation for achieving goals essential for a more mature adaptation to her current life?

The patient's inability to face her deep-seated resentment toward her father also motivated the development of significant defensive barriers. Her father visited the family after an absence in a nearby city for 25 years. She felt suspicious about his wants and was opposed to accommodating him in her home. She felt "*so sorry*" for him and turned over in her mind a variety of reasons for not taking him in. She advised her husband not to let her soften and became so disturbed that she almost called her therapist.

It was pointed out that the feeling she referred to as *sorrow* was preventing her from experiencing guilt for her deep-seated hostility towards her father.

The thought occurred to her repeatedly about telling him that he couldn't expect anything from her after 25 years. She wanted to ask him why he had come back but feared he would cry. The only good thing she could say about him was that he did not beat her; but the cursing was just as bad. She could not recall anything good about him.

The patient then complained that people stayed up nights trying to aggravate her.

"Are you not aggravating yourself?" It was suggested that she felt guilty about her hostility and the possibility of its expression.

She responded that she had no feeling for her father. She felt similarly about her mother. Did he expect them to throw their arms around him and greet him? The only time she ever did that was on a surprise visit from the Army. However, he left while the children were in school and didn't kiss them goodbye. She cried. Her sister teased her about it. After she grew up, he embarrassed her when she dated. She would wipe the make-up from her face before coming home, fearful that he might see her. He maintained that nice girls did not use make-up. He would "holler" at her if he saw make-up on other girls. Yet she always felt "*so sorry*" for him, especially when he tried to economize rigidly. "If I can only stop feeling sorry for people. I can hate people for making me feel sorry for them," she expostulated.

"Is it sorrow or guilt?" she was asked.

"I don't know. I just want to make sure they have enough money. If I learned my father was poor it would be the end of me." She was also afraid to ask about her mother's finances.

"You feel it is your fault if they are in need," it was suggested.

"I have always felt the financial burden. I was so young when I felt that. I keep telling myself he's not my responsibility. He's been away more years than I had him for a father." When he left, she felt he did not have enough money. She gave him ten dollars. She felt like getting even with him. She could have been dead by now without his knowing. If he had visited her in the hospital she would have told others that she had not seen him for 25 years.

It was pointed out again how feeling sorry relieved her of guilt for hating.

She responded with, "I used to think I never hated anyone."

In this patient the feelings of sorrow and the need to be generous and brave were all part of a rigid reaction-formation that prevented the expression of any of the intense and strongly repressed hostility she harbored.

Case 3. This patient revealed the second type of defensive-verbal expression in her need to be *nice* and *honest,* and the first type in an expression of independence which merely repressed her intense dependent needs.

The patient was a still attractive, 50-year-old woman, who gave the immediate impression of being well-bred with polished behavior and aloof poise. She was reared in a busy household where her parents had little time for the children. She felt lonesome and deserted most of the time and was thoroughly incompatible with her older brother, who was a "bully," and her oldest sister, who was extremely aggressive and vicious.

The patient's illness began when she was 12 years old. She had a disabling migraine with scotomata, headaches, speech disturbance, and numbness in various parts of her body. Her husband also suffered from migraine. He was quite as restrained as she was.

The patient was active in business. On one occasion a customer had come in to pay $3,000 at a time when the cleaning woman was the only one in. The latter did not bother to call the patient. Though chagrined, the patient could not tell this woman that she should have called her, as this would not have been *nice.*

"You use *niceness* as a way to avoid giving expression to your feeling," it was suggested.

"I have seen others blow up and fear I will do the same," she responded. She went to pieces several times. It was so embarrassing. She apologized the next day. She could hurt a lot of people. When she was pregnant, while she was cooking eggs, her husband said something. She could not recall what it was, but she threw the pan of eggs at him. About

15 years before she could not go anywhere because she was unable to control her bowels. Yesterday, she had had cramps and frequent movements—like explosions.

This patient also gave verbal expression to other defensive processes that contributed to the maintenance of her passive-submissiveness. "I cannot tolerate *dishonesty*, or the avoidance of admitting a wrongdoing," she professed.

"Such extreme honesty, along with niceness, prevents any aggressiveness from being expressed," it was suggested.

She "couldn't even tell a white lie." Her mother and father were very honest and were taken advantage of by others. Many people failed to pay their bills but her parents never did anything about it.

Another commonly expressed defensive verbal production pertains to *independence*. This patient felt very "independent" as she grew up.

"Independent or isolated?" she was asked.

If hurt she went off by herself. She never asked for help. When ill she never bothered her parents. She had had an operation years before and hadn't bothered her parents or friends. (Compare this with case 2.) About three years before she had gone to Philadelphia for surgery and hadn't let her husband go with her.

The tendency to refer to a strong urge to isolate oneself from others, and thus repress or deny dependent needs by means of the defensive verbal expression, *independence*, is seen in patients who are contemplating leaving intolerable homes to become *independent*, but who are unable to do so because of deep-seated dependency and fear of isolation. They usually have no close ties to others outside the family.

Case 4. A similar defensive pattern was evident in a 33-year-old single woman who lived with her divorced mother, to whom she was completely subservient. The patient suffered severe headaches and was obsessively convinced that she had a brain tumor. She felt that she should be "nice" to every one. Being nice involved no display of temper or free expression of one's thoughts. "I usually don't say to others what I think or feel. Why don't I say it? I say I don't mind doing something when I really do; and that I'm not frightened when I'm scared to death." It was in this sense that she felt she had to be nice to her overbearing mother.

Case 5. Another very immature, 46-year-old woman, who had been extremely submissive to her parents and husband and who was over-solicitous about her children, suffered anxiety, periods of obsessive-compulsive behavior, and intermittent hypomania and depression. She maintained that she was scrupulously *honest.* "I never lie. People know me for telling the truth," she maintained. In her naive honesty, when hypomanic, she unwittingly gave expression to much that embarrassed others, as a child might. Her husband tried to point out the inappropriateness of some of her truthful remarks but to no avail. To the patient it was sufficient that what she said was the truth as she saw it. It was lying that was harmful. Aggression was tolerable to her so long as it was concealed by the defensive cloak of honesty. She derived some emotional gratification from such aggression. She did feel guilty, however, when exposed to her husband's criticism of her aggressiveness. Her defense did not afford adequate protection against his exposure of her hostility.

This patient also devoted considerable energy to being *nice* to others. After a period of relative comfort she became depressed for several days. She felt she had been too aggressive and decided she would rather be *nice.*

"Do you mean appeasing?" she was asked.

"So I don't feel guilty. I often try to be nice to G. [daughter] but she resents it. She realizes she is being appeased."

Case 6. A very attractive but extremely immature 23-year-old young lady, whose parents were separated, lived with her mother, grandmother, and several other unbearable relatives. She was self-supporting and devoted much time to the issue of leaving her home and becoming *independent.* (See case 3.) Yet she did not dare to make the move. It was only when she became aware of how the idea of *independence* was concealing an ambivalent urge for isolation from those who failed to gratify her immature, dependent needs, and of the continuing but futile drive to achieve such gratification from them, that she gained some insight into her very dependent adaptation and was able to give up the defensive fantasy that independence or maturity was attainable by merely living alone.

Case 7. A rather common defensive verbal expression is that of *devotion.* A 35-year-old unmarried, boyish-looking, capable professional man could not accept responsibility without anxiety and feelings of inadequacy, or become intimately involved with people without much anguish and self-debasement. He often projected his feelings and was convinced that others found him rather incompetent. He was a product of a veritable Xanthippe of a mother and a nice, passive father. He felt eternally guilty about having deserted his mother when he left home, yet he could not recall many happy moments under her domination. Within this framework he expressed intense regressive feelings as follows: "I must not forget my mother. One should always be *devoted*. Respect, my father used to repeat. Honor your father and mother. My mother would never let me express myself as a child, yet I have to be devoted to her." His mother would not let the children go anywhere for fear they would tell others about the discord at home. However, when they were more grown she would complain because they did not go out and try to exonerate herself with the formula, "Am I holding them?"

After the patient gained some insight into the defensive role of the expression of devotion and realized that it made his submissiveness morally tenable, he was able to become aware of and give expression to his deep-seated resentment toward his mother.

Summary

Psychotherapy is a communication process involving mutual interchange between patient and therapist. This interchange involves nonverbal behavior and verbal or symbolized communication.

Defensive adaptations are often expressed verbally, and these are of two types: 1. Defensive verbal communications which may represent and may also give inadvertent expression to repressed hostile feelings, but which serve fundamentally as a basis for the continuation of repressed hostility to a high degree. The patients fantasy their defensive behavior and attitudes as being represented by these aggressive verbal communications which are quite intolerable, and they are thus motivated to continue their defensive behavior and attitudes. 2. Defensive verbal communications which may symbolize a rigid, defensive character formation that maintains repressed intense feelings, such as hostility, which cannot be expressed without experiencing overwhelming guilt.

Effective interpretation of defensive verbal communications is conducive to the release of repressed feelings and attitudes. However, as stressed by Fenichel, effective interpretation involves repeated working through of the superficial defenses to deeper levels; "—an interpretation is most effective when that which has just been described in words can be demonstrated simultaneously to the patient in his behavior at another point where he does not expect it, at another level."[1]

REFERENCES

1. Fenichel, O.: Problems of psychoanalytic technique. New York Psychonal. Quart. Inc., 1941.
2. Freud, A.: The Ego and the Mechanisms of Defense. New York, International Universities Press, 1954.
3. Reich, W.: Character-Analysis. New York, Orgone Institute Press, 1954.
4. Selye, H.: The Physiology and Pathology of Exposure to Stress. Montreal, Acta, 1950.

16

CHANGES IN LANGUAGE PATTERN AS ADAPTIVE MECHANISMS

By EDWIN A. WEINSTEIN, M.D.*

THE DEVELOPMENT OF IDEAS of the relationship of language and behavior in the past few decades, particularly in the work of Mead,[1] Sapir,[2] and Whorf,[3] has shown that language cannot be identified with individual physiological or perceptual processes. Rather, language is a type of social behavior that transcends the functions of the individual psychophysical organism. Sapir has pointed out that linguistic terms cannot be directly equated with the events of the physical world, but in both its structural and semantic aspects language is the product of an interaction in the environment. Sapir stressed that even our "oh's," "ah's," and "ouches" are not manifestations of biologically instinctive processes but are conventional systems of sound symbols which are socially determined. In the concept of the phoneme, sounds which are phonetically and physiologically distinct are heard as the same sound or felt to be insignificantly different variants of the same sound. Such classifications are purely arbitrary ones, to quote Sapir, "Romantic intrusions into the austere continuities of nature." The individual in his language organizes the environment and expresses a relatedness in it. Ordinarily the individual is quite unconscious of the degree to which his language classifies the environment and expresses this interaction. These formulations have become known in linguistics and anthropology as the Sapir-Whorf hypothesis. They are of particular significance for psychiatry where language has generally been regarded as the representation of perceptual and cognitive processes, and verbal expression has been equated with biological drives as affect or as manifestations of such faculties as memory, judgment, and insight.

Sapir and his student, Whorf, were led to their ideas by studies of North American Indian languages. They found that the speakers of these languages were able to form ideas and communicate in a gram-

* Neuropsychiatry Division, Walter Reed Army Institute of Research, Washington, D. C.

matical structure far different from that of the European languages. The speakers of any language are apt to believe that they designate the environment and use a logical system of thought in the only way in which it is possible to represent such reality. It was Whorf's belief that our space-time-matter classification of the environment is a manifestation of the organization of our language, or, as he put it, "language dissects nature." For example we use three tenses of verbs, past, present, and future, while in many Indian languages there are no such verb forms yet meanings are conveyed quite satisfactorily. The Indian verb suffix rather tells the relation of the speaker to the event, whether he saw it with his own eyes or saw evidence of it, as a footprint, or if it is something that he was told. In our speech these ideas are apt to be conveyed in more implicit fashion, through the largely unconsciously perceived aspects of the social situation. Whorf felt that in our language we concretize and spatialize time, forming what to the analyst of language are arbitrary units like ninepins in a row. Thus, to us 10 days is a "natural" unit or concept. To the Hopi Indian this has no validity, though he may use the term the "tenth day." Whorf also notes the absence of metaphor from Hopi speech. He points out that we use physical-spatial metaphors constantly in expressing ideas as in "our attention wandering," "losing the thread," etc. According to Whorf, the Hopi do not use space terms where space is not involved.

Now even in our own everyday speech the syntactical forms of our language do not have arbitrary meaning in the sense of directly reflecting the physical world. Events of the past may be related in the present tense, in the so-called dramatic present—as in a Damon Runyon story. The editorial "we" usually accompanies an expression of the opinions of an individual person. When one uses a metaphor such as "pulling the wool over one's eyes," speakers and listeners do not feel that the phrase concerns sheep. In a sentence such as, "The path goes down to the lake," it is not actually the path that "goes" or moves; movement, if any, is in ourselves. In all of these examples both the average speaker and his auditors are quite unconscious of the fact that his syntax in any way departs from a factual representation of the situation. Sapir has also pointed out that the use of many syntactical forms is quite unnecessary for the conveying of meaning such as case form in Latin, gender in German and French, and our use of the plural where one might use the expression "two man" as well as "two men." These redundancies may persist because language has other functions than simply the designation of "reality."

The study of the language of patients with brain damage and of those in whom brain function has been altered by drugs furnishes a unique opportunity to examine the role of language as a measure of interaction in the environment and to evaluate the role of changes in language pattern as a mode of adaptation to stress. (In such a study we exclude those patients in whom the process of symbol formation itself is affected, as in aphasia.) The disability and hospitalization provide the conditions of stress, and the language of the patient may be observed at successively changing levels of brain function and/or under changing degrees of stress. Interviews are structured and the questions are those used in routine clinical examination. They concern the reason for coming to the hospital, the nature of the patient's disability, his knowledge as to where he is, the identification of hospital personnel, orientation for time, and ability to name various objects. The same type of interview is held twice weekly during the patient's hospitalization and the patient's responses to identical questions compared.

These procedures yield a number of phenomena which illustrate the principle of interaction in the environment. These are usually designated clinically as disorientation for place and time, reduplication for place, time and person, paraphasia and confabulation. Disorientation for place is the term that describes the statement by the patient that he is in a place or location other than the one where he is actually. The responses given by these patients not only designate a place or location but express an attitude of the patient. Thus he names a hospital near his home or one where he has been treated for some illness in the past, or refers to "Walter Reed Repair Shop" or "Walter Reed Prison." I recall a woman with a brain stem lesion with weakness of both lower extremities and a tracheotomy who called the hospital the "Fresh Air Roller Skating Academy." Usually, one portion of the response includes either the designation "hospital" or its proper name, and the other expresses the patient's attitude toward his situation. In reduplication these aspects are more distinctly separated, as when the patient says that there are two Walter Reed hospitals. He may locate one correctly and the other in his home town. Or he may state that only one performs operations. Some patients name and locate the hospital correctly but greatly condense the distance between the hospital and home. Thus a patient seen in Washington stated that his home in Detroit was only 10 miles away.

Now why is disorientation for place considered as a form of language rather than a manifestation of "confusion" or as a defect in memory, perception, calculation, judgment or insight? First, the patient frequently names the hospital correctly in another context. Thus he may say he used to be in Walter Reed Hospital, that a member of his family is, or that he was supposed to go there. It can hardly be a defect in memory in the ordinary sense in which the term is used, as the patient persists in using the fictitious term even after being repeatedly told the correct name. Often the name is in plain sight on a pillow case or piece of hospital equipment. One man, in writing a letter, crossed out the Walter Reed inscription and substituted "Fort Sill" where he had served on duty. Patients who condense the distance from home to hospital may do quite well on calculation tests and again may give the correct distance in another context of language. I refer to the man who stated that he was only 10 miles from his home in Detroit. In discussing a forthcoming visit from his family he stated that he expected them at a certain time in the afternoon as they would be leaving Detroit that morning, giving the exact mileage in his account. Such patients may even give accurately the distance say from Detroit to Washington but insist they are only 10 miles from home. Here the spatial concept "10 miles" and the temporal concept "10 minutes" serve not only purposes of reference but also as figures of speech to express a feeling of closeness to home. The patient may be quite conscious of his need or desire to be at home but he seems quite unaware of how he is expressing this in his language.

The most common form of reduplication involves the misidentification of other people. The patient will state that another man on the ward is a boy with whom he went to school, a cook or a radio repair man (patient's own occupation) with whom he worked. One patient stated that a man in a nearby bed was an automobile racing driver. Another said that an attendant was a "bachelor from home who took things easy and knew what it was all about." Another was identified as R——, a fellow from North Carolina. In all of these designations patients are expressing ideas about themselves and they are most apt to appear when the patient is talking about himself. When the patient addresses the misidentified person he usually calls him by his proper name and behaves toward him in a manner compatible with his actual status. The use of these reduplications in the maintenance of self-concepts is brought out by comparisons of the pattern in which the concept appears at successive stages in recovery from brain injury. Thus the one patient first confabulated that he, himself, was an automobile racing driver, then identified the other man as one, and ultimately talked about his ambition to be one. The patient who called the attendant "a bachelor who took things easy," to judge from the content of later interviews was talking about what he would do after being discharged from the Army.

Paraphasia is a phenomenon in which the patient misnames an object in terms of some selected aspects of its structure or function. He may call a hypodermic needle a "tie-pin," a wheel-chair a "stroller," or a slipper a "bank"—because you can keep money in it. When a number of objects of equal familiarity and complexity are shown, the patient usually misnames only those which he relates to his personal problems, particularly those of his illness. The name that is given not only structures and classifies the environment but expresses the individual's feeling about himself in terms of the spatial environment. An excellent example of such interaction was afforded by an electronics engineer severely incapacitated by a head injury, who called an electric light bulb a "used-up old radio tube." Like disorientation, paraphasia cannot be attributed to a defect in perception or memory nor is it an aphasic deficit despite the name "paraphasia." First there is the motivated selectivity. Second, the patient often can give the correct and incorrect names side by side, commenting "but I call it——." The rhythm of speech is normal, words are not garbled, nor is there perseveration in the aphasic patient. Further the patient seems quite unaware of any error and does not become at all upset when one is called to his attention. While these examples are taken from the language of people with brain disease, others can be chosen from poetry (metonymy) slang, nicknames, and even prayer.

Just as disorientation, reduplication, and paraphasia illustrate modes of interaction in the spatial aspects of the environment in terms of places, persons, and things, so does confabulation involve interaction in the temporal aspects in terms of events. Confabulation may be defined as the narrating of a fictitious version of a past event. Among patients with head injuries the most frequent confabulation concerns the manner in which the injury was sustained. Patients who have been hurt in automobile accidents tell stories of having been in an airplane crash, parachute accident, or atomic explosion, or of having been wounded in combat. A soldier sustaining a head injury in combat fabricated an account of having been hit on the head by his wife, while another told a story about developing a headache on duty. In these cases it becomes apparent that while the story refers ostensibly to an incident in the past, that is the accident, it is also the representation of some current problem. These problems concern the patient's incapacity, economic and social consequences, and his relationships with his family and hospital personnel. A patient who became blind after a craniotomy for a brain tumor referred to the onset of his illness as having been "beaten up and rolled in a blind alley." A supply officer sustained a head injury in a jeep accident in Korea and was left with a mild weakness of his right side, inability to write, and a very slight dysphasia. He told a story that he had had an important "intelligence job" and had been shelled by the enemy while bringing in some spies who had committed a "security offense." In relating the story he spoke in seemingly rambling fashion of "writing all the evidence down," of having "enough written so that any jury in its right senses would be sure to convict." In each interview over a period of several months the patient would repeat this story in identical fashion including the words "intelligence," "writing," "right senses," and "security." In subsequent interviews, after the confabulation was no longer present, the patient expressed his concern about his intelligence, his writing disability, and his financial security in less metaphorical and more referential language. It is of interest that when the patient changes his story about the accident and adds some new detail it is related to the occurrence of some new stressful incident in the hospital.

Usually the patient does not give up the confabulation abruptly but continues to offer its content in another language pattern. Thus the patient tells the story in the form of a rumor that someone said such and such happened or that he was "told" the story. There is commonly a stage at which both the true and false versions are given, indicating that the confabulation is not simply a result of the patient's not "knowing" what happened. He may relate the events of the confabulation as if they had happened to another person. One man stated at first that he had been killed, then said that his brother had been killed. Some patients retain some of the content of the story in a statement about the future. After apparent recovery a patient who confabulated that he had been in an atomic explosion talked a great deal about his plan to get a job making atomic bombs.

Commonly the patient introduces a true or approximately accurate version of the accident in altered language patterns, involving changes in tense, person, number, and grammatical mood. He describes an automobile accident which happened in the past or talks about having sustained injuries identical with the current ones at some past time. Or he talks of the injuries, accident, or circumstances of hospitalization as having happened to another person, commonly a member of his family. Thus one patient described an automobile accident identical to his own that he said had happened to his brother on the day that he was taken to the hospital. This use of the "third person" is very frequent. Patients state that a member of the family is in the hospital, one boy saying that his brother was in the next bed. A girl with a self-inflicted gun shot wound claimed that a girl from her neighborhood had been shot. These statements are often not strictly confabulatory. A patient may have had a car accident in the past. One man told a story about his father having been hospitalized that was in the main true. It included an account of how "the doctors did not let him (the father) go home until he had a good job ready for him." Another use of the third person occurs in an obsessive kind of worrying about the health of family members even though they are quite well. Yet the patient expresses the idea that they may meet with an accident.

It is important to recognize that this use of the "third person" is a device of language in which the patient is talking about himself and primarily his feelings about himself. Thus when the other person is said to be injured or killed, the patient is not necessarily expressing hostility toward him in a referential sense or liberating some repressed wish. It is of interest that the patient never expresses surprise at seeing the putatively dead or injured relative at visiting hours. This use of language is reminiscent of the "imaginary companion" of children—some fictitious character spills the milk, pulls up the plants, etc. Changes in number are less frequent. Here the patient talks of several head injuries or operations, multiplies the number of accidents, and talks of owning several automobiles. One patient told of how five people had been killed in the accident, when in fact only one had died.

The use of the negative mood usually appears as "I don't know" or "I don't remember" when the patient is asked about his accident. Clinically this is regarded as "amnesia" but we have considered it in the context of language rather than as a manifestation of "loss of memory" for several reasons. First, no patient in our experience who has had a severe head injury remembers the actual accident but when asked about it, most give the essential facts. Second, the initial "I don't know" is often followed by a statement of the accident utilizing the third person as, "They told me I was driving along and hit a car," etc. Long after a patient seems to have completely recovered, he prefaces any account of the accident with, "I don't remember, but." It seems evident that this use of the negative mood is expressing the patient's feeling about the situation.

In some patients delusions and confabulations are succeeded by other language patterns which include threats, jokes, vows and resolutions, slang, profanity, and clichés. Some patients talk about the head injury for the first time in the form of a threat. One man, for example, threatened to knock another patient's head off if he didn't keep quiet. A woman who had shot herself joked about the "misfraction" of her head. Several joked about a "hole in the head." Vows and resolutions about not drinking, for example, are common. In some patients the confabulation is replaced by clichés. One man, following the news that his wife was seeking a divorce, attributed on old scar on his knee to his wife's having tried to shoot him in the back. Several days later he referred to the matter in such expressions as, "Let nature take its course."

During the period of disorientation and confabulation the patient appears to be without anxiety in the usual clinical sense and seems relatively unconcerned about his disability and its consequences. In some cases anxiety and depression are observed with improvement in brain function and the disappearance of confabulation, but usually anxiety is avoided when the confabulation is succeeded by the other language patterns that have been mentioned. It is significant that the delusions and confabulations are usually expressed without apparent emotion, leading to the designation "lack of affect." The threats and vows, however, are apt to be uttered in a paranoid or euphoric fashion. We are accustomed to regard such language as simply the means of liberating emotion which has hitherto been "repressed." Yet it may be that the emotion is a means of changing the threshold of brain function and temporarily restoring a milieu of function in which the previous pattern of interaction may be established. This hypothesis is an attractive one when we consider the transitory nature of these emotional outbursts, hardly outlasting the verbal expressions themselves.

The question arises as to how such changed organizations of language function as modes of adaptation, particularly if we reject the "release of hostility" theory. Sapir contrasts the two sentences, "The grass waves in the wind," and "The wind causes the grass to wave." The second is a closer approximation of the events of the physical world. Yet the first creates for some of us a poetic quality or "feeling," possibly by reason of the change in the level of interaction, expressing a greater unity with our concept of nature. The "feeling" of humor is similarly associated with a shift in symbolic level. In our patients the alterations in language seem to have provided a means of identification with such aspects of the cultural environment as health and illness, home and work, violence and death. In earlier studies of denial of illness,[4] it was pointed out that the adaptive nature of this phenomenon lay not simply in the expression of a wish to be well. It was also a means of relating in a culture in which to be ill was in effect not to exist as a person, and in which not only denial but shame and guilt about illness were means of relating. While the patient is quite aware of his wish to be well, he is generally unconscious of the role of his language in expressing such an identification in his environment. It may seem paradoxical to describe such distortions of reality as occur in confabulation as a means of establishing a feeling of "existing" or "belonging," but one's *feeling* of reality or truth may be more closely related to one's relationship in his environment than to any more logical thought process.[5]

Such language patterns of course are not limited to patients with brain disease but are noted in all forms of our language that serve as modes of adaptation to stress. These include such diverse forms of speech as humor, myth, vows, resolutions, poetry and prayer, fable and drama, proverb and prophecy, clichés, curses, slang, and profanity. The representation of some ostensibly past event, as in myth, and a statement about some putative future occurrence, as in a vow, may both be expressions of an identification of the individual with socially significant aspects of his environment. Thus the vows of the medieval knight were concerned with fasting, sexual abstinence, the representation of suffering, maiming, and death in various forms. Regardless of the purpose of the vow given by the speaker, they all are the expression of his identification with significant aspects of his culture expressed also in his religion, e.g., ideas of chivalry. Whether or not the vow was fulfilled, it still served an important function. Similarly our patients who resolve "no more drinking, no more cussin', no more women" are hardly forecasting future behavior but are expressing an identification with significant social values. This may help to explain the behavior of one patient who repeatedly vowed to "get closer to the Lord" but with equal frequency used the Lord's name in profanity. When we refer to death in everyday speech in such expressions as "I almost died laughing," "this will be the death of me," or "this will slay you," we are not expressing hostility or a wish to die but indicating a relationship to a significant aspect of the cultural environment. One gets satisfaction out of proverbs and homilies not because one necessarily believes that "early to bed and early to rise" make one healthy, wealthy, or wise, but because the language itself expresses an identification with cultural values by a process of which we are largely unconscious.

The purpose of this paper has been to consider the role of language as a mode of adaptation to stress in line with some of the implications of the Sapir-Whorf hypothesis of language. Language cannot be equated with individual psychological or physiological entities but rather is the means whereby the individual organizes the environment and expresses his relationship in it. Delusions and confabulations concerning place, time, person, and event and changes in person, tense, number, and grammatical mood illustrate altered patterns of interaction in the environment and serve as modes of adaptation to stress by reason of the change in the level of interaction. The findings may also contribute to the understanding of how such forms of language as humor, prayer, vows, myths, slang, poetry, and proverb serve to relate the individual in his cultural environment.

REFERENCES

1. MEAD, G. H.: Mind, Self and Society. Chicago, University of Chicago Press, 1934.
2. MANDELBAUM, D. G., Ed.: Selected Writings of Edward Sapir. Berkeley, University of California Press, 1949.
3. WHORF, B. L.: Language, Thought and Reality. New York, Wiley, 1956.
4. WEINSTEIN, E. A., AND KAHN, R. L.: Denial of Illness. Springfield, Ill., Thomas, 1955.
5. ——, ——, AND MALITZ, S.: Confabulation as a Social Process. Psychiatry *19*: 383-96, 1956.

17

PROBLEMS OF COMMUNICATION BETWEEN PHYSICIANS AND SCHIZOPHRENIC PATIENTS

*By JOHN C. WHITEHORN, M.D.**

IN A RECENT STUDY by Barbara Betz and myself of the psychotherapeutic relationships between physicians and schizophrenic patients,[1] we reported that improvement in the schizophrenic patient is most likely to occur in cases in which the physician records statements that indicate he has gained some "grasp of the personal meaning and motivation of the patient's behavior, going beyond mere description and narrative biography."

In this study of the transactions between patients and physicians we noted too that the more favorable outcomes were associated with evidence of a more confidential relationship in which the patient had brought to the physician's attention highly personal problems, sought the physician's help in evaluating his behavior in worrisome situations, and participated with the physician in trying to work out practical solutions, i.e., what it would be best to do in some of these situations.

These findings have psychiatric relevance in several different ways. Today, I use them to highlight the strategic importance of the communication process. Obviously there can be no partnership in efforts at problem solving without a fairly high level of communicative rapport.

The problem of establishing effective communication with schizophrenic patients is notoriously difficult as well as strategically crucial. In a brilliant article in the short-lived *Bulletin of the Isaac Ray Library*, Manfred Bleuler has given an account of his father's success in establishing meaningful communication with schizophrenic patients at Burgholtzli by reason of his familiarity with the local dialect. Bleuler's account of this experience accentuates the verbal factor. Through his account one may perceive also the probable importance of other than verbal factors in communication—a perceptiveness regarding gestures,

* Johns Hopkins University, Baltimore, Maryland.

moods, and values—also contingent upon having shared a common social milieu.

Communication depends not merely upon the proper emission and correct reception of verbal messages—what the words denote—but also upon some community of values or emotional communion which carries the connotations. To complicate these difficulties still further, one may note the special problem raised in the case of schizophrenic patients by the disinclination of many such patients to submit graciously to the other person's occasional need for clarification and concretization, for the schizophrenic does not like to be pinned down and tends to be resentful of the implied coercion when tacitly or overtly requested to conform to the other person's mode of thought or frame of reference.

These verbal and nonverbal types of communication problems constitute the topic which I am to discuss briefly today. A few illustrative examples of thwarted or unsuccessful schizophrenic communication will be useful.

Many years ago, a male schizophrenic patient whom I knew only slightly used to send me occasional written messages consisting of a sheet of paper covered completely with adjectives, fifty to a hundred of them, enough to cover the sheet, with no salutation, no articulative terms, no nouns, no verbs—just adjectives. When I saw him to thank him for his message, he would smile with apparent appreciation but never offered any explanation or clarification even when urged. Then, weeks later, I might get another such message. I never understood what he meant.

Another schizophrenic patient, a middle-aged woman, had a habit of preparing by hand a sort of private news sheet, greatly resembling a newspaper at a casual glance, with headlines and areas blocked out as if for illustrations, and all carefully drawn by hand in an alphabet of her own invention somewhat resembling Greek. One day she saw me walking on the hospital grounds with my young daughter and the next day she showed and read to me from her newspaper an account of her own daughter's wedding, all quite mythical. Otherwise her newspapers, so laboriously and so meticulously gotten up, seemed to serve no practical communicative purpose.

On another occasion, when on duty in the ward, I was suddenly asked by a male schizophrenic patient who had long been mute whether I read poetry. Although a bit startled by this query, I acknowledged that

I sometimes did read poetry, whereupon he apparently decided he could talk to me and told me of his changed aspirations. He said he had just decided to go live in a small Italian village and sing opera, giving up his previous almost exclusive preoccupation with visions of the Virgin Mary. After a few interviews on this topic, he again changed his mind and told me that he had resumed his belief in the multiplication table and was prepared to resume his regular occupation, which was that of a school teacher.

One day, when I was on duty in a disturbed women's ward, one of the patients said she wanted to talk with me. This was a schizophrenic patient who had for months made life embarrassing for the nurses by shouting obscenities and had persistently and loudly demanded sexual intercourse. This time she started the conversation by asking me quietly, whether I believed in the sun or in the moon. Noting, tactfully, that I seemed a bit nonplussed by this curious question, she hastened to say that she herself believed in the sun but her sister believed in the moon. I perceived or thought I perceived by this that she was presenting the issue of frankness, and that she was choosing to uphold the rightness of complete and utter frankness in the expression of feminine desires, and assigning to her sister the misty and romantical "moonlight" approach to sex—the polite, evasive romanticization of sex. We then had a quiet and interesting discussion of this issue in which I took the position that there was value both in sunlight and in moonlight. I even went so far as to express the opinion that, men being the way they are, a woman might more effectively achieve the consummation of her sexual desires by the moonlight approach than by the glaring light of the sun. She remained unconvinced, but pleasantly argumentative, as we talked over this issue of the sun versus the moon for about an hour, somewhat to the bewilderment of the listening nurses, who must have wondered from my manner of speech whether I had suddenly gone schizophrenic.

These examples form a roughly graded series, illustrating the range from apparently meaningless utterance to clearly meaningful though highly symbolic communication on significant personal issues.

These examples also serve to raise the question, "Can one learn to talk schizophrenese?" Can one, by taking thought, develop the capacity to manage the metaphorical or symbolistic patterns in which a schizophrenic patient chooses to speak?

I have had the opportunity for much observation of young psychiatrists trying to communicate with schizophrenic patients and I have been much impressed by the likelihood that much depends upon the physician's native aptitude and a kind of temperamental preparedness to grant the patient a wide range of poetic license, so to speak. There are factors which hinder such capacities, and in respect to some of these hindrances assistance can be given the young physician, enabling him better to utilize what talent he may have for such communication.

One of the hindrances is the oppressive sense of obligation about getting material into the record, an admirable aim but one likely to desiccate a conversation quickly. The young resident eager to get down material which will contribute to an impressive case report to the staff is influenced thereby to quiz the patient and try, too obviously, to get definitive statements, thereby drying up the spontaneous flow which is necessary to keep effective conversation afloat.

For example, a schizophrenic patient, a housewife, was reported as obsessively preoccupied with the idea that she was "a bee, dead," or, rather, she was compulsively denying it. She was reported to have said that the neighbors first insinuated then openly accused her of being "a bee dead." This was given in the case report as a bizarre idea, in support of the schizophrenic diagnosis. When I asked if this issue had been further discussed with the patient I was told that there wasn't any issue, this was just a bizarre idea she had, and pains were taken to prove it by voluminous references to nurses' notes and statements by the patient to other physicians denying that she was "a bee dead." Further questioning brought to light the fact that she had also mentioned, with a meaningful smile, that she understood about "the bees and the birds." I took this familiar phrase to signify that she had meant to set up a frame of references to processes of sexual reproduction and that, in denying she was "a bee dead," she meant to deny that her sexual enthusiasm had died. In this instance I presume that the young physician's preoccupation with the clerkish task of recording a bizarre idea and of underlining its differential diagnostic significance had hindered him from using the opportunity to have a meaningful conversation on an issue of great personal significance to the patient.

To some extent it is possible to discuss this problem of the hindrances to communication and to liberate the young, obsessive doctor from a too literal-minded preoccupation with diagnostic meanings. It is quite possible to learn to be alert both to the diagnostic meaning and to the more personal communicative significance of the patient's speech.

I have observed another artificially induced impediment to communication between physician and patient. The modern injunction to young psychiatrists to listen and let the patient do the talking can also become a hindrance to effective communication when it induces such a degree of restraint as to inhibit the doctor's responsiveness to a patient's behavior. It is hard for the patient to talk to the great stone face.

One of the greatest hindrances to effective communication between physician and schizophrenic patient arises from a cause much more difficult to resolve: the difference in personal background and orientation to life which may exist between patient and physician. This difference can be statistically made manifest in a graphic way by arranging the human material by categories of socioeconomic class origins, by which it appears that doctors come mainly from middle class families and schizophrenic patients come mainly from lower class families. This statistical class difference does not in general mean, in America, so great a difference in dialect or in grammatical correctness as to set a real hindrance to communication. Nor does the communicative problem between middle class doctor and lower class schizophrenic lie in a distinction between the literate and the illiterate. Both are likely to be literate but in different ways. The doctor is likely to be conceptually literal-minded and the patient perhaps literal-minded in an embarrassing body- and action-conscious way, like a certain schizophrenic female who claimed that Dr. Smith had taken her pulse and who implied thereby that he had incurred some obligation or responsibility by taking away something from her or subtly invading her privacy.

Even when the schizophrenic patient tries earnestly to communicate what it is that he is distressingly mindful of, the physician, coming from a different socioeconomic class or a different type of background, may not know what the patient is talking about because he lacks an appreciation of the patient's personal background of experience. This point was made clear to me by a young schizophrenic girl with whom I was laboriously trying to discuss her life situation. She finally said, impatiently, "Do you know my Aunt Sophia?" When I said, "No," she said, "Then there's no use trying to talk with you. You couldn't understand my problem if you didn't know Aunt Sophia." I came to understand later that Aunt Sophia was considered to be the domineering, autocratic tyrant in her family, and that the patient had been particularly sensitive about this domination.

This issue between the schizophrenic patient and an allegedly domineering or coercive authority figure is very common—I think a practically universal issue—in the thinking and feeling of schizophrenic patients. This issue is not always appreciated correctly by the physician nor perceived by him in the patient's emotional frame of reference because that frame of reference does not fit very well the physician's set of attitudes regarding freedom or domination. The patient's choice of language in stating a declaration of or a demand for independence is often misleading in its connotations for the physician. Indeed, it seems often to mislead the patient himself into situations with which he cannot cope. I observe that a misunderstanding on this issue is often a considerable hindrance to effective communication between a doctor and his schizophrenic patient. I have also found that it has frequently been possible for me to clarify this issue in consultation with the young physician, thereby facilitating his communications with his patient.

I will therefore attempt to make a generalized statement about this matter, which is much harder to state in general terms than in particular specific cases where the concrete details are available.

When the schizophrenic patient puts into words his feeling of objection to coercive influence, it sounds to practical ears like a demand for independence. At least the words used can have such meanings. But it isn't quite that way with the schizophrenic patient in its emotional connotations. The independence, if granted, is like the "independence of a hog on ice"—unconstrained but incapable of locomotion. The schizophrenic patient demanding independence from coercive influence or domination does not ordinarily have a clear and decisive program of action for which he needs the demanded freedom nor would he enthusiastically use it. Sometimes he merely means to express petulant annoyance at the irksomeness of being bothered by others or at being ignored by others or both. Frequently he is also expressing a markedly dependent need for support and approval. A schizophrenic complaint against a "domineering" parent and the demand for more independence very often means that the patient is really demanding not merely the opportunity to do something on his own, but strong assurance that it is all right for him to do so. This is not real independence but an inverted kind of extreme dependence.

For the clarification of this issue one can quote the aphorism, "It is in the nature of freedom that it is not *granted;* if it is real freedom it is always *taken.*" For physicians this aphorism may provide an illuminating insight, but some patients may take it in an annoyingly literal sense.

To have meaningful communications with a schizophrenic on this issue of independence versus influence, it is also helpful to recognize that the irksomeness of feeling under authority, domination, or influence depends upon an implicit hopelessness or lack of aspiration or expectation of ever being really free. The satisfaction, enthusiasm and eager use of a real state of freedom is foreign to one who has not been accustomed to exert decisive, spontaneous choice of action. For many schizophrenics a fearful and hateful self-distrust impedes such exercise of inner power. Even when no really strong authoritative prohibition is exerted against him, i.e., even in highly permissive settings, this type of schizophrenic will probably be so disinclined by habit to exercise freedom that he will invent a prohibitive authority figure, or grossly magnify whatever slight authoritarianism is perceptible to his over-sensitive disposition, and then complain resentfully against this coercion.

One such patient, during a tearful and pathetic interview with me, stared for a moment at her hand, which was tightly grasping my thumb, and yelled at me, "Let go my hand, you brute." In terms of who held whom, this was an obvious absurdity; in terms of resentful dependency it was a perfectly clear communication.

The physician, differently oriented from the patient by his accustomed habits of exercising freedom and responsibility, is likely to interpret according to his own meanings the schizophrenic's complaint about coercion or influence. The physician may even try to manipulate the life situation of the schizophrenic patient prematurely in the direction of freedom and responsibility and thereby throw upon him too great or too sudden a burden of freedom of action before the issue has been communicatively clarified for the schizophrenic so as to help him get his relatively feeble powers of spontaneity exercised enough to have a constructive chance of success in real freedom.

Obviously, if the physician does not understand this type of issue he cannot gain a very sympathetic appreciation of how the patient stands on it, nor help him very effectively to grope his way to increased spontaneity despite self-distrust.

At an earlier stage of this discussion, I referred to a statistical difference in socioeconomic class origins between schizophrenic patients and physicians, schizophrenic patients being principally of lower class origin and doctors being principally of middle class origin. While I believe this to be a statistically significant statement, it is far from being a universal rule. There are many schizophrenic patients of upper or middle class origin, and fortunately, despite the soaring costs of medical education in money and in years, there are still some physicians, technically speaking, of "lower class" origin, some of them capable of bringing to their professional work an appreciation of the values and emotional orientations of their lower class origins.

Nearly all of our psychiatric and psychodynamic theorizing has been done, however, by those of upper or middle class orientations, with a characteristically high regard for intelligent self-understanding and self-directed living—specially idealized for the medical profession in the picture of the ideal physician with scholarly detachment yet sympathetic appreciation. The emotional attitudes which give high value to that ideal are not strongly shared by many patients in any real and striving sense. Such values are likely to seem to many lower class people, if they ever think about them, as being as remote and unreal as life on Mars. Picture a properly-brought-up, ambitious, and highly self-respecting young psychiatric resident and a schizophrenic patient of lower class origin and orientation to values whose world of existence operates by influences far beyond his hopes of managing. It is not difficult to foresee that they are not going to understand each other very well, nor are they likely to persist very long in so-called psychotherapeutic interviews.

I do not advocate that we should, because of the obvious difficulties in communication, abandon such therapeutic efforts; rather I think we should recognize here a special responsibility to persevere and to seek to overcome by sympathetic and imaginative study these barriers to communication. The task has also a theoretical fascination to gratify the most scholarly taste.

Those problems of communication which depend upon different class origins have been given much emphasis here. Some may think too much emphasis. Our culture is characterized by a high degree of social mobility up and down the ladder and one's class origin may not correspond to one's psychological orientation to values. This very motility not only creates or accentuates special problems within the life experience of individuals but it also creates complexities of emotional connotations which form part of the communication problem.

Many of the young psychiatrists now moving into the emotionally rewarding private practice of psychiatry, to the neglect of those great masses of patients in the state hospitals, are influenced in making such decisions by comparing their pleasant and effective communications with patients of their own class with the baffling problems and boredom of cross-class communications.

Furthermore, from the theoretical point of view, which is the proper business of my discussion, there are significant psychological similarities in the value systems of upper class schizophrenic patients and lower class schizophrenic patients (and with lower class persons in general).

It has seemed to me that the inner sense of power is in general rather deficient in those persons who develop schizophrenic illness. They are likely to have lacked zest, enthusiasm and the feeling of power and spontaneity that goes with enthusiasm. They are therefore expecting the universe to be run by others and expecting to dislike it. In this respect, their psychological orientation parallels the actual life situation characteristic of persons of lower class origins. Both groups, so to speak, pronounce "They" with a capital T in such expressions as, "They ought to pass a law." The powers-that-be are, for them, other persons—third or second person pronouns, not the first person "We" as used by middle class and upper class people who are aware of power and responsibility. Because of this degree of parallelism in viewpoint, which in a fashion identifies upper class schizophrenics with lower class attitudes of futility, much of what I have been trying to say in class terms has some validity in clarifying the issues likely to be involved in communications with any schizophrenic patient of whatever class origin. Those from educated families are of course likely to have a different vocabulary which may favor better communication or may harmfully complicate communication. The upper class vocabulary may hinder the understanding of schizophrenics because it echoes the words used by the family in their ambitious efforts to stir the patient out of the lethargy of futility. Consequently, what one hears from such a schizophrenic may represent him and his feelings much less accurately than it serves to mirror the pressures put upon him.

In the study of the communication problems with schizophrenic patients, verbal behavior has received considerable emphasis. As I have sought to indicate already, schizophrenic word salads which seem to defy understanding may still have meanings and these meanings can sometimes be deciphered. Schizophrenic patients are noted for neologisms. It was my good fortune at one time to have the assistance of George Zipf[2] in studying, by a special statistical technique, the written speech patterns of schizophrenic patients, some of them much inclined to neologistic habits. We found a relatively constricted style, tending to a high degree of repetitiousness and a low degree of diversification in word usage—a pattern which reflects autistic preoccupation and an inadequate regard for the needs of the reader. The speech patterns appeared therefore to reflect something of the schizophrenic's same ineptitude in rapport which has been inferred from direct clinical study. The technique which we used for studying the speech patterns in schizophrenic communications was an exceedingly laborious one—too laborious for extensive use.

In bringing to a close these remarks regarding the problems of communication between schizophrenic patients and their physicians, I wish to re-emphasize the possibilities that exist for being helpful to these sick people when one can succeed in useful measure, although not completely, in understanding some of the problems with which they are bemused and about which they communicate so confusedly. Such aid to individual patients can be gratifying experience, but the larger possibilities of benefit seem to lie in broader preventive or supportive measures. We all know markedly schizoid or mildly schizophrenic persons who have been able to live useful and gratifying lives with a certain measure of support, and we also know that the genetic factors conducive to schizophrenic illness are fairly widely distributed in the population, often along with factors of a more socially constructive character, which, under favorable circumstances, may enable the patient to maintain or regain better balance.

Perhaps in time we may find chemical agencies useful in radical ways for correcting the presumed biochemical basis of the schizophrenic's temperamental deviation from the standard norm. This is a popular hope in the year 1956. Meanwhile, we have clear evidence that it does make a significant difference in altering the course of schizophrenic illness if the patient has a physician who seeks with some success to understand his special life problems and who offers understanding aid in resolving them with him. To seek to develop, through appreciative communication, a transmissible knowledge and understanding of what life is like for the schizophrenic is a task of direct and demonstrable value in this "meanwhile" period of our basic ignorance, and the task appears to have a very long-term significance, also, from the likelihood that we will have for a long time in our population many persons with schizophrenic potentialities whose relative effectiveness and comfort may depend upon the psychiatric profession's knowledge of the kind of life problems they have and the ways in which they are capable of dealing with those life problems constructively, with minimal appreciative support.

REFERENCES

1. Whitehorn, J. C., and Betz, Barbara: A Study of psychotherapeutic relationships between physicians and schizophrenic patients. Am. J. Psychiat. *111*: 321-331, 1954.
2. ——, and Zipf, George K.: Schizophrenic language. Arch. Neurol. & Psychiat. *49*: 831-851, 1943.

Discussion of Chapters 14-17

By JEROME D. FRANK, M.D.*

A THEME which can be singled out of this afternoon's presentations is that certain aspects of language behavior can best be understood as adaptive mechanisms by which a person, as Dr. Weinstein puts it, organizes his environment and expresses his relationship to it. It seems convenient to use the term "circumstances" to refer to the environment as objectively described, and "situation" to the environment as perceived by the person. Language, then, is one of the means by which a person creates meaningful situations out of circumstances.

By studying the patient's language behavior under the special set of circumstances of the psychiatric interview, the psychiatrist tries to infer the kind of situation the patient is creating from them. From this inference he draws others as to the types of situation the patient habitually tends to create in circumstances important in his life. Finally, from both kinds of inferences the psychiatrist draws a further set as to how he should behave so as to be of most help to the patient.

It is astonishing to me that this piling of one inference on top of another works as well as it does. The success of this process seems partly related to special properties of the psychiatric interview which are calculated to help the patient express, honestly and fully, his significant and enduring attitudes to persons important to him. These properties are essentially that the physician is competent and kindly, that is, that he knows how to help the patient and is disposed to do so, and that the patient can obtain his help only by making a clean breast of his problems and feelings, however intimate or shameful they may be. Perhaps it would be more accurate to say that this is the psychiatrist's definition of the interview situation. To the extent that the patient appears to accept this definition, his language is taken by the psychiatrist as an accurate expression of his feelings and problems.

The psychiatrist, however, is especially interested in evidence that the patient does not accept his definition of the interview situation, but invests it with meanings of his own. Often these meanings tend to be threatening or anxiety-provoking. The nature of the perceived threat depends partly on culturally determined attitudes and partly on personality characteristics of individual patients. The patient tries to meet the threat by various defensive or adaptive language maneuvers, from which the psychiatrist infers how the patient perceives the situation.

Examples of defensive maneuvers which are primarily culturally determined are found in patients' statements as to why they have come to a psychiatric clinic. These can often best be understood as indications that they view the situation as carrying the stigma of being mentally ill and are attempting to deal with the resultant threat to their self-respect. Recently we have reviewed the reasons given by about 60 patients for coming to the Phipps Outpatient Department. About half of the reasons could be classed as statements defending against the ego-damaging implications of mental illness. One such defense was to relate the clinic visit to the marital situation—the patient came to please the spouse, to prove that the spouse is the one who really needs treatment, to forestall the husband's getting military orders to go overseas, and so on. Another group of defensive reasons attributed the clinic visit to job circumstances, such as having been sent by the plant physician, or to get a release from the psychiatrist so that the patient could return to work. Other patients stated outright that they came to prove they weren't crazy or to get the psychiatrist to confirm that their illness was physical and not mental.

Patients' communications indicating acceptance of psychotherapy might also be defensive attempts to deal with the situation, rather than expressions of genuinely favorable attitudes to treatment. That is, patients might appear to welcome psychiatric help when they had no intention of returning as a means of fobbing the doctor off or to avoid having to face his displeasure. The fact that many of the patients' statements reflected attempts to deal with threatening aspects of the treatment situation as they initially perceived it rather than a genuine attraction to or aversion for psychotherapy is supported by the finding that there was no relation between the reasons the patients gave for coming to the clinic and whether or not they actually accepted psychotherapy, or whether those who accepted therapy improved. A similar lack of relationship holds with respect to patients' expressed attitudes to group therapy and whether or not they accept it.

Since cultural factors cause many patients to see roughly the same kind of threat in the interview situation, they tend to resort to similar language behavior to deal with it, and this behavior is therefore relatively easy to interpret. Language behavior based on the attempt to cope with organically determined personality deficits is more difficult to analyze. However, since the defects tend to be similar regardless of the life experience of the individual patient, it is possible to trace out consistencies in language behavior from one patient to another as Dr. Weinstein has so brilliantly done, and the interpretation of these consistencies would tend to receive assent from psychiatrists with widely differing backgrounds. Now that Dr. Weinstein has called attention to the adaptive functions of disorientation, reduplication, paraphrasia, confabulation and other language behavior in persons with central nervous system damage, everyone can see them.

The more a patient's language in the psychiatric interview is determined by his personal life experiences rather than by cultural factors or organic defects, the harder it is to be sure that one's interpretation of his meaning is correct; and the more threatening the interview situation appears to the patient, the more difficult it may be to penetrate through his defensive barrage.

The problem is seen in its severest form with schizophrenics, and Dr. Whitehorn has outlined in his usual penetrating and thoughtful fashion some of the aspects of the psychiatrist's class background, personality and behavior which contribute to the difficulty. But the problem is often not much less difficult with neurotics, as Dr. Teitelbaum's interesting paper illustrates. With both schizophrenics and neurotics the psychiatrist's interpretation of what the patient really means has to be based partly on his own theory of personality functioning, and psychiatrists with different outlooks may interpret the same language behavior in very different ways. My reaction to Dr. Teitelbaum's paper is an example of this. He presents clinical examples of two types of defensive verbalizations. In one the patient refers to his behavior or feelings in exaggeratedly derogatory terms; in the other he conceals them under socially sanctioned terms. Dr. Teitelbaum sees the major function of both these forms of communication as efforts to maintain repression. My predilection would be to regard them as attempts by the patient secretly to gratify his infantile needs and wishes while avoiding the anticipated unpleasant consequences of this gratification. According to this viewpoint, by using exaggeratedly derogatory terms for his feelings the patient may be trying to achieve one or more of several ends. He may be trying to maneuver others into reassuring him that he really isn't as bad as all that, to forestall criticism by berating himself first, or to punish himself in advance for the gratification he is about to enjoy, though the gratification may occur only in fantasy. By going to the other extreme and using socially approved terms for his antisocial feelings, the patient may be attempting to disguise their true nature from himself and others so as to be able to indulge them more easily. To quote Dr. Teitelbaum with respect to case 5, "aggression was tolerable to her as long as it was concealed by the defensive cloak of honesty."

All of this simply demonstrates that patients' communications can be interpreted in many different ways, any of which can be helpful if both the doctor and the patient believe them to be true.

If the psychiatrist is very intuitive and attentive and has an opportunity for prolonged work with the patient, he may arrive at an interpretation of the patient's communication which is essentially correct, that is, one which secures general agreement from his colleagues as well as the patient. This laborious and uncertain process can sometimes be appreciably speeded up by observation of the patient in circumstances other than those of the interview. One indirect way of doing this is by obtaining the impression of another informant who sees the patient in significant life situations, though here the informant's bias must be taken into account.

A valuable setting for direct observation of patients is the therapeutic group. In their efforts to deal with peers, patients often reveal therapeutically relevant aspects of their difficulties in social adaptation which may never emerge directly in the private interview. Better yet would be direct observation of the patient in his daily life activities, especially with members of his family. Sociologists such as Strodbeck have shown that the family on its native hearth can be the object of rigorously scientific and highly illuminating study—an example which may encourage resumption of the practice of house visits by psychiatric social workers.

Lacking an opportunity to see the family at home, the next best thing is to observe family members interact in the clinic, especially members who are of supreme importance to each other. Drs. Layman and Lourie deserve our gratitude for their very interesting reminders as to how much that is extremely valuable can be learned from observation of patients in relatively unguarded moments when they communicate with someone important to them. I hope that they will continue to develop this line of study and that their paper will persuade others to do the same.

By SANDOR RADO, M.D.*

I HAVE LISTENED to Dr. Whitehorn with keen interest and enjoyed greatly the scientific and aesthetic qualities of his paper. He told us that under favorable circumstances the physician may be able to engage the schizophrenic patient in conversations meaningful and significant to both of them. His report made us almost feel that we had actually participated in his observations.

Theoretically, his chief aim was to disclose some of the obstacles which make communication with the schizophrenic patient so difficult, if not impossible. The patient speaks an idiom which Dr. Whitehorn aptly termed "schizophrenese." In this idiom the established conventions of language may be distorted beyond recognition. The patient may use words as symbols in the psychiatric sense, coin new words and symbols presumably pregnant with hidden meaning, and supplant structural rules by a structural freedom of his own. In short, he ignores language as spoken in the community and turns it from a collective means of communication into an individual enterprise; his idiom is an expression of his private universe, comparable to a work of surrealistic art. It requires of the physician exceptional perceptivity to sense the patient's meaning and reply to him accordingly. Imagine what a dogmatic interpreter would have done with the symbols of sun and moon used by one of Dr. Whitehorn's patients.

While there is considerable literature on the peculiarities of schizophrenic language, to my knowledge no attention has been called previously to the important fact that physician and schizophrenic patient so often have different backgrounds and belong to different socioeconomic classes or groups. While the difficulties of understanding thus created apply to the entire population they also form a hindrance in our efforts to reach the schizophrenic patient. Differences in dialect, vocabulary, grammar, grade of literacy, and the like, are obvious and not too difficult to overcome. However, Dr. Whitehorn stresses a far more subtle and penetrating point here. Every culture is marked by its particular belief systems, that is, systems of shared emotional and intellectual values which are reflected in the language concerned and are in turn continuously developed by it. Within a culture, these belief systems show differences of shading from group to group, which

* State University of New York.

may change the connotations and even the meaning of the same words. To exemplify this, Dr. Whitehorn points to the physician's high ideal of "scholarly detachment yet sympathetic appreciation." "Such values," he continues, "are likely to seem to many lower class people, if they ever think about them, as being as remote and unreal as life on Mars." The relativity of values and language is a *cultural* problem upon which the patient superposes the *pathological* problems of his idiom of schizophrenese. Psychodynamics will have to assimilate the comparative cultural point of view, some other aspects of which are also discussed in Dr. Weinstein's paper.

Dr. Whitehorn's clinical observations on the part played in the schizophrenic patient's imagination and actual doings by an allegedly tyrannic authority figure touches upon a cardinal feature in the psychopathology of this disorder. He gives a superb description of the patient's struggle against this alleged coercive influence which looks to the physician like a struggle for independence. However, when independence is achieved the patient cannot cope with it; what he really needs is reassurance and support.

I have a good personal reason to be delighted with Dr. Whitehorn's observations because they strikingly corroborate certain propositions I have advanced in recent years in my theory of schizotypal organization.* According to this theory, the schizotype is marked by two innate defects: deficiency of the motivating power of pleasure, and proneness to a distorted awareness of bodily self. The impaired organism automatically evolves a reparative system of schizo-adaptation which rests on a combination of three processes: (1) a "scarcity" economy of pleasure, (2) a security system featuring overdependence, and (3) a replacement technique of central integration in which the job ordinarily done by pleasurable feeling and thought is shifted to unemotional thought. Relevant to Dr. Whitehorn's observation is the second process, the patient's compensatory overdependence, which I have described as defective from the outset, for since childhood the patient's responses to parental figures are largely limited to fear or rage, blind obedience or blind defiance; the important range "between" is undeveloped. Clearly, in the phases of defiant rage, the patient is just as overde-

* Rado, Sandor: Dynamics and classification of disordered behavior. In Psychoanalysis of Behavior. Collected Papers. New York, Grune & Stratton, 1956, p. 268; Schizotypal organization. In Rado, S., and Daniels, G. E., Eds., Changing Concepts of Psychoanalytic Medicine. New York, Grune & Stratton, 1956, p. 225.

pendent as in the phases of apprehensive obedience. An example is the young schizophrenic woman who runs away defiantly from her devoted husband or parent without whom she cannot exist.

Time does not permit me to elucidate here the many other fine points in Dr. Whitehorn's paper. Aside from offering my wholehearted endorsement of his entire approach, I should like to make only one more comment on his closing remarks. I also share in what he describes as a "popular hope in the year 1956" that discovery of the presumably inherited specific biochemical traits of schizotypal organization will place its psychodynamics on a firm physiological basis and open up truly radical ways of treatment. I also fully agree with his position that this advance will make the psychodynamic approach even more fruitful than it is today.

APPENDIX

Official Membership List of the American Psychopathological Association

E. Stanley Abbott, M.D.*
P. O. Box 119
Wayland, Massachusetts

Theodora M. Abel, Ph.D.
815 Park Avenue
New York, New York

David Abrahamsen, M.D.
1035 Fifth Avenue
New York, 28, New York

Nathan Ackerman, M.D.
42 East 78th Street
New York 21, New York

Alexandra Adler, M.D.
32 East 39th Street
New York 16, New York

Leo Alexander, M.D.
433 Marlborough Street
Boston, Massachusetts

Edward B. Allen, M.D.
21 Greenridge Avenue
White Plains, New York

George S. Amsden, M.D.*
Acworth, New Hampshire

Victor V. Anderson, M.D.*
Anderson School
Staatsburg, New York

Leslie R. Angus, M.D.
138 Greenwood Avenue
Jenkintown, Pennsylvania

* *Associate Member*

Irma Bache, M.D.
1 East 368
The Pentagon
Washington, D. C.

Lauretta Bender, M.D.
140 West 16th Street
New York 11, New York

Daniel Blain, M.D.
American Psychiatric Assoc.
3126 Woodley Road, N.W.
Washington 8, D. C.

Joseph V. Brady, Ph.D.
Walter Reed Army Medical Center
Washington 12, D. C.

Albert N. Browne-Mayers, M.D.
55 East 86th Street
New York 28, New York

A. Louise Brush, M.D.
55 East 86th Street
New York, New York

Dexter M. Bullard, M.D.
Chestnut Lodge Sanitarium
Rockville, Maryland

Ernest W. Burgess, Ph.D.
University of Chicago
1126 East 59th Street
Chicago 37, Illinois

Donald Ewen Cameron, M.D.
1025 Pine Avenue, West
Montreal 2, Canada

Norman Cameron, M.D.
Northford, Connecticut

Carl D. Camp, M.D.*
304 South State Street
Ann Arbor, Michigan

Douglas G. Campbell, M.D.
490 Post Street
San Francisco, California

G. Colket Caner, M.D.
63 Marlborough Street
Boston, Massachusetts

Edward J. Carroll, M.D.
121 University Place
Pittsburgh, Pennsylvania

James P. Cattell, M.D.
11 East 68th Street
New York 21, New York

Brock Chisolm, M.D.†
World Health Organizations
Geneva, Switzerland

Robert Clark, M.D.
Friends Hospital
Roosevelt and Adams Avenues
Philadelphia 24, Pennsylvania

Hollis E. Clow, M.D.
121 Westchester Avenue
White Plains, New York

Eugene Davidoff, M.D.
1101 Nott Street
Schenectady 8, New York

Oskar Diethelm, M.D.
525 East 68th Street
New York 21, New York

John M. Dorsey, M.D.
1401 Rivard Street
Detroit 7, Michigan

Roy M. Dorcus, Ph.D.
University of California
Los Angeles 24, California

Franklin S. DuBois, M.D.
Silver Hill Foundation
Valley Road
New Canaan, Connecticut

H. Flanders Dunbar, M.D.
1 East 69th Street
New York, New York

William W. Elgin, M.D.
Sheppard and Enoch Pratt Hospital
Towson 4, Maryland

Milton H. Erickson, M.D.
32 West Cypress
Phoenix, Arizona

Robert H. Felix, M.D.
National Institute of Mental Health
U. S. Public Health Service
Bethesda 14, Maryland

Arthur N. Foxe, M.D.
25 West 54th Street
New York 19, New York

Jerome D. Frank, M.D.
Johns Hopkins University
School of Medicine
Baltimore 5, Maryland

Richard L. Frank, M.D.
745 Fifth Avenue
New York, New York

† *Honorary Member*

Fritz A. Freyhan, M.D.
Farnhurst, Delaware

Freida Fromm-Reichmann, M.D.
Chestnut Lodge Sanitarium
Rockville, Maryland

Daniel H. Funkenstein, M.D.
74 Fenwood Road
Boston 14, Massachusetts

William Goldfarb, M.D.
Henry Ittleson Center for Child Research
5050 Iselin Avenue
Riverdale 71, New York

William Horsley Gantt, M.D.
Johns Hopkins Hospital
Baltimore 5, Maryland

Francis J. Gerty, M.D.
University of Illinois College of Medicine
912 South Wood Street
Chicago, Illinois

Arnold Gesell, M.D.
185 Edwards Street
New Haven, Connecticut

Bernard Glueck, M.D.
7 Parkway Road
Briarcliff, New York

Bernard Glueck, Jr., M.D.
Department of Psychiatry
University Hospitals
Minneapolis, Minnesota

Jacques Gottlieb, M.D.
Lafayette Clinic
951 East Lafayette Street
Detroit 7, Michigan

Ernest M. Gruenberg, M.D.
746 Irving Avenue
Syracuse 10, New York

Roscoe W. Hall, M.D.
St. Elizabeth's Hospital
Washington, D.C.

Volta R. Hall, M.D.
422 Beacon Street
Boston, Massachusetts

A. Irving Hallowell, Ph.D.
Box 14, Bennet Hall
University of Pennsylvania
Philadelphia, Pennsylvania

Donald M. Hamilton, M.D.
121 Westchester Avenue
White Plains, New York

Irving B. Harrison, M.D.
142 Garth Road
Scarsdale, New York

Harry H. Harter, M.D.
82-42 Kew Gardens Road
Kew Gardens 15, New York

Lynwood Heaver, M.D.
61 Irving Place
New York 3, New York

Morris Herman, M.D.
30 East 40th Street
New York, New York

Paul H. Hoch, M.D.
1165 Park Avenue
New York, New York

Lesile B. Hohman, M.D.
Duke University Medical School
Durham, North Carolina

Bernard Holland, M.D.
722 West 168th Street
New York 32, New York

Justin Morrill Hope, M.D.
New England Center Hospital
Boston, Massachusetts

William A. Horwitz, M.D.
722 West 168th Street
New York 32, New York

Joseph Hughes, M.D.
111 North 49th Street
Philadelphia 39, Pennsylvania

William A. Hunt, Ph.D.
Northwestern University
Evanston, Illinois

George A. Jervis, M.D.
Letchworth Village Research Department
Thiells, Rockland County, New York

Ernest Jones, M.D.*
The Plat, Elsted
North Midhurst
Sussex, England

Lothar B. Kalinowsky, M.D.
115 East 82nd Street
New York, New York

Franz J. Kallmann, M.D.
722 West 168th Street
New York, New York

Abram Kardiner, M.D.
1100 Park Avenue
New York, New York

Solomon Katzenelbogen, M.D.
The Woodner
16th Street, Spring Road, N.W.
Washington, D. C.

William R. Keeler, M.D.
1712 Rhode Island Avenue, N.W.
Washington 6, D. C.

Edward J. Kempf, M.D.
Wading River, New York
Isabelle V. Kendig, Ph.D.
Ashton, Maryland

Richard D. Kepner, M.D.
P. O. Box 3119
Honolulu 2, Hawaii

Seymour S. Kety, M.D.
National Institute of Mental Health
U. S. Public Health Service
Bethesda 14, Maryland

Lawrence Kolb, M.D.
6645 32nd Street, N.W.
Washington 15, D.C.

Vojtech Adalbert Kral, M.D.
4145 Blueridge Crescent
Montreal, Quebec, Canada

Morton Kramer, Sc.D.
9612 Sutherland Road
Silver Spring, Maryland

David M. Levy, M.D.
15 East 91st Street
New York, New York

Zigmond M. Lebensohn, M.D.
1712 Rhode Island Avenue, N.W.
Washington 6, D. C.

Alexander H. Leighton, M.D.
Payne Whitney Clinic
525 East 68th Street
New York, New York

Nolan D. C. Lewis, M.D.
Neuropsychiatric Institute
Princeton, New Jersey

William T. Ihamon, M.D.
1 Blalock Circle
Houston, Texas

Vladimir T. Liberson, M.D.
62 Roslyn Street
Hartford, Connecticut

Howard S. Liddell, Ph.D.
Department of Psychology
Cornell University
Ithaca, New York

Reginald S. Lourie, M.D.
Children's Hospital
Washington 9, D. C.

Lawson Lowrey, M.D.
25 West 54th Street
New York 19, New York

John G. Lynn, M.D.
305 Royal Hawaiian Avenue
Honolulu 15, Hawaii

Charles A. McDonald, M.D.*
106 Waterman Street
Providence 6, Rhode Island

Edwin E. McNeil, M.D.*
3875 Wilshire Boulevard
Los Angeles 5, California

Donald J. MacPherson, M.D.
270 Commonwealth Avenue
Boston 16, Massachusetts

Benjamin Malzberg, Ph.D.
New York State Department of Mental Hygiene
Albany, New York

Edward E. Mayer, M.D.*
5601 Forbes Street
Pittsburgh 17, Pennsylvania

William C. Menninger, M.D.
Menninger Foundation
Topeka, Kansas

Joseph S. A. Miller, M.D.
Hillside Hospital
Glen Oaks, New York

John A. P. Millet, M.D.
25 East 92nd Street
New York 28, New York

J. Allison Montague, Ph.D.
25 East 10th Street
New York 3, New York

Thomas Verner Moore, M.D.†
Carthusian Foundation in America
Sky Farm
Whitingham, Vermont

Harry M. Murdock, M.D.
Sheppard and Enoch Pratt Hospital
Towson 4, Maryland

Henry A. Murray, M.D.*
48 Mount Auburn Street
Cambridge, Massachusetts

Leo P. O'Donnell, M.D.
Harlem Valley Hospital
Wingdale, New York

Raymond L. Osborne, M.D.
140 East 54th Street
New York 22, New York

Winfred Overholser, M.D.
St. Elizabeth's Hospital
Washington 20, D. C.

Benjamin Pasamanick, M.D.
1798 Ashland Avenue
Columbus, Ohio

Grosvenor B. Pearson, M.D.
5555 Forbes Street
Pittsburgh 19, Pennsylvania

Harris B. Peck, M.D.
135 East 22nd Street
New York, New York

Harry H. Pennes, M.D.
Eastern Pennsylvania Psychiatric Institute
Henry Avenue and Abbottsford Road
Philadelphia 29, Pennsylvania

Zygmunt A. Piotrowski, Ph.D.
New Jersey Neuropsychiatric Institute
Skillman, New Jersey

Phillip Polatin, M.D.
722 West 168th Street
New York 32, New York

Hyman L. Rachlin, M.D.
33 East 39th Street
New York, New York

Sandor Rado, M.D.
50 East 78th Street
New York, New York

George N. Raines, Capt. (MC) USN
U. S. Naval Hospital
Portsmouth, Virginia

F. C. Redlich, M.D.
333 Cedar Street
New Haven 11, Connecticut

Evelyn B. Reichenbach, M.D.
St. Elizabeth's Hospital
Washington, D. C.

David McK. Rioch, M.D.
Neuropsychiatric Division
Walter Reed Medical Center
Washington 12, D. C.

Margaret Rioch, M.D.
4607 Dorset Avenue
Chevy Chase 15, Maryland

Fred V. Rockwell, M.D.
Grasslands Hospital
Valhalla, New York

Howard P. Rome, M.D.
Mayo Clinic
Rochester, Minnesota

Theodore Rothman, M.D.
444 North Bedford Drive
Beverly Hills, California

William S. Sadler, M.D.*
533 Diversey Parkway
Chicago, Illinois

G. Wilson Schaffer, Ph.D.
Johns Hopkins University
Baltimore, Maryland

Isidor W. Scherer, Ph.D.
Veterans Administration Hospital
Northampton, Massachusetts

Charles Shagass, M.D.
1025 Pine Avenue, West
Montreal, Quebec, Canada

David Shakow, Ph.D.*
National Institute of Mental Health
U. S. Public Health Service
Bethesda, Maryland

Alexander Simon, M.D.*
Langley Porter Clinic
San Francisco, California

John L. Smalldon, M.D.
Norwich State Hospital
Norwich, Connecticut

George W. Smeltz, M.D.
Atlantic City, New Jersey

Lauren H. Smith, M.D.
111 North 49th Street
Philadelphia, Pennsylvania

Harry C. Solomon, M.D.
74 Fenwood Road
Boston, Massachusetts

Rene A. Spitz, M.D.
1150 Fifth Avenue
New York 28, New York

Edward J. Stainbrook, M.D.
University Hospital
150 Marshall Street
Syracuse, New York

Charles W. Stephenson, M.D.
South Hero, Vermont

Gregory Stragnell, M.D.
2314 La Mesa Drive
Santa Monica, California

Joseph G. Sutton, M.D.
Essex County Overbrook Hospital
Cedar Grove, New Jersey

Hans C. Syz, M.D.
The Lifwynn Foundation
Westport, Connecticut

William S. Taylor, Ph.D.
55 Dryads Green
Northampton, Massachusetts

Harry A. TeitelBaum, M.D.
1801 Eutaw Place
Baltimore, Maryland

William B. Terhune, M.D.
Box D
New Canaan, Connecticut

Charles B. Thompson, M.D.
The Lifwynn Foundation
Westport, Connecticut

Clara Thompson, M.D.
12 East 86th Street
New York, New York

Kenneth J. Tillotson, M.D.*
1265 Beacon Street
Brookline, Massachusetts

Vladimir G. Urse, M.D.*
1447 Keystone Avenue
River Forest, Illinois

Roy McL. Van Wart, M.D.*
10431 Bellagio Road
Los Angeles 24, California

Heinrich B. Waelsch, M.D.
722 West 168th Street
New York 32, New York

Raymond W. Waggoner, M.D.
University Hospital
1313 East Ann Street
Ann Arbor, Michigan

James Hardin Wall, M.D.
121 Westchester Avenue
White Plains, New York

George A. Waterman, M.D.*
200 Beacon Street
Boston, Massachusetts

David Wechsler, Ph.D.
Bellevue Hospital
New York, New York

Edwin A. Weinstein, M.D.
7101 Pyle Road
Bethesda, Maryland

Livingston Welch, Ph.D.
Hunter College
695 Park Avenue
New York, New York

Frederic Lyman Wells, Ph.D.†
19 Bowdoin Street
Newton Highlands 61, Massachusetts

Louis Wender, M.D.
59 East 79th Street
New York, New York

Frederick L. Weniger, M.D.
3811 O'Hara Street
Pittsburgh 13, Pennsylvania

Mary Alice White, Ph.D.
121 Westchester Avenue
White Plains, New York

Robert W. White, Ph.D.
Department of Social Relations
Harvard University
Cambridge, Massachusetts

John C. Whitehorn, M.D.
Johns Hopkins Hospital
Baltimore 5, Maryland

Cornelius C. Wholey, M.D.*
121 University Place
Pittsburgh, Pennsylvania

Robert S. Wigton, M.D.*
105 South 49th Street
Omaha 3, Nebraska

George B. Wilbur, M.D.*
South Dennis, Massachusetts

William P. Wislon, M.D.*
2604 Hillandale Road
Durham, North Carolina

Emanuel Windholz, M.D.
2235 Post Street
San Francisco 15, California

Cecil L. Wittson, M.D.
415 North 61st Street
Omaha 5, Nebraska

Lewis R. Wolberg, M.D.
55 East 86th Street
New York, New York

Lawrence Woolley, M.D.
490 Peachtree Street
Atlanta, Georgia

S. Bernard Wortis, M.D.
410 East 57th Street
New York, New York

Gregory Zilboorg, M.D.
33 East 70th Street
New York, New York

Joseph Zubin, Ph.D.
722 West 168th Street
New York 32, New York

Past and Present Officers of the American Psychopathological Association

Presidents

1912 Adolf Meyer
1913 James T. Putnam
1914 Alfred R. Allen
1915 Alfred R. Allen
1916 Adolf Meyer
1917 Adolf Meyer
1918 Smith Ely Jelliffe
1921 William A. White
1922 John T. MacCurdy
1923 L. Pierce Clark
1924 L. Pierce Clark
1925 Albert M. Barrett
1927 Sanger Brown, II
1928 Ross McC. Chapman
1929 Ross McC. Chapman
1930 William Healy
1931 William Healy
1932 J. Ramsay Hunt
1933 Edward J. Kempf
1934 Edward J. Kempf
1935 Nolan D. C. Lewis
1936 Nolan D. C. Lewis
1937 Nolan D. C. Lewis
1938 Samuel W. Hamilton
1939 Abraham Myerson
1940 Douglas A. Thom
1941 Roscoe W. Hall
1942 Roscoe W. Hall
1943 Frederick L. Wells
1944 Frederick L. Wells
1945 Bernard Glueck
1946 Robert P. Knight
1947 Frederick L. Wells
1948 Donald J. MacPherson
1949 Paul Hoch
1950 William B. Terhune
1951 Lauren H. Smith
1952 Joseph Zubin
1953 Clarence P. Oberndorf
1954 David McK. Rioch
1955 Merrill Moore
1956 Oskar Diethelm

Vice Presidents

1924 William Healy
George H. Kirby
1925 J. Ramsay Hunt
Sidney I. Schwab
1927 Ross McC. Chapman
Edward J. Kempf
1928 Edward J. Kempf
E. Stanley Abbot
1929 Edward J. Kempf
E. Stanley Abbot
1930 J. Ramsay Hunt
Herman N. Adler
1931 J. Ramsay Hunt
Herman N. Adler
1933 Albert M. Barrett
Trigant Burrow
1934 Albert M. Barrett
Trigant Burrow
1935 J. Ramsay Hunt
Smith Ely Jelliffe
1936 J. Ramsay Hunt
Smith Ely Jelliffe
1937 Samuel W. Hamilton
Ray G. Hoskins
1938 Lydiard H. Horton
Hans Syz
1939 Roscoe W. Hall
Douglas A. Thom
1940 George S. Sprague
Bernard Glueck
1941 Frederick L. Wells
Lowell S. Selling
1942 Frederick L. Wells
Lowell S. Selling
1943 Lowell S. Selling
Flanders Dunbar

Vice Presidents

1944 Lowell S. Selling
Flanders Dunbar
1945 Thomas V. Moore
Robert P. Knight
1946 Paul H. Hoch
Thos. A. C. Rennie
1947 William C. Menninger
Ruth Benedict
1948 Ruth Benedict
Lauren H. Smith
1949 Arthur N. Foxe
Norman Cameron
1950 Harry M. Murdock
William S. Taylor
1951 Harry M. Murdock
Lauretta Bender
1952 William Horwitz
S. Bernard Wortis
1953 David McK. Rioch
Merrill Moore
1954 Merrill Moore
Howard S. Liddell
1955 Oskar Diethelm
Howard S. Liddell
1956 Leslie B. Hohman

Secretaries

1921 H. W. Frink
1922 Sanger Brown, II
1923 Sanger Brown, II
1924 Sanger Brown, II
1925 Sanger Brown, II
1926 Sanger Brown, II
1927 Martin W. Peck
1928 Martin W. Peck
1929 Martin W. Peck
1930 L. Eugene Emerson
1931 L. Eugene Emerson
1932 L. Eugene Emerson
1933 L. Eugene Emerson
1934 L. Eugene Emerson
1935 L. Eugene Emerson
1936 L. Eugene Emerson
1937 L. Eugene Emerson
1938 L. Eugene Emerson
1939 L. Eugene Emerson
1940 Merrill Moore
1941 Merrill Moore
1942 Merrill Moore
1943 Merrill Moore
1944 Samuel W. Hamilton
1945 Samuel W. Hamilton
1946 Samuel W. Hamilton
1947 Samuel W. Hamilton
1948 Samuel W. Hamilton
1949 Samuel W. Hamilton
1950 Samuel W. Hamilton
1951 Samuel W. Hamilton
1952 Donald M. Hamilton
1953 Donald M. Hamilton
1954 Donald M. Hamilton
1955 Donald M. Hamilton
1956 Donald M. Hamilton

Treasurers

1924 William C. Garvin
1925 William C. Garvin
1926 William C. Garvin
1927 William C. Garvin
1928 William C. Garvin
1929 William C. Garvin
1930 William C. Garvin
1931 William C. Garvin
1932 William C. Garvin
1933 William C. Garvin
1934 William C. Garvin
1935 William C. Garvin

1936 William C. Garvin
1937 William C. Garvin
1938 William C. Garvin
1939 William C. Garvin
1940 William C. Garvin
1941 William C. Garvin
1942 William C. Garvin
1943 Joseph Zubin
1944 Joseph Zubin
1945 Joseph Zubin
1946 Joseph Zubin
1947 Joseph Zubin
1948 Joseph Zubin
1949 Joseph Zubin
1950 Joseph Zubin
1951 Joseph Zubin
1952 Bernard Glueck, Jr.
1953 Bernard Glueck, Jr.
1954 Bernard Glueck, Jr.
1955 Bernard Glueck, Jr.
1956 Bernard Glueck, Jr.

INDEX